CHEMICAL CALCULATIONS

An Introduction to the Use of Mathematics in Chemistry

CHEMICAL
CALCULATIONS

An Introduction to the Use of
Mathematics in Chemistry

SIDNEY W. BENSON

Professor of Chemistry

University of Southern California

NEW YORK · JOHN WILEY & SONS, INC.

LONDON · CHAPMAN & HALL, LIMITED

Library of Congress Catalog Card Number: 51-13458

PREFACE

The student beginning his studies in chemistry today undertakes a prodigious labor. He must learn rapidly an almost entirely new language, replete with names, symbols, and rules of grammar. Speed is essential since he is expected to use this language in thinking about and memorizing a huge amount of loosely related and descriptive material. Finally, he must absorb the theoretical structure, expressed in a mathematical language, which provides a basis for unifying a great deal of the subject material.

Although I shall not pretend to say here which part of this gargantuan body of knowledge is important and which is not, one thing is certain. For the student who plans to continue the study of chemistry, it is essential that he obtain a thorough understanding of the way in which mathematical thinking is incorporated into chemistry. It is for these students and for those others who, though taking chemistry for only one year, may be expected to master chemical calculations that this book is written.

The neophyte finds his greatest difficulty usually with chemical problems. I trust that he will not be too surprised when I say that this is not due to his inadequate understanding of mathematics. The amount of mathematical understanding required for 80 per cent of first-year chemistry problems is microscopically small. The student's difficulty in doing problems arises not from a lack of mathematical background but rather from a lack of familiarity with the way in which chemists use mathematics. Most college students have, or soon acquire, quite enough mathematical understanding to pay for a "coke," borrow money from a friend, and place bets in a card game. If they had the same familiarity with chemical terms and units that they do with these more eclectic enterprises, they would show an equal agility with their homework and examinations.

In the present book an attempt is made to cope with this very real difficulty by presenting all terms, units, and definitions that will be employed mathematically, in the form of equations. This approach provides a unified method for attacking chemical problems. The student using this book is urged first to read Chapters I and II on measurement and chemical units. Although a good part of these chapters may seem self-evident and oversimplified, they nevertheless contain precisely that material which in my own experience usually has been needed to clarify the thinking of the student and deepen his understanding of chemical calculations. If the student is to learn to do chemical arithmetic, then he should do it logically and well.

This book represents the cumulative experience of many years of experimenting with the presentation of chemical arithmetic. To the many hundreds of my own students who have borne patiently, if not ecstatically, the various phases through which these pedagogical researches have passed, this book is dedicated.

I wish to express my appreciation to Miss Diane Frost, Secretary of the Chemistry Department, for the very generous assistance given in typing this manuscript. I also wish to express my thanks to Victoria Von Hagen, without whom this book would have been ready six months earlier.

SIDNEY W. BENSON

Los Angeles
February, 1952

CONTENTS

CHAPTER I

Measurement

1. The Language of Chemistry

In this book we are going to be concerned with that part of chemistry which can be expressed in terms of numbers. To clarify our understanding of this area, something must first be said of its relation to the whole structure of the science.

One of the goals of chemistry is to make simple, compact statements about the properties of matter. These statements must be clear and, as far as possible, devoid of any ambiguity. For this purpose, the language of everyday conversation is inadequate. The statements of chemistry must be free from the kind of double meanings which might confound, for example, the conversation of the cannibal and the missionary's wife, each of whom can say, "I am fond of missionaries."

To achieve such clarity, chemists have had to construct a vocabulary in which each word is precisely defined. Thus one definition of an acid is: "A substance whose water solution will turn blue litmus red." Such a definition permits of a clear and simple test for an acid.

The beginning student of chemistry will find that a great deal of his difficulty arises from a lack of appreciation of the fact that he is using a precise language, and that the usual liberties taken with our everyday speech are not permitted. A vague understanding of a word, which may suffice for the general intent of an ordinary statement, may lead to a total block in understanding a chemical statement. To obtain a genuine mastery, the student must constantly subject his study to the self-criticism of definition: "What does this word mean?"

Such caution is doubly necessary when the statements are quantitative rather than descriptive. Quantitative statements are preferred in science since they are the most compact and the least subject to ambiguity. To say that lead has a density of 11.34 grams per cubic centimeter is much more precise and informative than to say that lead is a dense metal. Such compactness, however, is apt to be

1

misleading. Though we can read it and say it more quickly, until we are quite familiar with the terms used, it actually calls for far more thought and reflection than the almost equally brief but descriptive statement. The difference will be found in the loose, qualitative idea conveyed by the word "dense," as opposed to the precise meaning contained in the word "density."

2. Measurement

Chemistry, like most natural science, starts by making qualitative or descriptive statements about nature. Thus, "copper sulfate is a blue, crystalline material which is soluble in water." How does it proceed to the quantitative? What is required in order that we shall be able to make statements in the language of mathematics? The answer lies in what we mean by measurement.

We may observe that a certain stick is long. We may measure its length with a ruler and find it to be 14.5 inches.

A property such as length may be expressed quantitatively, that is, it may be measured, if:

1. We can define the property precisely (i.e., length is the shortest distances between two points).
2. We have a standard object with which we can compare our object to be measured (i.e., a ruler).
3. We have a means of making the numerical comparison between the property of the standard object (the ruler) and the object whose property we wish to measure (the stick). This will consist in placing the two objects side by side and reading, from the divisions on the ruler, the length of the stick.

To summarize, then, a property can be expressed or measured quantitatively if three conditions are satisfied: 1. *precise definition;* 2. *a standard;* 3. *a means of comparison.*

3. Standards

Not all properties are capable of being expressed in numerical fashion. Taste and smell, which are certainly distinctive properties of a great many substances, have so far defied attempts to reduce them to exact measurement.

Of the large number of other properties which have been reduced to quantitative measurement, however, a few have come to be considered as basic. Among these are mass, length, time, and temperature. It would be most agreeable if a single set of standards were adopted for the measurement of these quantities. Unfortunately, such is not the case, and there are at present two different sets of standards in common usage. One of them is known as the English system of units, and the other as the metric system. Since the metric system is the simpler, being based on a decimal system of subdivision, it is the one which is universally employed by pure scientists. The English system finds its adherents principally among engineers.

Table I indicates the definitions, units, and means of measurement employed.

TABLE I
BASIC STANDARDS FOR MEASUREMENT

| Quantity | Definition | Standard | | Common Method of Measurement |
		English	Metric	
Mass	Quantity of matter. Resistance offered by a body to a change in its velocity.	Pound (lb.)	Kilogram (kg.)	Balance
Length	Shortest distance between two points.	Foot (ft.)	Meter (m.)	Straightedge ruler
Time	Interval between two events.	Second (sec.)	Second (sec.)	Clock
Temperature	Degree of hotness or coldness which determines the flow of heat from one body to another.	Degree Fahrenheit (°F.)	Degree centigrade (°C.)	Thermometer

The actual systems which have been adopted are quite arbitrary. Thus there is a lump of platinum in the Bureau of Standards at Washington, D.C., which has a mass of 1 pound. This has become the primary standard of mass against which all other standards have been compared by means of a balance. A larger or smaller lump of platinum could equally well have been chosen, and the same applies for the standards of length, time, and temperature.

We can observe that each basic quantity has associated with it a standard of measurement and a unit designating the standard itself. Our principle of measurement is based on the assumption that we can so design our measuring apparatus (e.g., the ruler) that we can express a given property such as length in multiples or fractions of the standard unit. Thus an object may be 20 meters long; another object may be only $\frac{1}{25}$ (0.040) meter long. Without the ability to make these numerical comparisons, exact definitions and standards are of no avail for quantitative work. Thus we may take a sample of perfume to represent the standard scent of, perhaps, orange blossom. Until we can then devise an instrument or method for comparing some other sample with our standard perfume in such a way that the observer can say, "This is twice as 'odoriferous' as the standard," we will not be able to measure orange blossom quantitatively.

4. Units

It is frequently very clumsy or inconvenient to use the standard units directly. Thus a biologist measuring the diameter of a blood cell under the microscope will find it awkward to have to express his results as 0.0000075 meter. Similarly, a surveyor will not want to write his distances on maps as, perhaps, 1,432,000 meters. To obviate such inconveniences, subsidiary sets of units have been adopted which are exactly defined by means of algebraic equations in terms of the major units. In the metric system, these auxiliary units are defined by attaching appropriate prefixes to the standard unit. Some common prefixes are shown in Table II.

TABLE II
METRIC UNITS (PREFIXES)

Prefix	Definition
Mega-	One million (1,000,000) (1×10^6)
Kilo-	One thousand (1,000) (1×10^3)
Centi-	One hundredth (0.01) (1×10^{-2})
Milli-	One thousandth (0.001) (1×10^{-3})
Micro-	One millionth (0.000001) (1×10^{-6})

In terms of these units the diameter of the blood cell can now be written as 7.5 micrometers (generally shortened to microns) and our surveyor's distance as 1432 kilometers, or 1.432 megameters. (The reader can ponder on the savings in printers' ink and paper, if the Treasury Department, newspapers, magazines, etc., would refer to items such as our national debt in terms of megabucks, kilobucks, etc.)

It is unfortunate that the list of metric prefixes is so limited, since science is now measuring distances as small as 0.000000000001 meter and as large as 10^{20} meters. Because of this large range we will frequently find other auxiliary units defined. The angstrom unit is now in quite common usage in the discussion of sizes of atoms and molecules. It is defined as one-ten-billionth of a meter:

$$1 \text{ angstrom} = 0.0000000001 \text{ meter} = 1 \times 10^{-10} \text{ meter} \quad \text{(definition)}$$

With the development of supersensitive balances it is also quite common to hear talk of the gamma, defined as

$$1 \text{ gamma} = 0.000000001 \text{ gram} = 1 \times 10^{-9} \text{ gram} \quad \text{(definition)}$$

In the Table of Common Units (Appendix II) the student will find a more complete list of the metric units in common usage.

Do problems 1 and 2 at the end of the chapter.

5. Relations between Different Systems of Measurement

The existence of two such different systems as the English and the metric for measuring the same property requires some means for translation from one system to the other. This can be provided only by direct experiment. That is, we must take, for example, the pound and measure its mass in kilograms, or vice versa. Careful measurements have been made for all the different systems of units. A few of the results obtained are indicated by the following equations.

$$1 \text{ meter} = 3.2808 \text{ feet} \quad \text{(experiment)}$$

$$1 \text{ kilogram} = 2.2046 \text{ pounds} \quad \text{(experiment)}$$

As will be seen shortly, one such relation enables us to relate any auxiliary unit in one system to any auxiliary unit in the other. By means of the above equation for the relation between lengths in the metric and English systems, we can show that 1 inch = 2.504 centimeters, 1 millimeter = 0.03937 inch, etc.

It is important to observe the distinction between the equations given above for relating similar properties in two different systems, which must be determined experimentally, and the equations given in section 4, which relate auxiliary units to standard units and which are mathematically exact.

6. Intensive and Extensive Properties

Properties that depend on the quantity of matter being measured are known as *extensive* properties. Mass, length, and volume are examples. If we take twice as much matter of a given substance, it will contain twice as much volume and twice as much mass.

Properties that do not depend on the quantity of matter being measured are called *intensive* properties. They may be important properties because they often depend only on the nature of the material being measured and not on the quantity involved. Density and temperature are examples of *intensive* properties. The density of water is the same whether we measure the density of a drop of water or a quart, namely, 1 gram per cubic centimeter. This is then a property of water itself and can be used to identify water, since in general all pure liquids will have different densities. Intensive properties are also of considerable interest to scientists because they are characteristic of the nature of the substance studied. Studies of intensive properties may throw great light on the fundamental nature of substances. We shall observe this in many of the quantitative laws.

Do problem 3 at the end of the chapter.

7. Conversion of Units—Conversion Factors

When properties have been measured in one set of units, it frequently is necessary to know the property in a different set of units. This translation from one set of units into a different set of units may be performed mathematically and is known as a conversion.

Conversions can be performed only if we have an equation relating the two units in question.

Example: Mass: What is the mass in pounds of an object whose mass is 900 g.?
Answer: The two units in question are *pounds* and *grams*, and the fundamental equation relating them is

$$1 \text{ lb.} = 454 \text{ g.} \qquad \text{(see Table of Units)}$$

The answer is then

$$\frac{900}{454} = 1.983 \text{ lb}$$

From the preceding example we have seen that equations relating different units can be used to convert quantities expressed in one of these units to the other unit. However, it is not always obvious when to multiply and when to divide in such conversions. This difficulty is completely avoided if we put units in our mathematical operations and cancel and multiply them as if they were numbers. Conversions of units are most conveniently performed by means of what are known as conversion factors.

Definition: A conversion factor is a numerical ratio of units which is equal to the pure number 1.

Example: The ratio $\left(\dfrac{454 \text{ g.}}{1 \text{ lb.}}\right) = 1$; also: $\left(\dfrac{1 \text{ lb.}}{454 \text{ g.}}\right) = 1$. These relations fol-

lowed directly from our fundamental equation:

$$454 \text{ g.} = 1 \text{ lb.}$$

If we divide both sides of this equation by the quantity 1 lb., we obtain the first conversion factor. If we divide both sides by 454 g., we obtain the second conversion factor. These operations are valid since equals divided by equals remain equal.

$$\frac{454 \text{ g.}}{1 \text{ lb.}} = \frac{1 \text{ lb.}}{1 \text{ lb.}} = 1; \quad \text{or} \quad \frac{1 \text{ lb.}}{454 \text{ g.}} = \frac{454 \text{ g.}}{454 \text{ g.}} = 1$$

By similar treatment every equation involving units can be made to give conversion factors. The usefulness of these conversion factors lies in the fact that they are equal to 1. We can multiply or divide any quantity by a conversion factor and the result will still be equal to the original quantity. This follows since multiplication or division by the number 1 does not change the value of the original quantity. When this is done, so that the units of the original quantity are canceled by some units in the conversion factors, we have performed a conversion of units.

Example:

$$2 \text{ lb.} = 2 \text{ lb.} \times \left(\frac{454 \text{ g.}}{1 \text{ lb.}}\right) = 908 \text{ g.}$$

We see in the above example that by multiplying the quantity 2 lb. by the conversion factor relating pounds and grams we were able to convert from the units of pounds to grams. If we had multiplied by the second conversion factor (1 lb./454 g.) the units of pounds would not have been canceled and we would not have obtained an answer in grams. (The student should verify this.)

The following simple example is easily remembered and should serve as a guide in converting units.

Example: How many nickels are there in 6 quarters?
Answer: The fundamental equation is

$$1 \text{ quarter} = 5 \text{ nickels}$$

From this equation we want a conversion factor to cancel the units of quarters when we multiply it by 6 quarters. The conversion factor is

$$\left(\frac{5 \text{ nickels}}{1 \text{ quarter}}\right) = 1$$

Then

$$6 \text{ quarters} = 6 \text{ quarters} \times \left(\frac{5 \text{ nickels}}{1 \text{ quarter}}\right) = 30 \text{ nickels}$$

Summary

1. *In order to convert from one set of units to another we must first have an equation which gives a relation between these two units.** *(See Table of Units.)*

2. *By dividing one side of the equation by the other we obtain a conversion factor (equal to 1) which we can use to convert from one set of units to the other.*

3. *Since we can divide either side of an equation by the other, every equation will give two conversion factors. The one to use is the one that will cancel the units we wish to eliminate.*

Example: How many centimeters are there in 2 ft.?
Answer: The fundamental relations are

$$1 \text{ ft.} = 12 \text{ in.}$$

$$1 \text{ in.} = 2.54 \text{ cm.}$$

The conversion factors are

$$\left(\frac{12 \text{ in.}}{1 \text{ ft.}}\right) \quad \text{and} \quad \left(\frac{2.54 \text{ cm.}}{1 \text{ in.}}\right)$$

Then

$$2 \text{ ft.} = 2 \text{ ft.} \times \left(\frac{12 \text{ in.}}{1 \text{ ft.}}\right) \times \left(\frac{2.54 \text{ cm.}}{1 \text{ in.}}\right) = 61.0 \text{ cm.}$$

Example: A sign says, "Rowboats for rent, two bits per hour." What will it cost in dollars to rent a rowboat for two weeks?
Answer: (To the student: write down all the fundamental equations involved.)

$$\frac{2 \text{ bits}}{1 \text{ hr.}} = \left(\frac{2 \text{ bits}}{1 \text{ hr.}}\right) \times \left(\frac{1 \text{ dollar}}{8 \text{ bits}}\right) \times \left(\frac{24 \text{ hr.}}{1 \text{ day}}\right) \times \left(\frac{7 \text{ days}}{1 \text{ wk.}}\right) = \frac{42 \text{ dollars}}{\text{week}}$$

$$= \frac{84 \text{ dollars}}{2 \text{ weeks}} \text{ (multiplying top and bottom by 2)}$$

Note: The only way to achieve proficiency in problems is by practice. Most problems can be solved by using conversion factors, and with a little practice the answers can be written down on inspection. From the unit equations in the Table of Units, practice writing conversion factors and then obtain relations between units which are not given.

---

* Whenever a problem involving conversion of units is given, the first step is always to seek for the fundamental relation *or relations* which equate the units concerned. (More than one relation may be involved.)

The student will observe that every one of the quantities in parentheses is a conversion factor and numerically equal to unity. Multiplying a great many of these still preserves the value of the original quantity.

Example: A car is moving at a rate of 30 miles/hr. What is this in centimeters per second?

Answer: (To the student: Write down all the fundamental equations involved.)

$$\frac{30 \text{ miles}}{1 \text{ hr.}} = \left(\frac{30 \text{ miles}}{1 \text{ hr.}}\right) \times \left(\frac{5280 \text{ ft.}}{1 \text{ mile}}\right) \times \left(\frac{12 \text{ in.}}{1 \text{ ft.}}\right) \times \left(\frac{2.54 \text{ cm.}}{1 \text{ in.}}\right) \times \left(\frac{1 \text{ hr.}}{60 \text{ min.}}\right)$$

$$\times \left(\frac{1 \text{ min.}}{60 \text{ sec.}}\right) = \left(\frac{30 \times 5280 \times 12 \times 2.54}{60 \times 60}\right) \frac{\text{cm.}}{\text{sec.}} = 1342 \text{ cm./sec.}$$

The method outlined above for the conversion of one set of units to another may at first seem unorthodox or too obvious to be worth the effort of going through. However, it represents a fundamental approach to such problems and, as we shall see, to most of the problems in chemistry. The experience of the author has been that, once students overcome their conservatism and unfamiliarity and master the method, they will gain an extraordinary facility in doing problems. The method permits a rapid solution of the problem with an instant check on basic errors. Answers to problems can be written down very quickly, units canceled, and finally all numbers gathered so that the arithmetic may be left for last.

For the students who find the arithmetical steps or notation troublesome, a section on simple algebraic definitions and manipulations is included in Appendix I.

The Table of Common Units in Appendix II gives fundamental relations between some of the common units. However, from these it is possible to derive other fundamental relations by the previous method. Such relations can then be applied in future problems and so save work.

Example: Derive a relation between ounces (oz.) and milligrams (mg.), given 16 oz. = 1 lb.

Answer: Write the other relations needed:

$$1 \text{ oz.} = 1 \text{ oz.} \times \left(\frac{1 \text{ lb.}}{16 \text{ oz.}}\right) \times \left(\frac{454 \text{ g.}}{1 \text{ lb.}}\right) \times \left(\frac{1000 \text{ mg.}}{1 \text{ g.}}\right)$$

$$= 28{,}400 \text{ mg.}$$

Example: How many milligrams are there in 0.74 oz.?

Answer: This can be solved by usual methods. However, if we take the relation from the previous example,

$$1 \text{ oz.} = 28,400 \text{ mg.}$$

we can use it to give a direct conversion:

$$0.74 \text{ oz.} = 0.74 \text{ oz.} \times \left(\frac{28,400 \text{ mg.}}{1 \text{ oz.}} \right) = 21,000 \text{ mg.}$$

The student may find it useful to make up tables of such additional relations. Handbooks such as the *Chemical Rubber Handbook* and Lange's *Chemical Handbook* will be found to contain many such tables.

Do problems 4–7 at the end of the chapter.

8. Properties Expressed in Complex Units

In the previous sections we have placed principle emphasis on those properties which can be expressed in terms of single, basic units (e.g., length, mass). It is possible to define more complex properties having important physical meaning which are related to these basic properties.

The property of "area" is one example. The area of a rectangle is defined as the product of its width and its height. Expressed as an algebraic equation,

$$\text{Area} = \text{Width} \times \text{Height} \qquad \text{(definition)}$$

We can now inquire about the units in which area will be expressed. The width of a rectangle is a property expressed in the units of length. Similarly, the height of a rectangle is expressed in the units of length. If we multiply a unit of length by itself, as indicated in the above equation, we will obtain, following the notation of algebra, the units of length squared.

Example: What is the area of a rectangle whose width is 6 cm. and whose height is 3 cm.?

Answer:

$$\text{Area} = 6 \text{ cm.} \times 3 \text{ cm. (from above definition)}$$

$$= 18 \text{ cm.}^2 \text{ (or 18 sq. cm.)}$$

Proceeding from this definition, geometry has developed theorems which permit us to compute the areas of much more complex figures, such as triangles, circles, etc., in terms of their dimensions. In each one the final result, the area, will be expressed as the square of the unit of length.   How can we convert the units of a complex property, such as area, from one system to another?   The answer is given by the procedure already outlined.

Example: Express the results of the preceding example (Area = 18 cm.^{2}) in square inches.
Answer: From our Table of Units we find

$$1 \text{ in.} = 2.54 \text{ cm.}$$

If we square both sides of this equation we do not disturb the equality:

$$(1 \text{ in.})^2 = (2.54 \text{ cm.})^2$$

$$= (2.54)^2 \text{ cm.}^2$$

$$1 \text{ in.}^2 = 6.45 \text{ cm.}^2$$

This last equation now provides us with a fundamental relation between square inches and square centimeters, and thus a conversion factor between the two sets of complex units.   Hence

$$18 \text{ cm.}^2 = 18 \text{ cm.}^2 \times \left(\frac{1 \text{ in.}^2}{6.45 \text{ cm.}^2} \right)$$

$$= 2.79 \text{ in.}^2$$

In a similar fashion we find that the property of volume is expressed as the cube of the unit of length (i.e., cm.^{3} or in.^{3} or ft.^{3}, etc.).   The same methods can be applied to units of volume.

Example: The volume of a rectangular solid is given by the product of its length times its width times its height.   What is the volume of a rectangular solid whose dimensions are 60 cm. by 8 cm. by 10 cm.?   Express this in cubic feet.
Answer:

$$\text{Volume} = 60 \text{ cm.} \times 8 \text{ cm.} \times 10 \text{ cm.}$$

$$= 4800 \text{ cm.}^3 \text{ (i.e., cubic centimeters)}$$

$$= 4800 \text{ cm.}^3 \times \left(\frac{1 \text{ in.}}{2.54 \text{ cm.}} \right)^3 \times \left(\frac{1 \text{ ft.}}{12 \text{ in.}} \right)^3$$

$$= 4800 \text{ cm.}^3 \times \frac{\text{in.}^3}{(2.54)^3 \text{ cm.}^3} \times \frac{\text{ft.}^3}{1728 \text{ in.}^3} = \frac{4800 \text{ ft.}^3}{16.4 \times 1728}$$

$$= 0.169 \text{ ft.}^3$$

Some other important physical properties, together with their definition and units are given in Table III. (A more complete list will be
found in the Table of Units in Appendix II.)

TABLE III

DEFINITION AND UNITS OF SOME COMPLEX PROPERTIES

Property	Verbal Definition	Algebraic Definition	Usual Units
Velocity (v)	Distance traveled divided by the time of travel.	$\text{Velocity} = \dfrac{\text{Distance}}{\text{Time}}$	cm./sec. ft./sec. miles/hr.
Kinetic energy $(K.E.)$	One half of the mass of a body times the square of its ve-locity.	$K.E. = \dfrac{mv^2}{2}$	g.-cm.^{2}/sec.^{2} (1 g.-cm.^{2}/ sec.^{2} = 1 erg) lb.-ft.^{2}/sec.^{2}
Density (d)	The mass of a body divided by its volume.	$d = \dfrac{m}{v}$	g./cm.^{3} lb./ft.^{3}
Acceleration (a)	The amount by which the velocity of a body changes divided by the time during which it changes.	$a = \dfrac{\text{Change in velocity}}{\text{Time}}$	cm./sec.^{2} ft./sec.^{2}
Force (f)	The push or pull that is capable of changing the velocity of (i.e., accelerating) a body. More precisely, force equals the mass of a body times the acceleration imparted to it (Newton's Law).	$f = ma$	g.-cm./sec.^{2} $\left(1 \text{ dyne} = \dfrac{1 \text{ g.-cm.}}{\text{sec.}^2}\right)$ lb.-ft./sec.^{2} $\left(1 \text{ poundal} = \dfrac{1 \text{ lb.-ft.}}{\text{sec.}^2}\right)$
Pressure (P)	The force acting on an object divided by the area over which the force is exerted.	$P = \dfrac{f}{A}$	dynes/cm.^{2} $\left(\dfrac{1 \text{ dyne}}{\text{cm.}^2} = \dfrac{1 \text{ g.}}{\text{cm.-sec.}^2}\right)$ lb. force/in.^{2}

Note: There may be some confusion in the English system since units of pounds have sometimes
been used for the measurement of mass and sometimes for the measurement of force. Proper
usage is units of pounds for mass and units of *poundals* for force. When pounds are used to express
force, it should be observed that 1 lb. force = 32.2 poundals force = 32.2 lb.-ft./sec.^{2}. Similarly,
when grams are used to express force, 1 g. force = 980 dynes. In this book both pounds and grams
will be used as units of mass unless explicitly designated otherwise.

$1 \text{ Lb.}_f = 32.2 \text{ FT/SEC}^2 \times \text{LBm}$

As a final example of the conversion of units for these more complex
properties we shall take the following:

Example: The density of metallic mercury is 13.55 g./cm.^{3} at 0°C. Convert
this to pounds per cubic inch.

Answer: The student should write out the various fundamental equations and
compute the conversion factors given as follows.

$\text{LB}_f = \text{LB}_m \times g$

$$\frac{13.55 \text{ g.}}{\text{cm.}^3} = \left(\frac{13.55 \text{ g.}}{\text{cm.}^3}\right) \times \left(\frac{1 \text{ lb.}}{454 \text{ g.}}\right) \times \left(\frac{2.54 \text{ cm.}}{1 \text{ in.}}\right)^3 \times \left(\frac{12 \text{ in.}}{1 \text{ ft.}}\right)^3$$

$$= \left(\frac{13.55 \text{ g.}}{\text{cm.}^3}\right) \times \left(\frac{\text{lb.}}{454 \text{ g.}}\right) \times \left(\frac{16.4 \text{ cm.}^3}{\text{in.}^3}\right) \times \left(\frac{1728 \text{ in.}^3}{\text{ft.}^3}\right)$$

$$= \left(\frac{13.55 \times 16.4 \times 1728}{454}\right) \frac{\text{lb.}}{\text{ft.}^3}$$

$$= 846 \text{ lb./ft.}^3$$

Do problems 8–15 at the end of the chapter.

9. Relation between Different Properties

In the preceding section we have shown how complex properties may be defined in terms of simpler properties. We have been able to apply the laws of algebra to such defined properties because the definitions could be expressed in algebraic form. These definitions, given in the form of equations involving properties, can be treated as algebraic equations and "juggled" mathematically to give new equations.

Thus density is defined as the mass of an object divided by its volume. Expressed algebraically as an equation:

$$\text{Density} = \frac{\text{Mass}}{\text{Volume}}$$

If we multiply both sides of this equation by "Volume" we have:

$$\text{Density} \times \text{Volume} = \frac{\text{Mass}}{\text{Volume}} \times \text{Volume} = \text{Mass}$$

This is a new form of the original equation which tells us that multiplying the density of an object by its volume will give us the mass of the object. The student should verify the following relation which can be derived from the original equation:

$$\frac{\text{Mass}}{\text{Density}} = \text{Volume}$$

We observe that the original definition represents an algebraic relation between three properties: the mass, the volume, and the density of an object. The equations given above, which were derived from it, all represent the same relation but in different forms.

The original equation contained three properties. If we have numbers given for any two of the properties, it is always possible to calculate the numerical value of the third property from the equation. The derived equations merely represent convenient methods for doing this.

Example: The density of mercury (Hg) at 0°C. is 13.55 g./cm.^{3}. What volume will be occupied by 20 g. of mercury?

Answer: From our definition of density:

$$\text{Density} = \frac{\text{Mass}}{\text{Volume}}$$

we can write the derived equation:

$$\text{Volume} = \frac{\text{Mass}}{\text{Density}}$$

On substitution of the above numbers,

$$\text{Volume} = \frac{20 \text{ g.}}{13.55 \text{ g./cm.}^3} = \frac{20 \text{ g.-cm.}^3}{13.55 \text{ g.}} \quad \text{(inversion of fractions)}$$

$$= 1.48 \text{ cm.}^3$$

Observe that in this example, through consistent and correct use of units, the volume is calculated not only as a number but in the proper units of cubic centimeters (cm.^{3}). Had an error been made in the equation, it would have led to a result expressed in the wrong units. Thus the use of units provides an additional check on our method of calculation.

If it had been desired to express the answer in other units, conversion factors could now be applied to the present answer to change it.

10. An Interpretation and a General Method for Solving Problems

We can infer from the preceding discussion a general principle involved in calculations. If most problems are analyzed we will see that they can be interpreted as follows:

1. A property or set of properties is given, and we are requested to calculate from these some other property or set of properties.
2. The problem may have the added complication that the data given may be expressed in one set of units whereas the answer requested may be in a different set of units.

From this analysis of problems we can outline the following set of rules for solving the problem.

1. Write down the given data and the data requested in the answer. These will generally be properties of one kind or another.

2. The task of the problem is then to find a law, definition, or laboratory observation which relates the properties given to the properties requested. *This is the heart of the problem.*
3. The law, definition, or datum, once discovered, is expressed in algebraic form and rearranged to yield an equation which expresses the property sought for in terms of the properties given.
4. The numbers and *units* for the given data are now substituted in this derived equation and the appropriate arithmetic performed. Units are canceled and multiplied just as if they were numbers.
5. The answer obtained must have the proper units; otherwise a mistake has been made. If a different set of units is requested, appropriate conversion factors may be employed directly in the original equation or else in the final answer.

Example: The density of grain alcohol at 20°C. is 0.79 g./cm.^{3}. What is the mass of 250 cm.^{3} of alcohol?

Answer: The data (or properties) given are: density (0.79 g./cm.^{3}) and volume (250 cm.^{3}). We are requested to find *mass*. The relation between these properties is provided by the definition of density:

$$\text{Density} = \frac{\text{Mass}}{\text{Volume}}$$

Solving this for mass we find:

$$\text{Mass} = \text{Density} \times \text{Volume}$$

Substituting the proper numbers we find:

$$\text{Mass} = \frac{0.79 \text{ g.}}{\text{cm.}^3} \times 250 \text{ cm.}^3 = 198 \text{ g.}$$

Example: The density of water is 62.4 lb./ft.^{3} at 20°C. What is the volume in liters occupied by 800 g. of water?

Answer: The data (or properties) given are: density (62.4 lb./ft.^{3}) and mass (800 g.). We are requested to find volume (liters). Proceeding as formerly, we write the fundamental equation connecting these properties and rearrange to solve for volume.

$$\text{Volume} = \frac{\text{Mass}}{\text{Density}}$$

Substituting we have:

$$\text{Volume} = \frac{800 \text{ g.}}{62.4 \text{ lb./ft.}^3} = \frac{800 \text{ g.-ft.}^3}{62.4 \text{ lb.}} \quad \text{(by inversion of fraction containing units)}$$

We now apply the proper conversion factors to obtain the desired units.

$$\text{Volume} = \left(\frac{800 \text{ g.-ft.}^3}{62.4 \text{ lb.}}\right) \times \left(\frac{1 \text{ lb.}}{454 \text{ g.}}\right) \times \left(\frac{12 \text{ in.}}{1 \text{ ft.}}\right)^3 \times \left(\frac{2.54 \text{ cm.}}{1 \text{ in.}}\right)^3 \times \left(\frac{1 \text{ l.}}{1000 \text{ cm.}^3}\right)$$

$$= \left(\frac{800 \times 1728 \times 16.4 \text{ ft.}^3}{62.4 \times 454 \times 1000}\right) \times \left(\frac{\text{in.}^3}{\text{ft.}^3}\right) \times \left(\frac{\text{cm.}^3}{\text{in.}^3}\right) \times \left(\frac{\text{l.}}{\text{cm.}^3}\right)$$

$$= 0.800 \text{ l.}$$

Once facility is gained in doing such problems, the student will find that he can combine the substitution in the fundamental equation together with the conversion factors and write the answer as one single equation combining both.

Do problems 16 and 17 at the end of the chapter.

11. Property Conversion Factors

A definition or a law or a direct observation may be thought of as expressing a relation between two different kinds of properties. Thus the definition of density expresses a relation between the property of mass and the property of volume. The complex property of density can be thought of as a conversion factor which can be used to convert from the property of mass to the property of volume or vice versa.

When we say that the density of mercury is 13.55 g./cm.^{3} at 0°C., we are in effect saying that 13.55 g. of mercury are the same as 1 cm.^{3} of mercury. Algebraically:

$$1 \text{ cm.}^3 \text{ Hg} = 13.55 \text{ g. Hg}$$

That is, the same quantity of mercury (Hg) has the volume of 1 cm.^{3} and the mass of 13.55 g. Either property thus provides an equally valid way of measuring out a quantity of mercury. The above equation expresses an equivalence between these two different properties of mercury and can be used to obtain conversion factors between the volume occupied by mercury and the mass of this same quantity of mercury.

In a similar fashion other complex properties (like density) can be looked upon as expressing an equivalence between two different sets of properties of a substance, and the algebraic relation stating this equivalence can be used to provide conversion factors for going from one of these sets of properties to the other. Such conversion factors are not the same as the conversion factors connecting sets of units, and we shall designate them as *property conversion factors*. However, the use of these property conversion factors, mathematically, is exactly the same as ordinary conversion factors.

The above equation for the density of mercury provides us with two alternative property conversion factors: $\left(\dfrac{1 \text{ cm.}^3 \text{ Hg}}{13.55 \text{ g. Hg}}\right)$ and $\left(\dfrac{13.55 \text{ g. Hg}}{1 \text{ cm.}^3 \text{ Hg}}\right)$. (Note that we write the symbol for mercury as part of the unit, since it is not true or meaningful to say that 1 cm.^{3} is equivalent to 13.55 g.)

This way of regarding complex properties provides us with a short method of doing problems. We can now analyze a problem as consisting of a combination of property conversion steps and unit conversion steps.

Example: If 80 lb. of apples cost 63 cents, what is the cost in quarters of 200 kg. of apples?

Answer: We are given the mass of apples (80 lb.) and total cost (63 cents) and asked to find the total cost (quarters) of another mass (200 kg.) of apples. The given data provide an equivalence between two quantities, mass of apples and cents. Expressing this algebraically we find:

$$80 \text{ lb. apples} = 63 \text{ cents}$$

This will be used to get a conversion factor between pounds of apples and cents. To complete the problem we need regular conversion factors. Thus, to convert 200 kg. of apples to the equivalent number of quarters:

$$200 \text{ kg. apples} = 200 \text{ kg. apples} \times \left(\frac{1000 \text{ g.}}{1 \text{ kg.}}\right) \times \left(\frac{1 \text{ lb.}}{454 \text{ g.}}\right) \times \left(\left(\frac{63 \text{ cents}}{80 \text{ lb. apples}}\right)\right)$$
$$\times \left(\frac{1 \text{ quarter}}{25 \text{ cents}}\right)$$

$$= \frac{200 \times 1000 \times 63}{454 \times 80 \times 25} \text{ quarters}$$

$$= 13.9 \text{ quarters}$$

Note: The property conversion factor in the above equation has been placed in double parentheses for purposes of emphasis and to distinguish it from the other unit conversion factors.

---

12. Summary

1. *A unit conversion factor (or, simply, conversion factor) is a ratio of two different units which measure the same property. The ratio is numerically equal to unity.*

2. *Unit conversion factors are obtained from definitions or experiments and can be used for expressing a given property in one set of units if it has been expressed in a different set of units.*

3. *Scientific laws or direct observations may express an equivalence between two different properties of the same substance.   When expressed as equations, such laws or observations may be used to obtain ratios of two different sets of properties.   These are called property conversion factors and may be used to calculate one property if the related property is given.*

4. *Most calculations may be considered as involving sequences of unit conversion factors and property conversion factors.   If all the laws, observations, and definitions involved in the problem are known, then the answer may be written out as a product of such conversion factors.*

13. Problems

1. Express the following quantities with the metric prefixes:

   (a) 0.002 of an inch. *milli*
   (b) 0.01 mile. *centi*
   (c) 12,000 dresses. *kilo*
   (d) 100,000,000 years. *mega*
   (e) 7,000,000,000 watts. 1×10^9
   (f) 0.0000035 ton. 1×10^{-6} *micro*

2. Write as ordinary numbers in basic units:

   (a) 3.5 kilobucks. 3.5×10^3
   (b) 75 microns. 0.000075×10^{-6}
   (c) 42 kilowatts. 42×10^2
   (d) 0.16 megapound. 0.16×10^6
   (e) 95 gammas. 9.5×10^{-9}
   (f) 2.7 milligallons. 2.7×10^{-3}
   (g) 1.6 kilosheep. 1.6×10^3

3. Which of the following are extensive and which are intensive properties?

   (a) Density. *inten*
   (b) Weight. *ex*
   (c) Temperature. *inten*
   (d) Cost. *extent*
   (e) Color of copper. *in*
   (f) Color of the sky.

4. Convert 25 g. to pounds.

5. Convert 16 mg. to kilograms.

6. What is the weight in tons of 120 mg. of radium?

7. The selling price of radium is now $25,000 per gram.   How much will 2 lb. of radium cost?

8. Convert 20 sq. yd. to square centimeters.

9. A coal bin has the dimensions: 8 ft. by 12 ft. by 15 ft.   How many cubic meters capacity does it have?

10. The wavelength of the yellow light from a sodium lamp is roughly 5900 A. What is this in inches? in centimeters? in microns?

11. The density of carbon tetrachloride is 1.60 g./cm.^{3}.   What is it in tons per cubic yards?

12. A sign in a Mexican town gives the speed limit as 40 km./hr.   What is this in miles per hour? in centimeters per second?

13. The force of the earth's gravitational field will produce an acceleration of 32 ft./sec.^{2}.   What is this in centimeters per square second? in meters per square minute?

14. Convert a force of 980 g.-cm./sec.^{2} (980 dynes) to kilogram-meters per square minute.

15. The volume of a solid is stated by an eccentric person to be 70 in.^{2}-cm. Is this a possible set of units for a volume? Explain why and then proceed to express it in more conventional units.

16. 400 lb. of iron metal occupy a volume of 0.0234 m.^{3}. Calculate the density of iron in grams per cubic centimeter.

17. The density of benzene is 0.88 g./cm.^{3} at 20°C. How many milligrams of benzene are there in 25 cm.^{3}?

18. If 24 hens can lay 150 eggs in a week, how many days will it take 5 hens to lay 250 eggs? (*Note:* Calculate the rate at which one hen lays eggs. What are its units?)

19. An atom of oxygen has a mass of 2.68×10^{-23} g. How many atoms of oxygen are there in 10 lb. of oxygen?

20. A molecule of water has a cross-sectional area of 10 A.^{2}. (*a*) How many molecules of water will be required to cover a square centimeter of surface? (*b*) How many molecules will be required to cover the total surface of a cube whose edge is 1 mm.? (*Note:* Assume that the molecules have the shape of squares.)

CHAPTER II

Methods of Measuring
Quantities of Matter

In the first chapter we have outlined the basis for the measurement of properties of matter and a method for dealing with calculations involving these properties. The remainder of this book will be devoted to an application of these concepts to the solution of chemical problems. In the present chapter we shall turn our attention to the atomic theory of matter and the way in which it affords us a method of measuring quantity of matter in chemical units.

1. Practical Units

A straightforward method for measuring a quantity of matter would be in terms of mass. This is readily accomplished in the laboratory by means of a balance. This is, however, not always the most convenient method available. Thus it is more convenient to measure liquids by volume, with a graduated cylinder or burette. If we know the temperature and the density of the liquid at that temperature, we can easily convert the measured volume to its equivalent in terms

TABLE IV

PRACTICAL METHODS FOR MEASURING QUANTITIES OF MATTER

Physical State	Method Employed	Property Measured	Additional Data Needed To Convert to Mass
Solid	Balance	Mass	None
Liquid	Balance	Mass	None
	Pipette, burette, graduated cylinder	Volume	Temperature and density
Gas	Gas burette, graduated cylinder, tank	Volume	Temperature, pressure, and gas density

of mass units. Similarly, when dealing with gases it is very difficult, if not impossible, to measure a quantity of gas by means of a balance. In the laboratory we measure out quantities of gas by measuring the volume occupied by the gas, the temperature of the gas, and the pressure used to confine the gas to that particular volume. From a knowledge of the temperature, volume, and pressure of the particular gas we can then compute from the gas laws the quantity of matter in the gas. Table IV summarizes the customary methods employed in the laboratory for measuring quantities of matter.

2. Chemical Units

The practical units for measuring out quantities of matter, though the most direct, are not of the greatest significance. The atomic theory of matter tells us that matter is composed of units which we call atoms and molecules. The changes which occur in chemical transformations always involve whole numbers of atoms or molecules. From this theoretical point of view it is more significant to talk directly about the numbers of atoms or molecules which are reacting rather than some auxiliary property such as their mass or volume. In analogous fashion we might say that there are 185 g. of nickels in a dollar. This would hardly be as informative as saying that there are 20 nickels in a dollar. Similarly, the Census Bureau does not report the population of San Francisco as 40,000 tons of people but preferably as 600,000 individuals.*

How, then, can we go about expressing quantities of matter in terms of the number of molecules present? It would seem at first an impossible or at the very least a burdensome task, since even the smallest quantities of matter dealt with in the laboratory contain billions upon billions of molecules. And, further, how can we go about counting molecules, which, as everyone knows, are invisible? The answer to both of these difficulties is given by the atomic theory.

3. Chemical Formulae—Atomic Weights

Chemists have been able to develop methods (which we shall not discuss here) for measuring the weights of single atoms and molecules. They have also been able to determine through methods of chemical analysis the exact composition of compounds, that is, the relative number of atoms of each element that is present in a compound. This type of information is summarized in what we call chemical formulae.

----

* This assumes, of course, that the Census Bureau also has a conversion factor, namely, the average weight of a person.

Thus when we see the formula, NaCl, the symbols tell us that in any quantity of pure NaCl (sodium chloride) there will always be precisely 1 atom of sodium (Na) for every atom of chlorine (Cl). Similarly, the formula H_2SO_4 tells us that in pure sulfuric acid (H_2SO_4) there are precisely 4 atoms of oxygen (O) and 2 atoms of hydrogen (H) for every atom of sulfur (S). These formulae are determined by analysis and are brief, precise means of expressing the information gained by such analysis. If now we know the weights of the respective atoms in these compounds, we can calculate the weights of the molecule corresponding to the written formula. This information is provided by a Table of Atomic Weights.

Thus the weight of 1 molecule of sulfuric acid (H_2SO_4) is obtained by adding the weights of 1 atom of sulfur plus 2 times the weight of 1 atom of hydrogen plus 4 times the weight of 1 atom of oxygen. Performing these additions, we should find that the weight of 1 molecule of $H_2SO_4 = 32 + (2 \times 1) + (4 \times 16) = 98$.

But we are immediately struck by a difficulty. What are the units for this weight?* On further inspection of the table we find that the units are arbitrary. That is, the Table of Atomic Weights does not give the absolute weight of an atom in mass units such as grams but gives the relative weight of the atoms with respect to the weight of an atom of oxygen. Thus the atomic weight of sulfur (S), which is recorded as 32, simply means that an atom of sulfur is heavier than an atom of oxygen in the ratio of 32 to 16. If we knew the absolute weight of an atom of oxygen in grams, we could then calculate the weight of an atom of sulfur in grams. To designate the relative nature of the masses recorded in the Table of Atomic Weights we shall use the term, atomic mass units, and so for consistency we should write the atomic weight of sulfur as 32 a.m.u. (32 atomic mass units). Similarly the mass of 1 molecule of sulfuric acid computed above would then be properly written as 98 a.m.u. If we are now given the relation between atomic mass units and grams, we can quickly convert these relative weight units into grams. However, such information is seldom needed, as we shall soon see, and it is quite rarely that we are ever concerned with the absolute mass of atoms and molecules.

Do problem 1 at the end of the chapter.

---

* The Table of Atomic Weights should more properly be designated the Table of Atomic Masses, since we are really discussing the mass, not the weight. However, since common usage has been to call these quantities weights, we shall follow this designation with the understanding that masses are really meant.

4. Chemical Units—The Mole

Let us define a unit for the measurement of quantities of atoms and molecules as follows:

Definition:

1 mole of a compound = The formula weight of the
                       compound expressed in units of grams*

Examples:

1 mole NaCl	=	58.5 g.
1 mole O_2	=	32 g.
1 mole H_2SO_4	=	98 g.
1 mole $Al_2(SO_4)_3$	=	342 g.
1 mole $Al_2(SO_4)_3 \cdot 18H_2O$	=	666 g.
1 mole Fe	=	56 g.

Note: 1 mole of a monatomic element = atomic weight in grams.

The importance of this unit, the mole, which we have defined above is the following:

One mole of every compound contains the same number of molecules.

Thus 1 mole of H_2SO_4 will contain the same number of molecules (or formula units) of H_2SO_4 as 1 mole of O_2 or 1 mole of H_2O or 1 mole of Fe, etc. The truth of this statement may be demonstrated as follows:

If we take 1 molecule of a compound, let us call it A, and 1 molecule of a second compound, B, then the ratio of the weights of these 2 molecules will be in the ratio of the molecular weight of A to the molecular weight of B.

If we take not 1 but 10 molecules of A and 10 molecules of B, then the ratio of the total weight of the 10 molecules of A to the total weight of the 10 molecules of B will still be in the ratio of the molecular weight of A to the molecular weight of B.

In fact, it doesn't matter how many total molecules of each we have;

---

* Since there is considerable confusion about whether a certain molecule as expressed by its formula really exists, we shall avoid any ambiguity by referring always to the formula. Thus NaCl is the formula for sodium chloride and as such gives its composition. However, solid sodium chloride is made of ions, not molecules, of sodium chloride. By defining 1 mole of sodium chloride as equal to the formula weight of NaCl expressed in grams, such questions are avoided.

as long as we have *equal numbers of molecules of A and B*, the ratio of the total weight of A to B will always be in the ratio of their molecular weights.

Conversely, if we have a certain weight of A and a certain weight of B and these weights are in the ratio of the molecular weights of A and B, then the number of molecules of A and B must be equal.   This is illustrated in the following chart, with O_2 molecules and SO_2 molecules as examples.

Total Number of Molecules of O_2	Total Number of Molecules of SO_2	Ratio of Total Weights SO_2/O_2
1	1	$\dfrac{1 \times 64}{1 \times 32} = 2$
10	10	$\dfrac{10 \times 64}{10 \times 32} = 2$
500	500	$\dfrac{500 \times 64}{500 \times 32} = 2$
1×10^{20}	1×10^{20}	$\dfrac{1 \times 10^{20} \times 64}{1 \times 10^{20} \times 32} = 2$
X	X	$\dfrac{X \times 64}{X \times 32} = 2$

Thus we have succeeded in defining a unit, *the mole*, which is a direct measure of the number of molecules present in a compound and which also is capable of translation into practical units of grams.   The student should observe, however, that this is true only if we know the formula for the compound.

The definition of the mole gives us an algebraic relation between the units of moles and the units of grams and so allows us to obtain a conversion factor between the two sets of units.

Example: How many moles of H_2SO_4 are there in 25 g.?
Answer:

$$1 \text{ mole } H_2SO_4 = 98 \text{ g. } H_2SO_4$$

Then

$$25 \text{ g. } H_2SO_4 = 25 \text{ g. } \cancel{H_2SO_4} \times \left(\frac{1 \text{ mole } H_2SO_4}{98 \text{ g. } \cancel{H_2SO_4}} \right)$$

$$= 0.255 \text{ mole } H_2SO_4$$

Example: How many grams of $CaCl_2$ are there in 2.5 moles?
Answer:

$$1 \text{ mole } CaCl_2 = 111 \text{ g. } CaCl_2$$

Then

$$2.5 \text{ moles } CaCl_2 = 2.5 \text{ moles } CaCl_2 \times \left(\frac{111 \text{ g. } CaCl_2}{1 \text{ mole } CaCl_2} \right)$$

$$= 277.5 \text{ g. } CaCl_2$$

Example: Which will contain more molecules, 40 g. of H_2O or 60 g. of NaCl?
Answer:

$$40 \text{ g. } H_2O = 40 \text{ g. } H_2O \times \left(\frac{1 \text{ mole } H_2O}{18 \text{ g. } H_2O} \right) = 2.22 \text{ moles } H_2O$$

$$60 \text{ g. } NaCl = 60 \text{ g. } NaCl \times \left(\frac{1 \text{ mole } NaCl}{58.5 \text{ g. } NaCl} \right) = 1.03 \text{ moles } NaCl$$

Thus there are more molecules of H_2O.

Do problems 2 and 3 at the end of the chapter.

5. The Number of Molecules in a Mole—Avogadro's Number

In the preceding section we have seen how it is possible to define a unit, the mole, which is proportional to the number of molecules in a quantity of matter and at the same time can be translated into mass units of grams. This would be a perfectly satisfactory system of units even if we were never to know exactly how many molecules were present in a mole.

Scientists, however, are never long satisfied by such a challenge, and a number of ingenious laboratory experiments have been devised which make it possible to measure numerically the number of molecules in a mole of substance. This number, known as Avogadro's number, is equal to 6.0221×10^{23} molecules. Thus we can write the very important algebraic relation:

$$1 \text{ mole } = 6.02 \times 10^{23} \text{ molecules} \quad \text{(from experiment)}$$

This equation now gives us a means of translating from moles to number of molecules, and, since moles are related to units of grams, all three sets of units can be interconverted.

Example: How many molecules are there in 2 g. of water (H_2O)?
Answer: The two fundamental relations are:

$$1 \text{ mole } H_2O = 18 \text{ g. } H_2O$$

$$1 \text{ mole } H_2O = 6.02 \times 10^{23} \text{ molecules } H_2O$$

Then

$$2 \text{ g. } H_2O = 2 \text{ g. } H_2O \times \left(\frac{1 \text{ mole } H_2O}{18 \text{ g. } H_2O}\right) \times \left(\frac{6.02 \times 10^{23} \text{ molecules } H_2O}{1 \text{ mole } H_2O}\right)$$

$$= 6.69 \times 10^{22} \text{ molecules } H_2O$$

Example: What is the mass of 1 atom of oxygen?

Answer: (Student should supply the fundamental relations.)

$$1 \text{ atom } O = 1 \text{ atom } O \times \left(\frac{1 \text{ mole } O}{6.02 \times 10^{23} \text{ atoms } O}\right) \times \left(\frac{16 \text{ g. } O}{1 \text{ mole } O}\right)$$

$$= 2.66 \times 10^{-23} \text{ g. } O$$

The following example shows how these methods can be applied to obtain interesting information.

Example: What is the average volume occupied by 1 molecule of water (H_2O)?

Answer: We can calculate the mass of 1 mole of H_2O from its formula, namely, 18 g. We also know how many molecules there are in 1 mole (6×10^{23}). The problem asks us, however, to calculate the property of volume. To do this we need a relation between mass of water and volume. This relation is provided by the density of water. So we can look through a table of densities and find that the density of water at 0°C. is 1.00 g./cm.^{3}. We now have all the necessary information and can proceed to write out the fundamental relations. The student should do this and check the following:

$$1 \text{ molecule } H_2O = 1 \text{ molecule } H_2O \times \left(\frac{1 \text{ mole } H_2O}{6.02 \times 10^{23} \text{ molecules } H_2O}\right)$$

$$\times \left(\frac{18 \text{ g. } H_2O}{1 \text{ mole } H_2O}\right) \times \left(\frac{1 \text{ cm.}^3 H_2O}{1 \text{ g. } H_2O}\right)$$

$$= 2.99 \times 10^{-23} \text{ cm.}^3$$

Note: If we imagine the molecule as fitting into a cube, the length of one edge of this cube is obtained by taking the cube root of the above volume or 3.1 $\times$ 10^{-8} cm. = 3.1 A. This method represents a crude way of obtaining diameters of molecules.

Do problems 4–7 at the end of the chapter.

6. Volumes of Gases—The Molar Volume

A study of the properties of gases shows us that equal volumes of gases at the same conditions of temperature and pressure will contain equal numbers of molecules. This statement is known as Avogadro's hypothesis and can be proved from the kinetic-molecular hypothesis. The converse of this statement, which is also true, is that equal numbers of molecules of different gases will occupy equal volumes when measured at the same conditions of temperature and pressure. But, since 1 mole of any substance has in it the same number of molecules as 1 mole of any other substance, if the two substances are both gases, then they will occupy equal volumes if kept at the same temperature and pressure.

As a consequence of this extraordinary property of gases, we can define the molar volume of a gas:

Definition: Molar volume of gas = Volume occupied by 1 mole of a gas (at 0°C. and a pressure of 1 atm.)

The temperature of 0°C. and the pressure of 1 atm. have been arbitrarily selected as the standard conditions for gas measurement and are referred to as STP (i.e., standard temperature and pressure).

By experiment the molar volume of a gas has been determined to be 22.4 l. STP. We can thus write the following relation *valid for ideal gases:*

$$\text{1 mole gas} = \text{22.4 l. gas STP} \qquad \text{(experiment)}$$

This last relation is quite extraordinary in that it permits us to determine the molecular weight of a gas merely by weighing it, *without any prior knowledge of its formula or composition.*

Example: A sample of gas, occupying 150 cm.^{3} STP is found to weigh 0.624 g. What is its molecular weight?

Answer: The problem asks us to find the molecular weight, that is, the weight in grams, of 1 mole of the gas. We are told that 150 cm.^{3} STP = 0.624 g.

$$\text{1 mole gas} = \text{1 mole gas} \times \left(\frac{22.4 \text{ l. STP}}{1 \text{ mole gas}}\right) \times \left(\frac{1000 \text{ cm.}^3}{1 \text{ l.}}\right) \times \left(\frac{0.624 \text{ g.}}{150 \text{ cm.}^3 \text{ STP}}\right)$$

$$= \frac{22.4 \times 1000 \times 0.624}{150} \text{ g.}$$

$$= 93.2 \text{ g.}$$

The molecular weight is thus 93.2 g.

---

7. Summary

From the point of view of the atomic theory, the fundamental chemical units are atoms and molecules. A unit is defined, the mole, which is related to the number of molecules in a quantity of matter. Since laboratory practice requires that we measure quantities of matter in mass units or volume units, we need a set of relations which will allow us to relate these practical, laboratory units to the more significant theoretical units. These relations are the following:

(1)   1 mole = Formula weight of a substance in grams   (definition)

(2)   1 mole = 6.02×10^{23} molecules   (experiment)

(3)   1 mole = 22.4 l. STP (*for gases only*)   (experiment)

Auxiliary unit:

1 millimole (mmole) = One thousandth mole

$$= 1 \times 10^{-3} \text{ mole}   \text{(definition)}$$

From these relations we can derive conversion factors for converting from any one of these units to any other. Since all these units are in frequent use, the student should gain facility in these conversions.

Example: How many grams of NH_3 (ammonia) are there in 800 cm.³ STP of NH_3 gas?
Answer:

$$800 \text{ cm.}^3 \text{ STP } NH_3 = 800 \text{ cm.}^3 \text{ STP } NH_3 \times \left(\frac{1 \text{ l.}}{1000 \text{ cm.}^3} \right)$$
$$\times \left(\frac{1 \text{ mole } NH_3}{22.4 \text{ l. STP } NH_3} \right) \times \left(\frac{17 \text{ g. } NH_3}{1 \text{ mole } NH_3} \right)$$

$$= \frac{800 \times 17}{1000 \times 22.4} \text{ g. } NH_3$$

$$= 0.607 \text{ g. } NH_3$$

Example: How many millimoles of H_2SO_4 are represented by 2×10^{18} molecules of H_2SO_4?
Answer:

$$2 \times 10^{18} \text{ molecules of } H_2SO_4 = 2 \times 10^{18} \text{ molecules } H_2SO_4$$
$$\times \left(\frac{1 \text{ mole } H_2SO_4}{6 \times 10^{23} \text{ molecules } H_2SO_4} \right) \times \left(\frac{1000 \text{ mmoles}}{1 \text{ mole}} \right) = 3.3 \times 10^{-3} \text{ mmole } H_2SO_4$$

---

8. Problems

1. Compute the molecular weights of the following substances:

(a) ZnS.   *65.38 + 32 = 97*   (e) $CuSO_4 \cdot 5H_2O$.
(b) Na_2O_2. *(23 × 2) + (16 × 2) = 78*   (f) C_6H_6.
(c) $CuSO_4$.   (g) $Ba_3(AlO_3)_2$.
(d) $Na_2S_2O_3$.   (h) H_4SiO_4.

2. Make the following conversions:

(a) 6.0 g. of NH_3 to moles.
(b) 4.7 mmoles of HCl to grams.
(c) 2.7 moles of $Ca_3(PO_4)_2$ to grams.

(d) 0.026 g. of $Cu(NO_3)_2$ to millimoles.
(e) 0.18 kg. of $Ba(ClO_3)_2$ to moles.
(f) 1.8 lb. of $(NH_4)_2SO_4$ to millimoles.
(g) 24 g. of $CuSO_4 \cdot 5H_2O$ to moles.

3. Which has more molecules?

(a) 4 mmoles of HNO_3 or 80 mg. of HNO_3.
(b) 16 g. of NaCl or 20 g. of KCl.
(c) 4 moles of $Ca(NO_3)_2$ or 1 kg. of $PbCl_2$.

4. Make the following conversions:

(a) 0.24 mole of H_2O to molecules.
(b) 1.7 mmoles of HCl to molecules.
(c) 6.9×10^{16} molecules of CO_2 to moles.
(d) 2 lb. of Cl_2 to molecules.
(e) 6000 molecules of $Ca_3(PO_4)_2$ to tons.

5. How many millimoles of S are there in 20 mg. of H_2S?
6. If 1.8×10^{19} molecules of NO_2 are removed from 10 mg. of NO_2, how many moles of NO_2 are left?
7. The density of carbon tetrachloride (CCl_4) is 1.65 g./cc. at $-5°C$. What is the average volume occupied by 1 molecule of CCl_4 at this temperature?
8. Make the following conversions:

(a) 26 cc. STP of Cl_2 gas to millimoles of Cl_2.
(b) 2.1×10^{26} molecules of NO gas to liters STP of NO gas.
(c) 16 mg. H_2S to cubic centimeters STP of H_2S gas.
(d) 33 l. STP of SF_6 gas to kilograms of SF_6.

9. 620 mg. of an unknown gas occupy a volume of 175 cc. STP. What is the molecular weight of the gas?
10. One molecule of an unknown chemical compound is found to have a mass of 2.33×10^{-22} g. What is the molecular weight of the compound?
11. A 1-l. vessel is found to weigh 500.763 g. when evacuated. What will its weight be when it is filled with CO_2 gas STP? (Ignore buoyancy effects.)
12. It is found that 2.71×10^{19} molecules of an unknown compound have a mass of 3.76 mg. What is its molecular weight?
13. A 250-cc. flask has a weight of 261.023 g. when filled at STP with a gas. When evacuated its weight is 260.242 g. What is the molecular weight of the gas?
14. The density of CCl_4 (liquid) at $0°C$. is 1.600 g./cc. What is the volume occupied by 800 molecules of CCl_4? What is the volume occupied by a single molecule of CCl_4? From the latter result, what is the diameter in Angstroms of a molecule of CCl_4?

CHAPTER III

Chemical Formulae

1. Interpretation of Chemical Formulae

In Chapter II we stated that a chemical formula represents a concise method of giving the chemical composition of an element or compound. Let us now be more specific about the information conveyed by a chemical formula.

The symbol H_2O is interpreted as representing 1 molecule of water. It further means that in 1 molecule of water there are 2 atoms of hydrogen (H) and 1 atom of oxygen (O). We shall now extend this interpretation to include the following: H_2O may also mean 1 mole as well as 1 molecule of water. The full meaning conveyed is that 1 mole of water (H_2O) contains 2 moles of H and 1 mole of O. In similar fashion we shall interpret the formula H_2SO_4 as representing 1 mole of sulfuric acid which contains 2 moles of H, 1 mole of S, and 4 moles of O.

This may appear to the reader like a step backwards. Are we not adding confusion by giving a chemical symbol two different meanings? The answer is, of course, that we are. However, the confusion will be small if not negligible since it will generally be quite apparent from the way in which these symbols are used just which interpretation is meant. On the other hand, by making this additional interpretation we are making it possible to discuss formulae in terms of theoretical units (moles) which represent a certain large number of molecules and which at the same time may be related to practical units such as grams.

The student should convince himself that the two interpretations are consistent. This can be seen as follows:

If we have 6.02×10^{23} molecules of H_2O, we have $2 \times 6.02 \times 10^{23}$ atoms of H and 6.02×10^{23} atoms of O. But, by the relation, 1 mole $= 6.02 \times 10^{23}$ molecules, these numbers represent in turn 1 mole of H_2O; 2 moles of H, and 1 mole of O. Thus the two interpretations are consistent.

30

2. Molar Composition of Chemical Compounds

We have seen from the discussion above that a chemical formula summarizes our knowledge of the chemical composition of a compound. It presents this information concerning composition not in terms of practical or laboratory units, such as grams, but in theoretical units. That is, it tells us the relative number of atoms of each element present in the compound or, alternatively, the relative number of moles of each element present in the compound. Chemical formulae thus give us the *molar composition* of a compound.

How does a chemist obtain the information which enables him to write a chemical formula? That is, how does he obtain the *molar composition* from which a formula can be written? In answering this very important question, let us proceed backwards and first show that if we know the *molar composition* we can write the chemical formula.

Suppose we find that 0.100 mole of calcium (Ca) metal react precisely with 0.100 mole of oxygen (O) to produce the single, pure substance calcium oxide. We can infer from this that the formula for calcium oxide must be CaO, since our experimental observation has informed us that there is 1 mole of oxygen for every mole of calcium in the compound calcium oxide.

Example: It is found experimentally that a certain quantity of the compound, zinc sulfate, contains 0.241 mole of zinc (Zn), 0.241 mole of sulfur (S), and 0.964 mole of oxygen (O). What is its chemical formula?

Answer: The above analytical evidence shows us that for every 1 mole of Zn there are 1 mole of S and 4 moles of O present in zinc sulfate. The formula must be $ZnSO_4$.

Example: It is found that a certain quantity of the compound $Al_2(CO_3)_3$ on analysis will yield 1.32 moles of aluminum (Al). How many moles of carbon (C) and oxygen (O) were present in this quantity of the compound?

Answer: From the formula, the molar composition is 2 moles of Al, 3 moles of C, and 9 moles of O. Thus there will be $\frac{3}{2} \times 1.32$ moles of C = 1.98 moles of C and $\frac{9}{2} \times 1.32$ moles of O = 5.94 moles of O.

Do problems 1–7 at the end of the chapter.

3. Composition Conversion Factors

It is possible to set the information conveyed by a chemical formula in terms of algebraic relations such that our methods of conversion factors may be employed.

The formula for calcium chloride, $CaCl_2$, tells us that 1 molecule of $CaCl_2$ contains 1 atom of Ca and 2 atoms of Cl or, alternatively,

1 mole of $CaCl_2$ contains 1 mole of Ca and 2 moles of Cl. From this information, then, for the compound $CaCl_2$ we can write all of the following relations:

$$1 \text{ mole } CaCl_2 = 1 \text{ mole Ca}; \quad 1 \text{ mole } CaCl_2 = 2 \text{ moles Cl};$$

$$1 \text{ mole Ca} = 2 \text{ moles Cl}$$

But surely, you will protest, 1 mole of $CaCl_2$ is not equal to 1 mole of Ca. This objection is certainly true, and we must be careful, as we were in the discussion of complex properties (e.g., density), to place a restrictive interpretation on these equations. Strictly speaking, they represent properties of the same amount (1 mole) of a particular substance ($CaCl_2$), and as such they represent alternative methods of measuring this particular amount (1 mole) of this particular substance. Thus we can measure out 1 mole of $CaCl_2$ by taking that quantity of $CaCl_2$ which contains 1 mole of Ca or that which contains 2 moles of Cl.

From these relations between the composition properties of $CaCl_2$ we can make composition conversion factors that will be used like our regular conversion factors to convert from one aspect of the composition to another.

Example: How many moles of oxygen (O) are there in 0.265 mole of $CuSO_4$?
Answer:

$$0.265 \text{ mole } CuSO_4 = 0.265 \text{ mole } CuSO_4 \times \left(\frac{4 \text{ moles O}}{1 \text{ mole } CuSO_4} \right)$$

$$= 1.06 \text{ moles O}$$

Example: How many moles of Na_2CO_3 (sodium carbonate) will contain 0.124 mole of Na?
Answer:

$$0.124 \text{ mole Na} = 0.124 \text{ mole Na} \times \left(\frac{1 \text{ mole } Na_2CO_3}{2 \text{ moles Na}} \right)$$

$$= 0.062 \text{ mole } Na_2CO_3$$

Example: A certain quantity of barium phosphate, $Ba_3(PO_4)_2$, is found to contain 0.64 mole of O. How many moles of Ba were present also?
Answer:

$$0.64 \text{ mole O} = 0.64 \text{ mole O} \times \left(\frac{3 \text{ moles Ba}}{8 \text{ moles O}} \right)$$

$$= 0.24 \text{ mole Ba}$$

To summarize, we can say that the subscripts in a chemical formula represent the moles of each element present in 1 mole of the compound represented by that formula.

Composition conversion factors can be obtained by writing the ratio of the numbers of moles of each element present in the formula, and these can be used to convert from moles of one element present to moles of any other element or to moles of the parent compound.

4. Chemical Analysis—Weight Composition—Summary

We now come to the important question: How can we determine the formula of a compound? In order to determine the formula (that is, the molar composition) we must first know what elements are present, and, second, we must know the weight of each element present. This latter information is provided by the experimental techniques of quantitative analysis. The results of a direct experimental analysis generally give us the weight composition, that is, the weight of each element present in a compound. The formula can be obtained from this weight composition by conversion to molar composition with the atomic weights as conversion factors.

Example: It is possible by chemical analysis to show that in, let us say, 2.000 g. of copper chloride there is 0.945 g. of copper (Cu) and 1.055 g. of chlorine (Cl). From this information determine the formula for copper chloride.

Answer: We are given the weight composition and desire the molar composition.

$$0.945 \text{ g. Cu} = 0.945 \text{ g. Cu} \times \left(\frac{1 \text{ mole Cu}}{63.6 \text{ g. Cu}} \right) = 0.0148 \text{ mole Cu}$$

$$1.055 \text{ g. Cl} = 1.055 \text{ g. Cl} \times \left(\frac{1 \text{ mole Cl}}{35.5 \text{ g. Cl}} \right) = 0.0297 \text{ mole Cl}$$

Thus for the compound $CuCl_2$ there are 0.0297 mole of Cl for 0.0148 mole of Cu. Written algebraically:

$$0.0297 \text{ mole Cl} = 0.0148 \text{ mole Cu (for copper chloride)   (experimental)}$$

Dividing both sides by 0.0148 (the smaller of the two quantities), we have

$$2.006 \text{ moles Cl} = 1 \text{ mole Cu}$$

Allowing then for the error of 6 parts in 2000, we see that the formula is $CuCl_2$.

Example: In 4.50 g. of an organic compound, acrylic acid, there are found to be 2.25 g. of carbon (C), 2.00 g. of oxygen (O), and 0.25 g. of hydrogen (H). What is its formula?

Answer: Using atomic weights we convert this weight composition to molar composition:

$$2.25 \text{ g. C} = 2.25 \text{ g. C} \times \left(\frac{1 \text{ mole C}}{12 \text{ g. C}} \right) = 0.187 \text{ mole C}$$

$$2.00 \text{ g. O} = 2.00 \text{ g. O} \times \left(\frac{1 \text{ mole O}}{16 \text{ g. O}} \right) = 0.125 \text{ mole O}$$

$$0.25 \text{ g. H} = 0.25 \text{ g. H} \times \left(\frac{1 \text{ mole H}}{1 \text{ g. H}} \right) = 0.25 \text{ mole H}$$

Dividing each of these by the smallest, 0.125 mole O, we find the molar composition conversion factors:

$$\frac{0.187 \text{ mole C}}{0.125 \text{ mole O}} = \frac{1.5 \text{ moles C}}{1 \text{ mole O}}; \quad \frac{0.25 \text{ mole H}}{0.125 \text{ mole O}} = \frac{2 \text{ moles H}}{1 \text{ mole O}}$$

From this we can write the formula $C_{1.5}H_2O_1$. However, we want whole numbers in our formula, so we multiply all the subscripts by 2 and obtain $C_3H_4O_2$.

Do problems 8–14 at the end of the chapter.

Summary: *To obtain a chemical formula from the experimentally determined weight composition:*

1. *Convert the weights to mole composition, using the atomic weights as conversion factors.*

2. *Obtain composition conversion factors by dividing the number of moles of each element by the smallest number of moles of an element present.*

3. *Write the formula from the mole conversion factors using as subscripts the smallest whole numbers.*

5. Weight Per Cent

It is usual for analysts to express their results as weight per cent rather than in terms of grams. An analysis of the composition of water will be reported as 11.1% hydrogen (H) and 88.9% oxygen (O). This means that, if we take 100 weight units of water (100 lb., 100 g., etc.), 11.1 weight units will be hydrogen and 88.9 weight units will be oxygen. Thus, 100 tons of water contain 11.1 tons of hydrogen and 88.9 tons of oxygen. Percentage is an *intensive* property. It is independent of the quantity of material chosen. The percentage of hydrogen in a sample of water is always 11.1% even though the sample may weigh 1 g., 29.6 g., or 2 tons.

If a substance contains individual components A, B, C, D, etc., then the weight per cent of component A is given by the following definition.

Definition:

Wt. % A = Weight of A contained in 100 weight units of substance

or

$$\text{Wt. \% A} = \frac{\text{Weight of A}}{\text{Weight of substance}} \times 100$$

Example: What is the percentage of sulfur (S) in a mixture containing 80 lb. of sulfur and 70 lb. of iron?
Answer:

$$\text{Wt. \% S} = \frac{80 \text{ lb. S}}{150 \text{ lb. mixture}} \times 100$$

$$= 53.3$$

It is to be noted that the property of weight per cent (or, as generally abbreviated, %) can be used as a property conversion factor relating the number of weight units of a component to 100 weight units of the total sample.

To calculate formulae from composition reported as weight per cent we proceed by writing weight units, grams, in place of the units, per cent, and continue as usual.

Example: The composition of calcium pyrophosphate is: calcium (Ca) = 25.3%; phosphorous (P) = 39.2%; oxygen (O) = 35.5%.   What is its formula?
Answer:

Weight Composition for 100-g. Sample	Molar Composition	Dividing by the Smallest Quantity
$25.3 \% \text{ Ca} = 25.3 \text{ g. Ca} = 25.3 \text{ g. Ca} \times \left(\frac{1 \text{ mole Ca}}{40 \text{ g. Ca}}\right)$	$= 0.633 \text{ mole Ca} =$	1
$39.2 \% \text{ P} = 39.2 \text{ g. P} = 39.2 \text{ g. P} \times \left(\frac{1 \text{ mole P}}{31 \text{ g. P}}\right)$	$= 1.266 \text{ moles P} =$	$\frac{2 \text{ moles P}}{1 \text{ mole Ca}}$
$35.5 \% \text{ O} = 35.5 \text{ g. O} = 35.5 \text{ g. O} \times \left(\frac{1 \text{ mole O}}{16 \text{ g. O}}\right)$	$= 2.22 \text{ moles O} =$	$\frac{3.5 \text{ moles O}}{1 \text{ mole Ca}}$

The formula is thus: $Ca_1P_2O_{3.5}$ or, eliminating fractions, $Ca_2P_4O_7$.

Do problems 15 and 17–20 at the end of the chapter.

6. Empirical Formulae and True Formulae

The weight composition or molar composition of a compound tells us only the ratio of atoms of each element present in a compound; it tells us nothing about molecules.   Indeed, if sodium chloride is used as an example, there are no molecules which exist as such in a crystal of table salt.

The formula which we write on the basis of a chemical analysis is the simplest formula or the *empirical formula*. The analysis of water tells us only that for every atom of oxygen there are 2 atoms of hydrogen. We could write for the formula of water: H_2O; H_4O_2; H_6O_3; H_8O_4; etc. Chemical analysis alone cannot tell us which is the proper formula for a molecule of water or indeed whether there is any such thing as a molecule of water.

In order to write the correct molecular formula, rather than the empirical or simplest formula, we must know:

1. That a molecule really exists.
2. What the molecular weight is.

Water, for example, can exist as a gas which must be, by the molecular theory, made up of molecules. From the density of the gas (water vapor) the molecular weight can be calculated; it is 18. Comparing this with the molecular weights of the possible formulae shown above, we see that H_2O is the true molecular formula for water.

For salts made up of individual ions, there are no molecular units, and so empirical formulae are always written (e.g., $NaCl$, $CaSO_4$, $BaCl_2$, etc.).

Example: Benzene has the empirical formula CH. If its molecular weight (from gas density) is 78, what is its true molecular formula?

Answer: The true formula must be some multiple of CH, such as C_2H_2, C_3H_3, etc. One CH unit has a molecular weight of 13. Since the total molecular weight is 78, there are $78/13 = 6$ CH units in the molecule. Thus the true molecular formula is C_6H_6.

Do problem 16 at the end of the chapter.

7. Summary

1. The subscripts in a chemical formula give the number of atoms of each element present in the molecular unit designated by the formula.

2. The above molecular interpretation can be extended to include: The subscripts in a formula give the number of moles of each element present in 1 mole of the given formula.

3. From the ratio of any two subscripts we can obtain a composition conversion factor which enables us, for that particular compound, to convert from moles of one element to moles of another element.

4. Chemical analysis gives us the weight composition of a compound. To calculate the formula we must convert this to mole composition (by dividing by the atomic weights). From the mole composition we can obtain molar ratios and thus write the empirical formula for the compound.

5. *True molecular formula can be written only if we have additional information such as the molecular weight. Not all compounds are composed of molecules, notably salts!*

8. Problems

1. Interpret the following formulae in terms of molecules and atoms and in terms of moles. Which seem to be true formulae? Explain why.

(a) H_2O_2.
(b) Na_2SO_4.
(c) $Na_2SO_4 \cdot 10H_2O$.
(d) $Al_2(SO_4)_3$.
(e) CaC_2.
(f) N_2H_4.
(g) $2CaSO_4 \cdot H_2O$.
(h) $C_{10}H_{18}$.

2. How many moles of oxygen (O) are there in 0.28 mole of $Al_2(SO_4)_3$?

3. How many moles of sulfur (S) are there in 1.78 moles of $Na_4S_4O_6$?

4. How many moles of oxygen (O) are there in 0.12 mole of $Na_2CO_3 \cdot 10H_2O$?

5. How many moles of $CuSO_4$ will contain 6.3 mmoles of oxygen (O)?

6. How many moles of H_2O_2 will contain 24 mmoles of H?

7. A certain quantity of $Na_2B_4O_7$ contains 0.33 mole of O. How many millimoles of B does it contain?

8. How many moles of B are there in 20 g. of $Na_2B_4O_7$?

9. How many millimoles of S are there in 18 g. of $Al_2(S_2O_3)_3$?

10. How many grams of O are there in 64 mmoles of $CaSO_4$?

11. How many milligrams of Na are there in 240 mg. of Na_2CO_3?

12. How many grams of Ca are there in 1 ton of $Ca_3(PO_4)_2$?

13. How many atoms of O are there in 20 mg. of H_2O_2?

14. What is the weight per cent composition of the following:

(a) NaBr.
(b) $Ca(CN)_2$.
(c) $K_2S_2O_3$.
(d) $Na_2CO_3 \cdot 10H_2O$.
(e) $C_2H_4O_2$.
(f) $C_6H_5NO_2$.

15. Write the empirical formula for each of the following compounds whose weight per cent composition is given:

(a) Calcium (Ca) = 20.0%; bromine (Br) = 80.0%.
(b) Carbon (C) = 53.0%; oxygen (O) = 47.0%.
(c) Aluminum (Al) = 23.1%; carbon (C) = 15.4%; oxygen (O) = 61.5%.
(d) Strontium (Sr) = 65.7%; silicon (Si) = 10.4%; oxygen (O) = 23.9%.
(e) Manganese (Mn) = 56.4%; sulfur (S) = 43.6%.
(f) Calcium (Ca) = 18.3%; chlorine (Cl) = 32.4%; hydrogen (H) = 5.5%; oxygen (O) = 43.8%.

16. Given the following empirical formulae and molecular weights, compute the true molecular formulae:

Empirical Formula	Molecular Weight	True Formula
CH_2	84	
HO	34	
CH_2O	150	
HgCl	472	
HF	80	

17. 9.7 g. of a hydrate of $CuSO_4$ loses 3.5 g. of water on heating. What is the empirical formula for the hydrate?

18. 2.50 g. of a compound containing chromium (Cr) and sulfur (S) contains a total of 1.20 g. of sulfur (S). What is its formula?

19. When 3.75 g. of platinum chloride is heated, chlorine escapes and 2.17 g. of platinum is left. What is its formula?

20. 2.80 g. of $CuCl_2$ combines with 2.11 g. of NH_3 to form a compound. What is its formula?

CHAPTER IV

Chemical Reactions

1. Interpretation of Equations: Molecular

Just as a chemical formula is a concise way of representing the results of the analysis of a chemical compound in theoretical units (molecules, moles), so a chemical equation is an equally precise way of representing our *experimentally determined* information about a chemical reaction. Let us see how this information is acquired and how it is presented.

It is possible to determine in the laboratory that, when ferrous sulfide is heated in oxygen gas, the products of the reaction are ferric oxide and sulfur dioxide gas. We can represent this information as follows:

Ferrous sulfide + Oxygen (gas) → Ferric oxide + Sulfur dioxide (gas)

By chemical analysis we can determine the formulae for all the starting materials (reactants) and for the products. Substituting this information in our written equation we have:

$$FeS + O_2 \rightarrow Fe_2O_3 + SO_2 \quad \text{(skeleton equation)}$$

This skeleton, or unbalanced, equation, as it is called, now tells us what the reactants are, what the products of the reaction are, and also the composition of each of these. This equation may be "balanced"; that is, it can be written in such fashion as to tell us precisely what amounts of each substance takes part in the reaction. The justification for such balancing is provided by the atomic theory, which states that atoms can be neither created nor destroyed in chemical reactions.

This means that there must be the same number of atoms of each element present at the start and at the end of the reaction. (That is, there must be present the same number of atoms of each element distributed among the products of the reaction as there were in the reactants.)

39

The method of balancing is to put the *proper coefficients* before the formula for each substance in such a way that a final equation will result in which the equality of atoms is achieved. For simple equations this can be done by trial and error. For more complicated equations we shall develop special methods in a later chapter on oxidation and reduction.

The skeleton equation with which we started is balanced in the following form: FeS + O₂ → Fe₂O₃ + SO₂

$$4\text{FeS} + 7\text{O}_2 \rightarrow 2\text{Fe}_2\text{O}_3 + 4\text{SO}_2$$

Atoms Present in Reactants	Atoms Present in Products
Fe: 4 (in FeS)	Fe: 4 (in Fe_2O_3)
S: 4 (in FeS)	S: 4 (in SO_2)
O: 14 (in O_2)	O: 14 (in SO_2 and Fe_2O_3)

The equation can be interpreted in molecular terms:

4 molecules FeS + 7 molecules O_2 → 2 molecules Fe_2O_3
$$+ \text{ 4 molecules SO}_2$$

This is now a precise statement of the quantities of matter that take part in the chemical change.

Do problem 1 at the end of the chapter.

2. Chemical Conversion Factors: Molecular

The ratio of any two quantities in the balanced equation gives us a "chemical" conversion factor which allows us to convert from molecules of one substance to the equivalent number of molecules of the other substance involved in the particular reaction.

From the balanced equation:

$$4\text{FeS} + 7\text{O}_2 \rightarrow 2\text{Fe}_2\text{O}_3 + 4\text{SO}_2$$

we can write the following *chemical conversion factors:*

$$\left(\frac{4 \text{ molecules FeS}}{7 \text{ molecules O}_2}\right); \quad \left(\frac{4 \text{ molecules FeS}}{2 \text{ molecules Fe}_2\text{O}_3}\right); \quad \left(\frac{7 \text{ molecules O}_2}{4 \text{ molecules SO}_2}\right); \text{ etc.}$$

These conversion factors can now be used in performing calculations.*

* We will continue to use the word molecule to refer to the formula, even if the particular substance indicated by the formula is not composed of molecules.

Example: How many molecules of SO_2 can be made, using the above reaction, from 20 molecules of FeS?

Answer: Our conversion factor is

$$\left(\frac{4 \text{ molecules } SO_2}{4 \text{ molecules FeS}} \right)$$

Then

$$20 \text{ molecules FeS} = 20 \text{ molecules FeS} \times \left(\frac{4 \text{ molecules } SO_2}{4 \text{ molecules FeS}} \right)$$

$$= 20 \text{ molecules } SO_2$$

Example: How many molecules of O_2 are needed to react with 36 molecules of FeS?

Answer:

$$36 \text{ molecules FeS} = 36 \text{ molecules FeS} \times \left(\frac{7 \text{ molecules } O_2}{4 \text{ molecules FeS}} \right)$$

$$= 63 \text{ molecules } O_2$$

3. Chemical Conversion Factors: Molar

Molecules are not practical units for laboratory work. Thus the above interpretation of equations in terms of molecules is not very useful for actual experiments. We need another interpretation of equations in terms of some unit which will have the theoretical significance of molecules and which can be related to practical, laboratory units such as grams. This unit, as we have already seen, is the *mole*.

Just as formulae can be interpreted directly in terms of moles or of molecules, so equations can be also interpreted directly in terms of moles as well as molecules. To show this, let us multiply every term on both sides of our equation by the number 6.02×10^{23}. This does not alter the equality. The resulting equation is

$$4(6.02 \times 10^{23})FeS + 7(6.02 \times 10^{23})O_2 \rightarrow 2(6.02 \times 10^{23})Fe_2O_3 + 4(6.02 \times 10^{23})SO_2$$

But observe that 6.02×10^{23} molecules of a substance is precisely 1 mole of that substance. We can thus replace this number by its equivalent in moles, and our equation becomes

$$4 \text{ moles FeS} + 7 \text{ moles } O_2 \rightarrow 2 \text{ moles } Fe_2O_3 + 4 \text{ moles } SO_2$$

Thus we have shown that balanced equations can be interpreted directly in terms of moles as well as molecules. Since moles can be related directly to practical units of mass, this is the interpretation we shall most frequently make. Just as the ratio of any two quantities in an equation can be used to obtain chemical conversion factors in terms of molecules, our added interpretation allows us to obtain chemical conversion factors in terms of moles.

Thus we have the following conversion factors:

$$\left(\frac{4 \text{ moles FeS}}{7 \text{ moles } O_2}\right); \quad \left(\frac{7 \text{ moles } O_2}{4 \text{ moles } SO_2}\right); \quad \left(\frac{4 \text{ moles FeS}}{2 \text{ moles Fe}_2O_3}\right);$$

$$\left(\frac{2 \text{ moles Fe}_2O_3}{4 \text{ moles } SO_2}\right); \text{ etc.}$$

$$4FeS + 7O_2 \rightarrow 2Fe_2O_3 + 4SO_2$$

This can be used in solving problems in units of moles.

Example: How many moles of SO_2 can be made from 0.24 mole of FeS?
Answer:

$$0.24 \text{ mole FeS} = 0.24 \text{ mole FeS} \times \left(\frac{4 \text{ moles } SO_2}{4 \text{ moles FeS}}\right)$$

$$= 0.24 \text{ mole } SO_2$$

Example: How many moles of oxygen are needed to produce 2.50 moles of Fe_2O_3?
Answer:

$$2.50 \text{ moles Fe}_2O_3 = 2.50 \text{ moles Fe}_2O_3 \times \left(\frac{7 \text{ moles } O_2}{2 \text{ moles Fe}_2O_3}\right)$$

$$= 8.75 \text{ moles } O_2$$

Do problems 2–4 at the end of the chapter.

4. Summary

1. *Balanced chemical equations can be interpreted in terms of molecules or moles directly. The coefficients in the balanced equation indicate the number of moles (or molecules) of each substance taking part in the chemical reaction.*

2. *The ratio of any two coefficients in a chemical equation gives us a chemical conversion factor for converting from moles (or molecules) of one substance to moles (or molecules) of the other substance.*

5. Calculations in Mixed Units

From the foregoing discussion we have seen that problems concerning chemical reactions can be solved in one step by means of chemical conversion factors. This is true, however, only if the units are moles. But most practical questions involving chemical reactions are based not on molar units but rather on practical units such as grams, or, if gases are concerned, the volume of the gas at STP.

We have already seen, in Chapter II, how to convert these practical units directly to molar units and vice versa. Every calculation involving chemical reactions can be solved by the following scheme:

1. Convert given units (e.g., grams, volumes, etc.) to moles.
2. Convert from moles of given substance to moles of desired substance by means of the appropriate chemical conversion factor.
3. Convert from moles of desired substance to whatever units are requested in the answer.

Note that these three steps can be combined into a single product of conversion factors.

Example:

$$Na_2CO_3 + 2HNO_3 \rightarrow 2NaNO_3 + H_2O + CO_2$$

How many grams of $NaNO_3$ can be made from 10 g. of $NaCO_3$?
   Answer: (1) Convert 10 g. of Na_2CO_3 to moles. Fundamental equation is

$$1 \text{ mole } Na_2CO_3 = 106 \text{ g. } Na_2CO_3$$

Conversion factor is

$$\left(\frac{1 \text{ mole } Na_2CO_3}{106 \text{ g. } Na_2CO_3}\right)$$

Then

$$10 \text{ g. } Na_2CO_3 = 10 \text{ g. } Na_2CO_3 \times \left(\frac{1 \text{ mole } Na_2CO_3}{106 \text{ g. } Na_2CO_3}\right) = 0.094 \text{ mole } Na_2CO_3$$

(2) Convert moles of Na_2CO_3 to moles of $NaNO_3$. Fundamental equation is the balanced chemical equation. Chemical conversion factor is

$$\left(\frac{2 \text{ moles } NaNO_3}{1 \text{ mole } Na_2CO_3}\right)$$

Then

$$0.094 \text{ mole } Na_2CO_3 = 0.094 \text{ mole } Na_2CO_3 \times \left(\frac{2 \text{ moles } NaNO_3}{1 \text{ mole } Na_2CO_3}\right)$$

$$= 0.188 \text{ mole } NaNO_3$$

(3) Finally, convert moles of $NaNO_3$ to grams of $NaNO_3$. Fundamental equation is

$$1 \text{ mole } NaNO_3 = 85 \text{ g. } NaNO_3$$

Conversion factor is

$$\left(\frac{85 \text{ g. NaNO}_3}{1 \text{ mole NaNO}_3}\right)$$

Then

$$0.188 \text{ mole NaNO}_3 = 0.188 \text{ mole NaNO}_3 \times \left(\frac{85 \text{ g. NaNO}_3}{1 \text{ mole NaNO}_3}\right) = 15.98 \text{ g. NaNO}_3$$

Notice that the three steps could have been combined:

$$10 \text{ g. Na}_2\text{CO}_3 \times \overset{(1)}{\left(\frac{1 \text{ mole Na}_2\text{CO}_3}{106 \text{ g. Na}_2\text{CO}_3}\right)} \times \overset{(2)}{\left(\frac{2 \text{ moles NaNO}_3}{1 \text{ mole Na}_2\text{CO}_3}\right)} \times \overset{(3)}{\left(\frac{85 \text{ g. NaNO}_3}{1 \text{ mole NaNO}_3}\right)}$$
$$= 15.98 \text{ g. NaNO}_3$$

Example:
$$\text{MnO}_2 + 4\text{HCl} \rightarrow \text{MnCl}_2 + \text{Cl}_2 + 2\text{H}_2\text{O}$$

How many liters of Cl_2 gas STP can be made from 20 g. of HCl?
Answer:

$$20 \text{ g. HCl} = 20 \text{ g. HCl} \times \overset{(1)}{\left(\frac{1 \text{ mole HCl}}{36.5 \text{ g. HCl}}\right)} \times \overset{(2)}{\left(\frac{1 \text{ mole Cl}_2}{4 \text{ moles HCl}}\right)} \times \overset{(3)}{\left(\frac{22.4 \text{ l. STP}}{1 \text{ mole}}\right)}$$
$$= 3.07 \text{ l. STP Cl}_2$$

Example:
$$\text{Al}_4\text{C}_3 + 12\text{H}_2\text{O} \rightarrow 4\text{Al(OH)}_3 + 3\text{CH}_4$$

How many molecules of CH_4 will be produced when 0.2 g. of Al(OH)_3 are prepared?
Answer:

$$0.2 \text{ g. Al(OH)}_3 = 0.2 \text{ g. Al(OH)}_3 \times \overset{(1)}{\left(\frac{1 \text{ mole Al(OH)}_3}{78 \text{ g. Al(OH)}_3}\right)} \times \overset{(2)}{\left(\frac{3 \text{ moles CH}_4}{4 \text{ moles Al(OH)}_3}\right)}$$
$$\times \overset{(3)}{\left(\frac{6.02 \times 10^{23} \text{ mol.}}{1 \text{ mole}}\right)} = 1.16 \times 10^{21} \text{ molecules CH}_4$$

Example:
$$4\text{FeS} + 7\text{O}_2 \rightarrow 2\text{Fe}_2\text{O}_3 + 4\text{SO}_2$$

How many grams of Fe_2O_3 can be made, using 600 cc. STP of O_2?
Answer:

$$600 \text{ cc. O}_2 \text{ STP} = 600 \text{ cc. O}_2 \text{ STP} \times \left(\frac{1 \text{ l.}}{1000 \text{ cc.}}\right) \times \left(\frac{1 \text{ mole}}{22.4 \text{ l. STP}}\right)$$
$$\times \left(\frac{2 \text{ moles Fe}_2\text{O}_3}{7 \text{ moles O}_2}\right) \times \left(\frac{160 \text{ g. Fe}_2\text{O}_3}{1 \text{ mole Fe}_2\text{O}_3}\right) = 1.22 \text{ g. Fe}_2\text{O}_3$$

Do problems 5–18 at the end of the chapter.

6. Problems

1. Translate the following statements into chemical equations and then balance the equations (see text for formulae):

(a) Chlorine gas burns in hydrogen gas to give hydrogen chloride.

(b) Barium chloride reacts with zinc sulfate to give zinc chloride and a precipitate of barium sulfate.

(c) Calcium nitrate reacts with sodium phosphate to give sodium nitrate and a precipitate of calcium phosphate.

(d) Potassium chlorate, when heated, gives a mixture of potassium chloride and potassium perchlorate.

(e) Hydrogen sulfide gas burns in air to give water and sulfur dioxide.

(f) Aluminum metal replaces iron from ferric oxide, giving aluminum oxide and iron.

(g) Hydrogen gas combines with nitrogen to give ammonia.

(h) Copper dissolves in dilute nitric acid to give copper nitrate, water, and nitric oxide.

(i) Phosphorus burns in oxygen to give phosphorus pentoxide.

(j) Sodium metal reacts with water to give sodium hydroxide and hydrogen gas.

(k) Carbon disulfide burns in air to give carbon dioxide and sulfur dioxide.

(l) Sodium hypochlorite when heated gives a mixture of sodium chloride and sodium chlorate.

2. $4HCl + O_2 \rightarrow 2H_2O + 2Cl_2$. How many moles of HCl are needed to form 0.35 mole of Cl_2?

3. $16HCl + 2KMnO_4 \rightarrow 2MnCl_2 + 2KCl + 4H_2O + 5Cl_2$. How many moles of chlorine gas will be produced from 3.20 moles of hydrochloric acid?

4. $3CaCl_2 + 2K_3PO_4 \rightarrow Ca_3(PO_4)_2 + 6KCl$. How many moles of potassium phosphate are needed to produce 0.076 mole of potassium chloride?

5. $CS_2 + 3O_2 \rightarrow CO_2 + 2SO_2$. How many cubic centimeters STP of SO_2 will be produced by burning 3 g. of CS_2?

6. $FeS + 2HCl \rightarrow H_2S + FeCl_2$. How many grams of FeS are needed to produce 100 g. of H_2S? What volume does this occupy at STP?

7. $2KClO_3 \rightarrow 2KCl + 3O_2$. How many liters STP of oxygen will be produced by decomposing 25 g. of $KClO_3$?

8. $2NaOH + H_2SO_4 \rightarrow Na_2SO_4 + 2H_2O$. How many moles of sodium hydroxide are needed to neutralize 100 g. of sulfuric acid?

9. $2Na_2O_2 + 2H_2O \rightarrow O_2\uparrow + 4NaOH$. How many cubic centimeters STP of O_2 gas can be made from 224 mg. of Na_2O_2?

10. In the contact process for the production of sulfuric acid, the sulfur present in FeS_2 is eventually converted into H_2SO_4. Assuming that the conversion is complete, how many kilograms of H_2SO_4 may be made from 2 tons of FeS_2?

11. If the H_2SO_4 produced in the preceding problem has a density of 1.86 g./cc., what volume will it occupy?

12. $2C_4H_{10} + 13O_2 \rightarrow 8CO_2 + 10H_2O$. How many cubic centimeters STP of CO_2 can be produced from 15 cc. of liquid butane (C_4H_{10})? The density of liquid butane is 0.60 g./cc. at 0°C.

13. From the reaction indicated in problem 3, how many grams of $KMnO_4$ are needed to produce 200 cc. STP of Cl_2 gas?

14. $Al_4C_3 + 12H_2O \rightarrow 4Al(OH)_3 + 3CH_4$. How many grams of Al_4C_3 are required to produce 250 l. STP of CH_4? How many grams of water are needed for this reaction? What is the liquid volume occupied by the water? (Density $H_2O = 1.00$ g./cc.)

15. In the Fischer-Tropsch process, coal is made to react with water over a catalyst to produce hydrocarbons. In this step 34% of the coal is converted to hydrocarbons. Of the total hydrocarbons produced, 6% is hexane, C_6H_{14}. How many kilograms of hexane can be produced from 1 ton of coal? (Consider coal as carbon, C.)

16. A metallurgical process for the extraction of uranium starts with carnotite ore which is 3.5% U_2O_3. This is treated in a number of steps and finally converted to uranyl sulfate hydrate, $(UO_2)SO_4 \cdot 3H_2O$. What is the maximum number of kilograms of the hydrate which can be made from 1 ton of carnotite ore?

17. $Zn + 2HCl \rightarrow ZnCl_2 + H_2$.

    (a) If 2.0 moles of Zn is mixed with 1.6 moles of HCl, what substances will be present when the reaction is over? What is their quantity?

    (b) If 14 g. of Zn is mixed with 18 g. of HCl, what substances will be present when the reaction is over? What is the weight of each?

18. $3Cu + 8HNO_3 \rightarrow 3Cu(NO_3)_2 + 2NO + 4H_2O$.

    (a) If 4 moles of Cu is added to 16 moles of HNO_3, what substances will be present when the reaction is over? How many moles of each?

    (b) If 24 g. of Cu is added to 12 g. of HNO_3, what substances will be present when the reaction is over? How many grams of each?

CHAPTER V

Energy and Chemical Changes

1. Energy and Work—Conservation of Energy

Next to the direct analysis of the products of chemical reactions, the greatest insight into the structure of matter has been obtained through the consideration of the energy changes which accompany the transformation of matter.

All chemical changes are accompanied by the absorption or liberation of energy by the reacting system. These energy changes may be manifested as thermal energy (heat), mechanical energy (pressure of gases from an explosion, sound, etc.), radiant energy (light, infrared or visible, ultraviolet, X-rays, etc.), or electric energy (storage batteries, nerve cell stimulation, electric eels, etc.).

Before discussing these energy changes in detail, let us first define the terms we shall use.

Definition: By *energy* we shall mean that which is capable of doing work.

Definition: By *work* we shall mean mechanical work, that is, the result achieved when a force moves through a distance. (See Table III.)

Since, as we shall see, all types of energy can be transformed by various laboratory devices, one into the other, all types of energy may be transformed into mechanical work, and vice versa. These devices for transforming different types of energy into each other and into mechanical work also provide a means whereby the units for measuring these various types of energy can be related to the units for mechanical energy or work.

If a force is applied to an object, its application will be manifested as a change in the velocity of the object (acceleration). The product of the force times the distance along which the force moves is defined as mechanical work.

47

Definition:

Mechanical work = Force × Distance traversed by force

The product of the mass of an object times one-half its velocity squared is defined as its kinetic energy (energy of motion).

Definition:

$$\text{Kinetic energy} = \frac{1}{2} \times \text{Mass} \times (\text{Velocity})^2$$

The change in the velocity of an object when a force acts on it produces a change in its kinetic energy. If there is no production of other types of energy, then the mechanical work done by the force is transformed entirely into kinetic energy. This represents an illustration of a very important law of energy, the *law of conservation of energy.*

Law of conservation of energy: Energy can neither be created nor destroyed. It can only be transformed from one form into another.

2. Units of Energy and Work

In Table V are listed the more important types of energy and the units in which they are measured.

TABLE V

Types of Energy and Their Units

Types of Energy	Definition	Units
Mechanical	Force × Distance	dyne-cm; erg (1 erg = 1 dyne-cm.)
Kinetic	$\dfrac{\text{Mass} \times (\text{Velocity})^2}{2}$	$\text{g.-}\dfrac{\text{cm.}^2}{\text{sec.}^2}$; erg $\left(1 \text{ g.-}\dfrac{\text{cm.}^2}{\text{sec.}^2} = 1 \text{ erg}\right)$
Thermal	Quantity of heat. 1 cal. is the amount of heat necessary to raise the temperature of 1 g. of water by 1°C. at 15°C.	calorie; kilocalorie (1 cal. = 4.185 × 10^7 ergs)
Electrical	Work done by electrical forces. 1 joule = work done by electrical forces in moving 1 *coulomb* of charge through a potential drop of 1 volt.	joule (1 joule = 0.24 cal. = 1 × 10^7 ergs) (1 watt-sec. = 1 joule)

Do problems 1, 2, and 3 at the end of the chapter.

3. Heat—Temperature Scale

Temperature is a measure of the heat energy contained in a substance. We define a temperature scale as follows:

TABLE VI
TEMPERATURE SCALES

Standard	Centigrade Scale	Fahrenheit Scale	Absolute Scale (Kelvin)	Rankine Scale
The temperature of a mixture of pure ice and water.	0°C.	32°F.	273°K.	491.6°R.
The temperature of boiling water at a pressure of 76 cm. of Hg. (1 atm.)	100°C.	212°F.	373°K.	671.6°R.

We can see from this scale that the temperature interval between melting water and freezing water is divided into 100 parts in the centigrade scale and in the absolute scale, but into 180 parts in the Rankine and Fahrenheit scales. From the above definitions we can derive the following equations relating the various scales:

$$°C. = \frac{5}{9}(°F. - 32); \quad °F. = \frac{9}{5}°C. + 32; \quad °F. = °R. - 459.6$$

$$°K. = °C. + 273; \quad °C. = °K. - 273; \quad °C. = \frac{5}{9}(°R. - 491.6)$$

Observe, however, that a *change* of 1°C. is equivalent to a *change* of $\frac{9}{5}$°F., whereas a change of 1°C. is equal to a change of 1°K. That is, if the temperature of an object is 10°C. and changes to 11°C., in the Fahrenheit scale it will be 50°F. and change to 51.8°F. (a change of 1.8°F. = $\frac{9}{5}$°F.), whereas in the absolute or Kelvin scale it will go from 283°K. to 284°K. (change of 1°K.). Most of the time we are concerned with temperature changes rather than actual temperature, and the relations between temperature changes then become important.

Note that the apparatus for measuring temperature is the mercury thermometer. The property involved is the change in volume of the liquid mercury with temperature. Thus, by measuring the volume occupied by a drop of mercury in the thermometer bulb, we can relate this volume to the temperature of the mercury.

Do problems 4 and 5 at the end of the chapter.

4. Heat Energy—Specific Heat

Since the energy involved in chemical changes is usually in the form of thermal energy, this type of energy will be emphasized. We have seen that temperature is a measure of the intensity of heat energy of a body. When two bodies have the same intensity of heat energy they will be at the same temperature and if brought together no heat energy will pass from one to the other. When two bodies are at different temperatures, heat energy will flow from the hotter one to the colder one until they both come to the same temperature. The absolute temperature scale is theoretically important since 0°K. is the lowest attainable temperature (0°R. on the Rankine scale).

It is found experimentally that 1 cal. of heat energy is required to raise the temperature of 1 g. of water by 1°C. (starting at 15°C.). While defining the calorie of heat energy, this observation also defines an *intensive property* of water known as the *specific heat*. In general, 1 g. of each different substance will require a different number of calories to raise its temperature by 1°C. This number of calories is called the *specific heat* of the substance.

Definition:

$$\text{Specific heat of a substance} = \frac{\text{Heat energy}}{\text{Mass} \times \text{Temperature change}}$$

The units of specific heat are calories per gram per degree Centigrade (cal./g.-°C.). The following Table VII gives the specific heats of a few common substances.

TABLE VII
SPECIFIC HEATS OF SOME COMMON SUBSTANCES AT 15°C.

Substance	Specific Heat (cal./g.-°C.)	Substance	Specific Heat (cal./g.-°C.)
Water	1.000	Iron (α)	0.107
Mercury	0.0333	Zinc	0.092
Graphite (C)	0.17	Sodium chloride	0.206
Diamond (C)	0.12	Ammonium nitrate	0.398
Copper	0.092	Potassium chlorate	0.197
Iodine	0.052	Sulfuric acid	0.340
Lead	0.304	Ethyl alcohol	0.561
		Benzene	0.399

It should be pointed out that the specific heat of a substance is slightly different at different temperatures just as the density of solids and liquids is slightly different at different temperatures.

The specific heat is a complex property relating the number of calories required to change the temperature of 1 g. of an object and the temperature change brought about. As such it can be used as a conversion factor to relate heat energy per gram and temperature change of a given substance.

Example: 250 cal. of heat energy will raise the temperature of 50 g. of iron by 46.7°C. What is the specific heat of iron?

Answer:

$$\text{Specific heat} = \frac{\text{Heat energy}}{\text{Mass} \times \text{Temperature change}}$$

$$= \frac{250 \text{ cal.}}{50 \text{ g.} \times 46.7°\text{C.}} = 0.107 \frac{\text{cal.}}{\text{g.-°C.}}$$

Example: The specific heat of water is 1.00 cal./g.-°C. How many calories are required to raise the temperature of 20 g. of water by 15°C.?

Answer:

$$\text{Heat energy} = 15°\text{C.} \times \left(\frac{1 \text{ cal.}}{\text{g.-°C.}} \right) \times 20 \text{ g.}$$

$$= 300 \text{ cal.}$$

Thus it will require 300 cal. to raise the temperature 15°C.

Do problems 6–9 at the end of the chapter.

5. Molar Heat Capacity—Law of Dulong and Petit

The molar heat capacity is defined as the energy required to raise the temperature of 1 mole of a substance by 1°C. It is frequently used since it employs the theoretical units of moles rather than the practical mass units of grams. We can relate it to the specific heat by using the conversion factor of molecular weight.

Definition:

Molar heat capacity = Specific heat × Molecular weight

Its units are calories per mole per degree Centigrade (cal./mole-°C.).

Example: The specific heat of water is 1.00 cal./g.-°C. What is its molar heat capacity?

Answer:

$$\text{Molar heat capacity of water} = \left(\frac{1.00 \text{ cal.}}{\text{g.-°C.}} \right) \times \left(\frac{18 \text{ g. } H_2O}{1 \text{ mole } H_2O} \right)$$

$$= \frac{18 \text{ cal.}}{\text{mole-°C.}}$$

One of the interesting discoveries of the last century was that the molar heat capacity of metals is roughly 6 cal./mole-°C. This law, known as the Law of Dulong and Petit, is accurate to within about 10% for all metals. It was originally used to obtain crude atomic weights for the metallic elements.

Example: The specific heat of lead is 0.304 cal./g-°C. What is its atomic weight?

Answer: From the Law of Dulong and Petit: molar heat capacity of lead = 6 cal./mole-°C. From the definition of molar heat capacity:

$$\text{Atomic weight of lead} = \frac{\text{Molar heat capacity}}{\text{Specific heat}}$$

$$= \frac{6.0 \ \cancel{\text{cal.}}/\text{mole-}°\cancel{C}.}{0.304 \ \cancel{\text{cal.}}/\text{g.-}°\cancel{C}.} = 198 \ \text{g./mole}$$

which is pretty close to the true atomic weight of 207 g./mole.

Do problems 11–14 at the end of the chapter.

6. Heat Content

The fact that an object has the ability to change temperature indicates that it always possesses a certain amount of heat energy. At absolute zero, when it is incapable of being cooled further, it will have no more heat energy. However, substances contain another form of energy which is not capable of being removed simply by heating or cooling but can be released only when the atoms making up the substance are rearranged, as in a chemical reaction. This latent (hidden) chemical energy is also part of the total energy of the substance, just as the potential energy in a coiled spring must be counted as part of the energy of the spring. The sum of the heat energy and this internal chemical energy is called the *heat content* of a substance. There is no simple, direct way of measuring the total heat content of a substance, but we can measure the changes in heat content which occur when chemical changes take place, and these in turn can be related to the heat content. The heat content is also known as the *enthalpy*.

7. Heats of Formation

Since we can't have, or at least don't need, an absolute measure of the total heat energy or *heat content* of a substance, but merely a relative measure, we must establish a reference point or standard from which to measure this heat content for each substance. This can be done by measuring the heat content of a compound with respect to the elements which make it up. Thus we find that when carbon (graphite) reacts with oxygen (gas) at 20°C., carbon dioxide (gas) is produced and 94.4 kilocalories (kcal.) of heat are liberated for every mole of CO_2 (gas) produced. This thermal energy can be written in the balanced equation as one of the products:

$$C\ (s) + O_2\ (g) \rightarrow CO_2\ (g) + 94.4\ \text{kcal.}$$

The significance of this equation is that 1 mole of CO_2 (g) contains 94.4 kcal. less heat than the elements from which it is made. [Note that the parentheses refer to the physical state: (g), gas; (s), solid; (l), liquid.]

We will define the total heat content of a substance with reference to the elements from which it is made. To make an intensive property of it we will define it as the *heat content per mole* or molar heat content. By placing all free elements at zero on our reference scale, we see that the molar heat content of a substance is equal to minus the heat liberated or absorbed when 1 mole of the compound is formed from its elements. This quantity is also referred to as the heat of formation.

Definition:

Heat of formation = Molar heat content

= − (Heat liberated or absorbed when 1 mole of a compound is formed from the free elements)

Since the total heat energy depends slightly on temperature and pressure, we will take as our reference or standard set of conditions 25°C. and 1 atm. total pressure.*

From the example quoted, carbon dioxide at 25°C. and 1 atm. pressure has a heat of formation of −94.4 kcal./mole or, alternatively, a total heat content of −94.4 kcal./mole at 1 atm. pressure and 25°C.

Conversely this implies that if there were a way of breaking carbon dioxide back into its elements (the reverse reaction) it would require an amount of work equal to 94.4 kcal./mole.

In Table VIII are given heats of formation of a few compounds at standard conditions.

* In this chapter, all calculations of heats of chemical reaction should properly be called standard heats, since they refer to the heat change when the reaction occurs at 25°C. and 1 atm. pressure (standard conditions). It is possible to estimate from these standard heats what the heat changes would be at other temperatures if we know the molar heat capacities of each of the substances involved. From this latter information we can compute the heat contents of each of the substances at the different temperature and, from the difference in heat contents between reactants and products, the heat of reaction at that temperature.

TABLE VIII
SOME HEATS OF FORMATION AT STANDARD CONDITIONS

Substance	Heat of Formation (kcal./mole)	Substance	Heat of Formation (kcal./mole)
CO_2 (g)	−94.4	NaCl (s)	− 98.4
H_2O (l)	−68.4	$KClO_3$ (s)	− 89.9
SO_2 (g)	−70.2	H_2SO_4 (s)	−189.8
HCl (g)	−22.0	NaOH (s)	−101.9
NO (g)	+21.5	CH_4 (g)	− 19.1 (methane)
NO_2 (g)	− 7.4	C_2H_6 (g)	− 23.4 (ethane)
H_2S (g)	− 5.2	C_2H_2 (g)	+ 54.3 (acetylene)
NH_3 (g)	−10.9	C_6H_6 (l)	+ 13.4 (benzene)

A negative heat of formation (or heat content) signifies that heat is given out when the compound is formed from its elements (the reaction is *exo*thermic). Alternatively, a positive heat of formation signifies that heat is absorbed when the compound is formed from its elements (i.e., the reaction is *endo*thermic).

8. Heats of Reaction

If we know the heat contents of all the substances participating in a reaction (i.e., their heats of formation), then we can calculate the heat of the reaction. This follows since, from the law of conservation of energy, the heat of the reaction must simply be the difference in heat contents of the products and the reactants.

Definition:

$$\text{Heat of reaction} = \left(\begin{array}{c}\text{Total heat content}\\ \text{of products}\end{array}\right) - \left(\begin{array}{c}\text{Total heat contents}\\ \text{of reactants}\end{array}\right)$$

This equation simply expresses an energy balance for the reaction. If the total heat contents of the products are less than the total heat contents of the reaction, then heat must have been liberated (exothermic reaction). If the total heat contents of the products are greater than the total heat contents of the reactants, then heat must have been absorbed during the reaction and the reaction is endothermic.

Example:

$$2CO \ (g) + O_2 \ (g) \rightarrow 2CO_2 \ (g)$$

What is the heat of this reaction, given the heats of formation? $H_F(CO) = -28$ kcal./mole; $H_F(CO_2) = -94.4$ kcal./mole. *Note:* $H_F(O_2) =$ zero, since it is a free element.

Answer: By definition:

$$\text{Heat of reaction} = \begin{pmatrix} \text{Total heat contents} \\ \text{of products} \end{pmatrix} - \begin{pmatrix} \text{Total heat contents} \\ \text{of reactants} \end{pmatrix}$$

$$= [2H_F(CO_2)] - [2H_F(CO) + H_F(O_2)]$$

$$= (-2 \times 94.4) - [2(-28) + O]$$

$$= (-188.8) - (-56)$$

$$= -132.8 \text{ kcal.}$$

This means that the reaction is exothermic, since the total heat contents of the products are *less* (observe the minus sign) than the total heat contents of the reactants. That is, heat is a product of the reaction.

In similar fashion, if we know the heat of a reaction and the heats of formation of all but one of the compounds present in the equation, we can calculate the heat of formation of this compound.

Example:

$$2C_2H_6 \ (g) + 7O_2 \ (g) \rightarrow 4CO_2 \ (g) + 6H_2O \ (l) + 742 \text{ kcal.}$$

If the heats of formation are: $H_F(CO_2) = -94.4$ kcal./mole and $H_F(H_2O) = -68.4$ kcal./mole, what is $H_F(C_2H_6)$?

Answer: From the definition:

$$\text{Heat of reaction} = \begin{pmatrix} \text{Total heat content} \\ \text{of products} \end{pmatrix} - \begin{pmatrix} \text{Total heat content} \\ \text{of reactants} \end{pmatrix}$$

But the heat of reaction = -742 kcal., since the reaction is exothermic (i.e., heat is given out). Thus

$$-742 \text{ kcal.} = [4H_F(CO_2) + 6H_F(H_2O)] - [2H_F(C_2H_6)]$$

Solving for $H_F(C_2H_6)$ we have

$$H_F(C_2H_6) = 2H_F(CO_2) + 3H_F(H_2O) + 371$$

and, on substitution,

$$H_F(C_2H_6) = 2(-94.4) + 3(-68.4) + 371$$

$$= -188.8 - 205.2 + 371$$

$$= -23 \text{ kcal.}$$

Do problems 15 and 16 at the end of the chapter.

9. Heat Calculations

For calculating the amounts of heat liberated or absorbed when given amounts of a compound react in a chemical reaction, the balanced equation containing the heat of reaction can be used to obtain a heat-chemical conversion factor.

Example: The combustion of butane liberates energy according to the following:

$$2C_4H_{10} \ (g) + 13O_2 \ (g) \rightarrow 8CO_2 \ (g) + 10H_2O \ (g) + 1360 \ kcal.$$

How much heat will be liberated by burning 10 g. of C_4H_{10}?
Answer:

$$10 \ g. \ C_4H_{10} = 10 \ g. \ C_4H_{10} \times \left(\frac{1 \ mole \ C_4H_{10}}{58 \ g. \ C_4H_{10}}\right) \times \left(\frac{1360 \ kcal.}{2 \ moles \ C_4H_{10}}\right)$$

$$= 117 \ kcal.$$

Do problems 17 and 18 at the end of the chapter.

10. Heat Changes Accompanying Physical Changes—Intermolecular Forces

Heat changes generally accompany physical changes as well as chemical changes. Table IX lists some definitions of such heat changes. Remember, when heat change is negative, it means heat is liberated in the change.

TABLE IX
DEFINITION OF HEATS OF PHYSICAL CHANGES

Term	Symbol	Definition
Heat of vaporization	H_v	Heat *absorbed* when 1 mole of liquid or solid is changed to the gaseous state.
Heat of condensation	H_c $(H_c = -H_v)$	Heat *liberated* when 1 mole of gas is condensed to a liquid or solid. Opposite of H_v.
Heat of melting	H_m	Heat absorbed when 1 mole of solid is melted.
Heat of solution	H_s	Heat liberated *or* absorbed when 1 mole of substance (solute) is dissolved in a fixed quantity of solvent.

Before closing the chapter it is well to say something about the origin of these latent heat energies. Where do these energies of chemical change and physical change come from?

The answer to this question is to be found in the forces that act between molecules. The property that characterizes liquids and solids

$C° = \left(\frac{5}{9}F° - 32\right)$

is their cohesiveness. It takes work to separate the molecules in a liquid or a solid. This work we call the energy of vaporization, and it acts to overcome the attractive forces between the molecules making up the liquid or solid. Conversely, where we permit a gas to condense to a liquid or solid, the attractive forces this time do work, and it is released as heat energy.

A chemical change involves a rearrangement of the atoms in one or more compounds or elements. If energy is required to overcome the attractive forces in order to make the rearrangement, then we say that heat is absorbed. If, on the other hand, the attractive forces are greater in the rearranged form (their products), then these inter-molecular forces have performed work and heat energy is liberated.

Do problems 10, 19, and 20 at the end of the chapter.

11. Problems

1. If you push against a wall it does not move (usually), and thus, according to our definition, no mechanical work is done. Nevertheless, you will become tired from this effort. Explain.

2. The force of gravity is 980 dynes/g. If it acts on a 10-g. mass during the time in which the body falls a distance of 1 m., having initially been at rest, calculate the increase in kinetic energy of the body. What is the final velocity of the body?

3. Make the following conversions:

(a) 500 cal. to ergs.   (c) 8 joules to calories.
(b) 6×10^8 ergs to kilocalories.   (d) 60 ergs to microjoules.

4. Make the following conversions in temperature scale:

(a) 150°C. to °K.   (g) −100°F. to °K.
(b) 0°K. to °F. (absolute zero).   (h) 50°F. to °R.
(c) 0°K. to °C.   (i) 10°R. to °F.
(d) 1000°K. to °C.   (j) 500°C. to °R.
(e) 500°K. to °F.   (k) 90°R. to °K.
(f) −40°C. to °F.

5. When the temperature of a body increases by 15°C., what does this increase correspond to in °K.? in °F.?

6. From Table VII, calculate the number of calories required to raise the temperature of 40 g. of copper from 100°C. to 150°C.

7. How many calories are required to raise the temperature of 1 lb. of water from 0°C. to the boiling point?

8. Compute the specific heat of water in units of ergs/lb.-°F.

9. Assuming that the specific heat of iron did not change, calculate how many calories of heat would have to be removed to cool 1 mole of Fe from 25°C. to absolute zero?

10. Which would you think would require more energy to separate into its individual molecules, a substance at a high temperature or the same substance at a lower temperature? Explain your reasoning.

11. It takes 80 cal. to raise the temperature of 20 g. of wool by 16°C.   What is the specific heat of wool?

12. An unknown metal has a specific heat of 0.150 cal./g. °C.   What is the atomic weight of the metal, roughly?   Could you guess from the Table of Atomic Weights which metal this might be?

13. From the knowledge of the atomic weight of nickel (58.7), what would you estimate its specific heat to be?

14. How many ergs are required to raise the temperature of 1 molecule of water by 1°3.?

15. Calculate the heat of the following reactions (using the values for H_F in Table VIII):

    (a) $2NO + O_2 \rightarrow 2NO_2$.

    (b) $CH_4 + 2O_2 \rightarrow CO_2 + 2H_2O$.

    (c) $C + H_2O \rightarrow CO + H_2$ $[H_F(CO) = -28 \text{ kcal./mole}]$.

    (d) $C_2H_2 + 2H_2 \rightarrow C_2H_6$.

    (e) $2Na + 2H_2O \rightarrow 2NaOH + H_2$.

    (f) $H_2S + 2O_2 \rightarrow H_2SO_4$.

16. For the following reactions, calculate the heat of formation of the single compound which in each case is not listed in Table VIII:

    (a) $4C_3H_5(NO_3)_3 + 11O_2 \rightarrow 12CO_2 + 12NO_2 + 10H_2O + 1330$ kcal. (combustion of nitroglycerine).

    (b) $6CO_2 + 6H_2O \rightarrow C_6H_{12}O_6$ (sugar) $+ 6O_2 - 676$ kcal. (photosynthesis of fructose).

    (c) $2SO_2 + O_2 \rightarrow 2SO_3 + 43$ kcal.

    (d) $2NaOH + H_2SO_4 \rightarrow Na_2SO_4 + 2H_2O + 30$ kcal.

17. For the reaction shown in problem 16(a), how many liters of oxygen at STP are required to produce 500 kcal. of heat?

18. How many kilocalories of heat energy are required by a plant to produce 50 g. of fructose [reaction 16(b) above]?

19. The heat of vaporization of water is 540 cal./g.   How many calories are required to vaporize 200 g. of water?   What is the molar heat of vaporization of water?

20. The heat of fusion of ice is 80 cal./g.

    (a) What is the molar heat of fusion of ice?

    (b) How many calories are required to melt 500 g. of ice?

    (c) How many calories are required to transform 50 g. of water from ice at 0°C. to steam at 100°C.   (See problem 19 for heat of vaporization.)

CHAPTER VI

The Properties of Gases

1. Measurement of Gases

As noted in Chapter II, the method employed for measuring a quantity of matter depends on the physical state of the matter. For solids, direct weighing is most convenient. For liquids, direct measurement of volume proves to be most convenient, but additional information is needed to convert from volume units to mass units, namely, the density of the liquid.

For gases, direct weighing is extremely difficult because gases are so many times lighter than the containers needed to hold them. For this reason, gases are measured out in terms of volume, and to convert to mass units additional information is needed giving the density of the gas.

The density of a substance is defined as the mass divided by the volume. The volume of a given quantity of liquid or solid depends very little on its temperature or pressure. On the other hand, the volume occupied by a given quantity of gas is much more sensitive to its temperature and pressure. Fortunately, there are laws which enable us to calculate, if we know the volume occupied by a given quantity of gas at one temperature and pressure, precisely what the volume will be at any other temperature and pressure. Thus it is possible from a knowledge of the density of a gas at any one pressure and temperature to compute the density of the same gas at any other temperature and pressure. This is a great convenience in measuring quantities of gas.

2. Pressure

The pressure exerted by a gas upon the walls of its container is the same at every part of the vessel. It may be measured by a pressure gauge or a mercury manometer. The latter is more frequently used in the laboratory, and the principle on which it is based is that the pressure exerted by a gas on a liquid in a U-tube can be counterbalanced by the weight of liquid in the other arm of the U-tube (Figure 1).

The unbalance in the arms of the manometer is caused by the pressure of the gas on one of these arms.   We can measure the unbalance in units of length, and this provides a direct measure of the pressure exerted by the gas.   Thus it is customary to speak of a pressure of 20 cm. Hg, meaning that the unbalance in the arms of the manometer (i.e., the difference between the two levels) is 20 cm., and the manometer fluid is mercury.

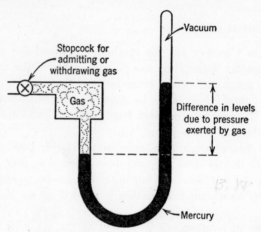

FIG. 1.   Mercury manometer.

These units can be related to the units of dynes by the properties of mercury (Hg).   The pressure 20 cm. below the upper level of a tube full of mercury is simply the force per unit area due to the weight of the mercury above.   The volume of a column of mercury 20 cm. high and having a cross-sectional area of 1 cm.^{2} is 20 cm.^{3}.   Multiplying this by the density we obtain the mass:

$$20 \text{ cm.}^3 \text{ Hg} = 20 \text{ cm.}^3 \text{ Hg} \times \left(\frac{13.55 \text{ g. Hg}}{1 \text{ cm.}^3 \text{ Hg}}\right) = 271.0 \text{ g. Hg}$$

The force of gravity is 980 dynes/g., and so the total force of gravity acting on this column of mercury is

$$\text{Force} = 271.0 \text{ g.} \times \frac{980 \text{ dynes}}{\text{g.}}$$

$$= 265,900 \text{ dynes} = 2.66 \times 10^5 \text{ dynes}$$

We thus have the total pressure in terms of force per unit area.

20 cm. Hg pressure $= \left(\dfrac{20 \text{ cm.}^3 \text{ Hg}}{\text{cm.}^2}\right) \times \left(\dfrac{13.55 \text{ g. Hg}}{1 \text{ cm.}^3 \text{ Hg}}\right) \times \left(\dfrac{980 \text{ dynes}}{\text{g. Hg}}\right)$

$$= 2.66 \times 10^5 \text{ dynes/cm.}^2$$

or

$$1 \text{ cm. Hg} = 1.33 \times 10^4 \text{ dynes/cm.}^2$$

Another unit for measurement of pressure is the atmosphere (atm.).

Definition:

$$1 \text{ atm.} = 76 \text{ cm. Hg}$$

Then

$$1 \text{ atm.} = 76 \text{ cm. Hg} \times \left(\dfrac{1.33 \times 10^4 \text{ dynes/cm.}^2}{1 \text{ cm. Hg}}\right)$$

$$= 1.01 \times 10^6 \text{ dynes/cm.}^2$$

The English system uses pounds force per square inch or simply pounds per square inch.   The student should show that this can be related to atmospheres:

$$1 \text{ atm.} = 14.7 \text{ lb./sq. in.}$$

Do problems 1–6 at the end of the chapter.

3. Boyle's Law—Pressure and Volume of a Gas

If a given mass of gas (m) is kept in a vessel and its volume changed, then its pressure will change in such a manner that the product of the pressure (P) and volume (V) do not change.   This is known as Boyle's law and is true only when the temperature (T) of the gas is kept fixed.   Algebraically:

Boyle's Law:

$$P \times V = \text{Constant} \quad \text{(if } T \text{ and } m \text{ are kept fixed)}$$

The constant in this equation will, of course, be different for each temperature and for each different quantity of gas.   It is, however, important to know that once these are fixed it is the same for each gas!   That is, 10 cc. of hydrogen gas and 10 cc. of oxygen gas behave in exactly the same way.

This law permits us to calculate the volume (of a fixed mass of gas, kept at constant temperature) at any pressure if we know the volume of the gas at any one pressure.

Example: What volume will be occupied by 10 l. of a gas originally measured at a pressure of 15 lb./sq. in. if it is compressed to 90 lb./sq. in.?

Answer: Since, from Boyle's law, $P \times V$ after the compression must be the same as $P \times V$ before the compression:

$$P_{\text{final}} \times V_{\text{final}} = P_{\text{initial}} \times V_{\text{initial}}$$

and, solving for the final volume:

$$V_{\text{final}} = \frac{P_{\text{initial}}}{P_{\text{final}}} \times V_{\text{initial}}$$

and substituting:

$$V_{\text{final}} = \frac{15 \text{ lb./in.}^2}{90 \text{ lb./in.}^2} \times 10 \text{ l.}$$

$$= 1.67 \text{ l.}$$

Do problems 7 and 8 at the end of the chapter.

4. Charles' Law—Temperature and Volume

It is found by experiment that, if the temperature of a given quantity of gas (m) is changed, then its volume will change in a corresponding manner such that the ratio of the volume (V) to the *absolute temperature* (T) does not change. This is known as Charles' law and is true only if the pressure of the gas is kept fixed. Algebraically:

Charles' Law:

$$\frac{V}{T} = \text{Constant} \quad \text{(if } P \text{ and } m \text{ are kept fixed)}$$

Once again, the constant in this equation will be different for each different pressure and each different quantity of gas (m), but, once these two are fixed, the ratio does not change.

Example: A quantity of gas at 20°C. and 1 atm. pressure occupies a volume of 200 cc. What volume will it occupy at −40°C., the pressure being kept fixed?

Answer: From Charles' law, the ratio of the volume to *absolute* temperature must be the same before and after the experiment:

$$\frac{V_{\text{final}}}{T_{\text{final}}} = \frac{V_{\text{initial}}}{T_{\text{initial}}}$$

Solving for V_{final} (the final volume):

$$V_{\text{final}} = \left(\frac{T_{\text{final}}}{T_{\text{initial}}}\right) \times V_{\text{initial}}$$

and substituting:

$$V_{\text{final}} = \left(\frac{233°\text{K.}}{293°\text{K.}}\right) \times 200 \text{ cc.}$$

$$= 159 \text{ cc.}$$

Do problems 9 and 10 at the end of the chapter.

5. Combined Form of Gas Laws

In the usual experiment it is rare that the pressure and temperature are kept fixed, and it is important to have a law which tells us how the volume of a gas will change under these circumstances.

Charles' and Boyle's laws can be combined into a single law which states:

Combined Gas Law: The product of the pressure and volume of a given quantity of gas divided by the absolute temperature is a constant which does not change. Even though the individual properties may change in an experiment, this ratio does not.

Algebraically:

$$\frac{P \times V}{T} = \text{Constant} \qquad \text{(if } m \text{ is fixed)}$$

From this combined law we can calculate the way in which the volume or pressure or temperature changes if the initial conditions (P, V, T) are known and two of the final conditions are known (i.e., two of the three quantities, P, V, T).

Example: A quantity of gas has a volume of 180 cc. at 40°C. and a pressure of 80 cm. Hg. What will this volume be at standard conditions (0°C. and 76 cm. Hg)?

Answer: From the combined gas law:

$$\frac{P_{final} \times V_{final}}{T_{final}} = \frac{P_{initial} \times V_{initial}}{T_{initial}}$$

Solving for V_{final}:

$$V_{final} = V_{initial} \times \left(\frac{P_{initial}}{P_{final}}\right) \times \left(\frac{T_{final}}{T_{initial}}\right)$$

and, substituting, we have

$$V_{final} = 180 \text{ cc.} \times \left(\frac{80 \text{ cm. Hg}}{76 \text{ cm. Hg}}\right) \times \left(\frac{273°K.}{313°K.}\right)$$

$$= 165 \text{ cc. STP}$$

Note: In the preceding examples, it should be noted that cooling a gas causes it to contract and heating causes it to expand. Similarly, compressing a gas reduces its volume and decreasing its pressure increases the volume. These rules provide a quick check on possible errors.

Thus, in the above example we must cool the gas from 40°C. (313°K.) to 0°C. (273°K.). This should reduce its volume, and accordingly we observe that the initial volume of 180 cc. is multiplied by a fraction ($273/313$) which is less than 1.

Also we must expand the gas to change its pressure from 80 cm. Hg to 76 cm. Hg. Again observe that the initial volume of 180 cc. is multiplied by the fraction ($80/76$) which is greater than 1.

Do problems 11, 12, and 13 at the end of the chapter.

6. Ideal Gas Law

We may now ask, how do the variables P, V, and T behave when the mass of gas is not held constant? The answer to this is found experimentally, and we find that the ratio PV/T is proportional to the mass (m) of the gas taken. Algebraically:

Gas Law:

$$\frac{P \times V}{T \times m} = \text{Constant}$$

This constant is now a fixed number for each gas but different for different gases. It is found, however, that it is inversely proportional to the molecular weight of the gas. Thus the constant for oxygen gas ($O_2 = 32$) is $\frac{1}{16}$ as large as the constant for hydrogen ($H_2 = 2$). This permits us to write an equation which includes the molecular weight (M) of the gas.

Ideal Gas Law:

$$\frac{P \times V \times M}{T \times m} = \text{Constant} = R$$

In this last equation the constant is now the *same* for every gas. It is known as the *universal gas constant* and given the symbol R. The ideal gas law, as it is called, now tells us that the product of the pressure, volume, and molecular weight of a gas, divided by the absolute temperature and mass of the gas, is a number R, which is the same for all gases. R can be calculated experimentally from the measurement of the properties of any gas.

Example: 32 g. of oxygen gas (O_2) at 0°C. and 1 atm. pressure is found to occupy a volume of 22.4 l. Calculate the value of R.

Answer:

$$R = \frac{P \times V \times M}{T \times m}$$

and on substitution:

$$R = \frac{1 \text{ atm.} \times 22.4 \text{ l.} \times 32 \text{ g./mole}}{273°\text{K.} \times 32 \text{ g.}}$$

$$= 0.0821 \frac{\text{l.-atm.}}{\text{mole-°K.}}$$

or, converting to different volume units:

$$R = 0.0821 \frac{\text{l.-atm.}}{\text{mole-°K.}} \times \left(\frac{1000 \text{ cc.}}{\text{l.}}\right) = 82.1 \frac{\text{cc.-atm.}}{\text{mole-°K.}}$$

R can be expressed in many other units as well. In addition to the ones shown in the example, which are most frequently used, we have $R = 1.99$ cal./mole-°K. and $R = 8.31 \times 10^7$ ergs/mole-°K.

The ideal gas law equation can be rearranged and written as follows:

$$PV = \frac{m}{M} RT$$

but, since the mass (m) of a gas divided by its molecular weight (M) is simply the number of moles of the gas, $n = m/M$. This equation can be written in its more usual form:

$$PV = nRT$$

Do problem 14 at the end of the chapter.

7. Molecular Weight of Gases

The molecular weight of a gas may be calculated if we know the volume occupied by a given mass of the gas (i.e., the density of the gas).

This calculation is possible since we know that 1 mole of a gas will occupy a volume of 22.4 l. at STP. If we know the volume occupied at any other temperature and pressure, the combined form of the gas laws permits us to calculate the volume at STP, and using the density of 1 mole as a conversion factor we can calculate the molecular weight.

Example: 5.75 g. of a gas occupy a volume of 3.4 l. at a temperature of 50°C. and a pressure of 0.94 atm. What is its molecular weight?

Answer: Using the combined form of the gas laws:

$$V_{STP} = 3.4 \text{ l.} \times \left(\frac{273°\text{K.}}{323°\text{K.}}\right) \times \left(\frac{0.94 \text{ atm.}}{1.00 \text{ atm.}}\right)$$

$$= 2.7 \text{ l. STP}$$

From the given data: 5.75 g. = 2.7 l. STP. This provides a conversion factor:

$$1 \text{ mole} = 22.4 \text{ l. STP} \times \left(\frac{5.75 \text{ g.}}{2.7 \text{ l. STP}}\right)$$

$$= 47.6 \text{ g. (molecular weight)}$$

The ideal gas law, however, allows us to perform the same calculations in one step. The equation representing the ideal gas law has in it six quantities: M, m, R, T, P, V. If we know five of these we can always solve for the sixth. Since R is a known constant, this leaves only four experimental properties to be measured in order to compute the unknown. The following example illustrates the application of this equation to the problem already solved.

Example: Use the data from the previous example to calculate the molecular weight of the gas, making use of the ideal gas law.

Answer: Solving the ideal gas law equation for the molecular weight:

$$M = \frac{m \times R \times T}{P \times V}$$

Substituting the data:

$$M = \frac{5.75 \text{ g.}}{0.94 \text{ atm.}} \times 0.0821 \frac{\text{l.-atm.}}{\text{mole-}^\circ\text{K.}} \times \frac{323^\circ\text{K.}}{3.4\text{ l.}}$$

$$= \frac{5.75 \times 0.0821 \times 323}{0.94 \times 3.4} \frac{\text{g.}}{\text{mole}}$$

$$= 47.6 \text{ g./mole}$$

(which checks with the previous calculations)

Do problems 15 and 16 at the end of the chapter.

8. Dalton's Law—Mixtures of Gases

Quite frequently it is convenient to collect gases in vessels above the surfaces of liquids such as water. The gases that we collect will not be pure but will consist of a mixture of the original gas plus the vapor of the liquid used to confine it. For mercury the amount of mercury vapor included is so small as to be negligible. However, for water, the amount of water vapor is quite significant. How can we estimate the composition of a gas collected above water?

The answer to this question is provided by Dalton's Law.

Dalton's Law: The total pressure exerted by a mixture of gases is simply the sum of the partial pressures which each gas would exert if the others were not present.

Now if a gas is collected above water and the result is a mixture of water vapor with the original gas, the total pressure of the mixture is equal to the sum of the pressures exerted by the original gas and by the water vapor, each acting as if the others were not there. If we could know what pressure the water vapor exerted, we could subtract this from the total, observed pressure, and the difference would then be the true pressure exerted by the original gas in the vessel.

This information about the pressure of water vapor can be obtained from a table of vapor pressures for water.

Example: A sample of oxygen is collected by displacing water from an inverted tube. The temperature is 25°C., the pressure is 750 cm. Hg (barometric pressure), and the volume occupied is 280 cc. What is the true volume of oxygen at STP?

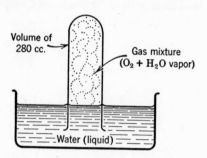

Volume of
280 cc.

Gas mixture
(O_2 + H_2O vapor)

Water (liquid)

Answer: From the table of vapor pressures we find the vapor pressure of water to be 23.5 mm. Hg at 25°C. The partial pressure of oxygen in the tube is thus equal to 750 − 23.5 = 726.5 mm. Hg. Now, using the gas laws:

$$V_{\text{STP}} = V_{\text{initial}} \times \left(\frac{P_{\text{initial}}}{P_{\text{final}}}\right) \times \left(\frac{T_{\text{final}}}{T_{\text{initial}}}\right)$$

$$= 280 \text{ cc.} \times \left(\frac{726.5 \text{ mm. Hg}}{760 \text{ mm. Hg}}\right) \times \left(\frac{273°\text{K.}}{298°\text{K.}}\right)$$

$$= 245 \text{ cc. STP}$$

Do problems 17 and 18 at the end of the chapter.

9. Gas Densities—Molecular Weights

The density of a gas is given by the ratio of its mass to its volume:

$$d = \frac{m}{V}$$

But the volume of a gas depends on its temperature and pressure. Using the ideal gas law:

$$PV = \frac{m}{M} RT$$

we can rearrange the equation to obtain the ratio m/V:

$$\frac{m}{V} = \frac{MP}{RT} = d \quad \text{(density)}$$

Thus the ideal gas law gives us a direct relation between the density of a gas and its other properties.

In particular, if we know the density of a gas at a given pressure and temperature we can calculate its molecular weight.

Example: The density of a certain gas at 30°C. and 1.3 atm. pressure is 0.027 g./cc. What is its molecular weight?

Answer: Rearranging the above equation to solve for M:

$$M = \frac{dRT}{P}$$

Substituting:

$$M = \frac{\left(\dfrac{0.027 \text{ g.}}{\text{cc.}}\right) \times \left(\dfrac{82.1 \text{ cc.-atm.}}{\text{mole-°K.}}\right) \times 303°\text{K.}}{1.3 \text{ atm.}}$$

$$= \frac{0.027 \times 82.1 \times 303}{1.3} \frac{\text{g.}}{\text{mole}}$$

$$= 516 \text{ g./mole}$$

This same formula gives us a method for obtaining molecular weights by a comparison of the densities of two gases, measured at the same temperature and pressure. If d_1 refers to gas 1 and d_2 refers to gas 2 we have:

$$d_1 = \frac{M_1 P}{RT}; \quad d_2 = \frac{M_2 P}{RT} \qquad \text{(same } P \text{ and } T\text{)}$$

Dividing these two equations, we have (P, T, and R cancel):

$$\boxed{\frac{d_1}{d_2} = \frac{M_1}{M_2}}$$

This tells us that the densities of two different gases (measured at the same T and P) will be in the ratio of their molecular weights. If we know the molecular weight of one of the gases, this equation then permits us to calculate the molecular weight of the other.

Example: The density of a certain gas is 1.64 g./l. At the same temperature and pressure, oxygen (O_2) has the density of 1.45 g./l. What is the molecular weight of the gas?

Answer: From our equation, solving for M_1:

$$M_1 = M_2 \left(\frac{d_1}{d_2}\right) \qquad \text{(let subscript 2 represent oxygen)}$$

$$= \left(\frac{32 \text{ g. } O_2}{\text{mole}}\right) \times \left(\frac{1.64 \text{ g./l.}}{1.45 \text{ g. } O_2/\text{l.}}\right)$$

$$= 36.2 \text{ g./mole}$$

Finally, we can use our original equation to obtain the density of a gas at any temperature and pressure, if we know its density at a given temperature and pressure.

Let d_1 be the measured density of a gas at T_1 and P_1 and d_2 the desired density at different conditions T_2 and P_2. We can write two equations:

$$d_1 = \frac{MP_1}{RT_1}; \quad d_2 = \frac{MP_2}{RT_2} \quad (M \text{ is the same, since the gas is the same})$$

Dividing these two equations we have:

$$\boxed{\frac{d_2}{d_1} = \left(\frac{P_2}{P_1}\right) \times \left(\frac{T_1}{T_2}\right)} \qquad (M \text{ and } R \text{ cancel})$$

Thus we have derived an equation giving the change in density of a gas with temperature and pressure.

Example: The density of a certain gas is 1.85 g./l. at 80 cm. Hg and 50°C. What is it at STP?

Answer: Solving the above equation for d_2:

$$d_2 = d_1 \times \left(\frac{P_2}{P_1}\right) \times \left(\frac{T_1}{T_2}\right)$$

Letting subscript 1 refer to given conditions and 2 to STP:

$$d_2 = \left(\frac{1.85 \text{ g.}}{1.}\right) \times \left(\frac{76 \text{ cm. Hg}}{80 \text{ cm. Hg}}\right) \times \left(\frac{323°\text{K.}}{273°\text{K.}}\right) = 2.08 \frac{\text{g.}}{\text{l. STP}}$$

Note: We can check the calculation by observing that going from 80 cm. Hg to 76 cm. Hg (standard pressure) represents an expansion in volume and thus a decrease in density (ratio 76/80 is less than 1). Similarly going from 50°C. to 0°C. represents a contraction in volume on cooling and thus an increase in density (ratio 323/273 is greater than 1).

10. Problems

1. The difference between two arms of a mercury manometer is 40 cm. Hg. If the lower arm is exposed to a gas while the upper arm is evacuated, what is the pressure of the gas in atmospheres?

2. If the difference between the two arms in the preceding problem were 10 in., calculate the pressure in centimeters Hg; in atmospheres.

3. If a gas is confined by a water instead of a mercury manometer and the water level exposed to the gas is 90 cm. lower than the other arm which is exposed to the air (whose pressure is 75 cm. Hg), calculate the gas pressure in centimeters Hg; in atmospheres. (Density Hg = 13.55 g./cc.).

4. Make the following conversions:
  (a) 250 mm. Hg to dynes per square centimeters.
  (b) 35 cm. Hg to atmospheres.
  (c) 3 lb./sq. in. to centimeters Hg.
  (d) 60 dynes/cm.^{2} to atmospheres.

5. A block of iron rests on a base whose area is 3 cm.^{2}. If the volume of the block is 25 cm.^{3} and the density of iron is 7.8 g./cm.^{3}, calculate the pressure on the base in dynes per square centimeters.

6. A phonograph pickup weighs 2 oz. It rests on a needle whose tip has a contact area of 0.045 sq. mm. Calculate the pressure exerted by the pickup on a record in pounds per square inch.

7. What is the volume occupied by 10 l. of gas at 76 cm. Hg after it has been compressed at constant temperature to 5 atm.?

8. What pressure is required to compress 180 cc. of gas at constant temperature to a volume of 24 cc. if the initial pressure is 30 cm. Hg?

9. 23 l. of gas is heated from 30°C. to 150°C. at constant pressure. What is its final volume?

10. To what temperature must 280 cc. of CO_2 be cooled for its volume to decrease to 130 cc.? The initial temperature is −20°C., and the gas is kept at constant pressure.

11. What is the volume of 600 cc. STP of N_2 at 45°C. and 2 atm. pressure?

12. 720 cc. of nitrogen gas is collected over mercury at −10°C. and 25 cm. Hg pressure. What is this volume at STP?

13. In each of the following problems, what information is lacking to calculate the answer?
  (a) A volume of gas is compressed from 10 atm. to 1 atm. at constant temperature. What is its final volume?
  (b) What volume will 15 cc. of gas occupy when cooled to −30°C. at constant pressure?
  (c) 80 cc. of gas at −38°C. is heated to 40°C. and 80 mm. Hg pressure. What was the initial pressure?

14. Using conversion factors, convert the value of R from 82.1 cc.-atm./mole-°K. to units of:
  (a) cc.-mm. Hg/mole-°K.
  (b) l.-lb./sq. in./mole-°K.
  (c) ergs/mole-°K.

15. 820 cc. of an unknown gas at 35°C. and 80 cm. Hg is found to weigh 2.46 g. What is its molecular weight?

16. What volume will be occupied by 1.5 g. of NO gas at 75°C. and 300 mm. Hg pressure?

17. 1.47 l. of a gas is collected over water at 30°C. and barometric pressure of 744 mm. Hg. If the gas has a weight of 1.98 g. and the vapor pressure of water at 30°C. is 32 mm. Hg, what is the molecular weight of the gas?

18. 250 cc. of a gas is collected over acetone at −10°C. and 85 cm. Hg pressure. If the gas weighs 1.34 g. and the vapor pressure of acetone at −10°C. is 39 mm. Hg, what is the molecular weight of the gas?

19. The density of a gas is found to be 2.07 g./l. at 30°C. and 2 atm. pressure. What is its density at STP?

20. The density of Cl_2 gas is 3.17 mg./cc. at STP. What is its density at 100°C. and 70 cm. Hg pressure?

21. The pressure of the atmosphere 100 miles above the earth is about 2×10^{-6} mm. Hg, and the temperature is about −180°C. How many molecules are there in 1 cc. of gas at this altitude?

22. What is the density of SO_2 gas at STP? at 40°C. and 80 cm. Hg pressure?

23. It is found that an unknown gas has a density 2.5 times as great as that of oxygen (O_2) at the same T and P. What is its molecular weight?

24. At a given T and P, CO_2 has a density 1.32 times less than that of a gas X. What is the molecular weight of X? What is the density of X at STP?

CHAPTER VII

The Concept of Combining Power—Valence

1. The Equivalent Weights of Elements

In the present chapter we shall investigate the concept of "valence" which is so frequently used in chemistry.

It was early discovered that elements seem to combine with each other in weight ratios which, in many cases, were simply related to their atomic weight. Thus it was found that 8 g. of oxygen (O) will react with precisely 20 g. of calcium (Ca) to form calcium oxide. It was further found that 8 g. of oxygen (O) would react with precisely 1.0 g. of hydrogen to form water. Then when the reaction of calcium with hydrogen was investigated it was discovered that 20 g. of calcium would react with just 1.0 g. of hydrogen to form calcium hydride. Many more illustrations of this type of relation could be given for other elements.

We can compile from such evidence an experimental table of weights for each element which gives that weight of the element which will combine with 8.00 g. of oxygen. These weights can be measured very precisely. The table is known as the Table of Combining Weights, or, according to current practice, the Table of Equivalent Weights. Table X contains the equivalent weights of a few common elements.

TABLE X
EQUIVALENT WEIGHTS OF A FEW COMMON ELEMENTS

Element	Equivalent Weight (grams)	Element	Equivalent Weight (grams)
Oxygen	8.000*	Aluminum	9.00
Hydrogen	1.008	Calcium	20.04
Sulfur	16.000	Zinc	32.7
Carbon	3.000	Sodium	23.00
Chlorine	35.46	Potassium	39.10
Bromine	79.92	Lead	103.61

* 8.000 g. of oxygen is the standard unit for the table.

The usefulness of such a table is that in most cases, if we want to know what weight of one element will react with a given weight of another element, these weights will be in the ratio of the equivalent weights.

Thus from the table we can predict that 1.008 g. of hydrogen will react with 16.000 g. of sulfur; 32.7 g. of zinc will react with 35.46 g. of chlorine, etc.

From these equivalent weights chemical weight conversion factors can be obtained which can be used to determine the weight of one element that will react with another.

Example: What weight of aluminum (Al) will combine with 5.00 g. of chlorine (Cl)?

Answer: From the table:

$$9.00 \text{ g. Al} = 35.46 \text{ g. Cl}$$

Then:

$$5.00 \text{ g. Cl} = 5.00 \text{ g. Cl} \times \left(\frac{9.00 \text{ g. Al}}{35.46 \text{ g. Cl}} \right)$$

$$= 1.27 \text{ g. Al}$$

Example: 7.95 g. of an element X will combine with 3.47 g. of oxygen. What is the equivalent weight of the element?

Answer: By equivalent weight, we mean that weight which will combine with 8.000 g. O.

$$8.000 \text{ g. O} = 8.00 \text{ g. O} \times \left(\frac{7.95 \text{ g. X}}{3.47 \text{ g. O}} \right)$$

$$= 18.32 \text{ g. X}$$

The significance of these results is that 1 equivalent weight of an element has precisely the same *power* for chemical combination as 1 equivalent weight of any other element, and all of these have the same chemical combining power as 8.000 g. of oxygen (standard).

Do problems 1, 2, and 3 at the end of the chapter.

2. The Equivalent—Units

We can define the following useful unit:

Definition:

1 equivalent of an element = The equivalent weight of the
element in grams

From the preceding discussion we see that the unit "equivalent" is well chosen since 1 equivalent of one element is indeed equal (or equivalent) in *chemical combining power* to 1 equivalent of any other element.

Conversely, we may conclude, when two elements react to form a compound, equal numbers of equivalents of both must react.

Example: How many equivalents of zinc (Zn) will react with 20 g. of bromine (Br)?

Answer: From Table X:

$$20 \text{ g. Br} = 20 \text{ g. Br} \times \left(\frac{1 \text{ eq. Br}}{79.92 \text{ g. Br}} \right)$$
$$= 0.250 \text{ eq. Br}$$

By the principle of equivalence, this will require precisely *0.250 eq. Zn*, or, in grams:

$$0.250 \text{ eq. Zn} = 0.250 \text{ eq. Zn} \times \left(\frac{32.7 \text{ g. Zn}}{1 \text{ eq. Zn}} \right) = 8.18 \text{ g. Zn}$$

It would thus appear that the Table of Equivalent Weights gives all the information needed to perform calculations for chemical reactions. This statement is subject to some restriction as we shall see later.

When two different elements react to form a compound, the latter will contain two elements and so is called a binary compound (e.g., $NaCl$, HCl, $ZnCl_2$, etc.). But, by the principle of equivalence, a binary compound will contain equal numbers of equivalents of each element present in it. Thus we can define the equivalent weight of a binary compound:

Definition:

The equivalent weight of = That weight of the compound which
    a binary Compound   contains 1 equivalent of each element

Similarly we can definite a unit:

Definition:

1 equivalent of a compound = The equivalent weight in grams

Example: What is the equivalent weight of sodium chloride?
Answer: We don't need to know the formula! From the table and the definition:

Eq. wt. of sodium chloride = Eq. wt. of Na + Eq. wt. of Cl
                           = 23.00 g. + 35.46 g.
                           = 58.46 g.

In a similar fashion we can obtain the equivalent weight of any binary compound by adding the equivalent weights of the elements present in it. For this we do not need to know the formula! Thus the equivalent weight of calcium oxide is 28.04 g.; of aluminum bromide, 88.92 g.; of potassium sulfide, 55.10 g.

3. Radicals

The chemical behavior of most inorganic compounds containing more than two elements is such that they may be considered as being composed of only two groups, one of which may be an element and the other a complex group containing more than one element. Thus calcium sulfate ($CaSO_4$) behaves chemically as though it were made of the two groups, calcium (Ca) and sulfate (SO_4). The sulfate (SO_4) preserves its identity in many chemical reactions of the compound $CaSO_4$. Such groups are known as radicals, and their equivalent weights may be obtained experimentally by determining the weight of the group that will combine with 1 equivalent of an element whose equivalent weight is known.

Thus it can be shown by direct analysis that 20 g. of calcium (1 equivalent) will combine with 48 g. of sulfate (SO_4), and so the equivalent weight of the sulfate radical (SO_4) is 48 g. Table XI lists some of the more common radicals and their equivalent weights.

TABLE XI

EQUIVALENT WEIGHTS OF SOME RADICALS

Radical	Formula	Equivalent Weight (grams)
Sulfate	SO_4	48.0
Nitrate	NO_3	62.0
Ammonium	NH_4	18.0
Carbonate	CO_3	30.0
Chromate	CrO_4	58.0
Chlorate	ClO_3	83.5
Hydroxide	OH	17.0

For compounds containing such radicals, 1 equivalent of the compound will contain 1 equivalent of the element and 1 equivalent of the radical. Thus the equivalent weight of sodium sulfate is 71.0 g.; of ammonium chloride, 53.5 g.; of aluminum chromate, 67.0 g.; etc.

Do problem 4 at the end of the chapter.

4. The Principle of Equivalence—Chemical Reactions

When reactions occur between elements or compounds, the principle of equivalence predicts that 1 equivalent of each substance will react and 1 equivalent of each product will be found.

Thus when zinc reacts with sulfuric acid (hydrogen sulfate) we can represent the reaction as:

1 eq. zinc + 1 eq. sulfuric acid → 1 eq. zinc sulfate + 1 eq. hydrogen

Similar equations can be written for all such reactions. Only for those reactions in which radicals are destroyed or lose their identity does this principle fail or, rather, need modification.

It appears, then, that if we are provided with a Table of Equivalent Weights we can dispense with the writing and balancing of chemical equations since the principle of equivalence tells us precisely the weight relationships in all chemical reactions, namely, 1 equivalent per 1 equivalent for all substances in the reaction.

Example: Ammonium sulfate reacts with calcium chloride to produce ammonium chloride and a precipitate of insoluble calcium sulfate. How much calcium sulfate will be produced from the reaction of 14.0 g. of ammonium sulfate?

Answer: The student should check the origin of all the conversion factors:

$$14.0 \text{ g. ammonium sulfate} = 14.0 \text{ g. amm. sulf.} \times \left(\frac{1 \text{ eq. amm. sulf.}}{66.0 \text{ g. amm. sulf.}} \right)$$

$$\times \left(\frac{1 \text{ eq. cal. sulf.}}{1 \text{ eq. amm. sulf.}} \right) \times \left(\frac{68 \text{ g. cal. sulf.}}{1 \text{ eq. cal. sulf.}} \right)$$

$$= 14.4 \text{ g. calcium sulfate}$$

Do problem 5 at the end of the chapter.

5. Combining Power—The Unit of Valence

We can now ask, how is this new system of units, *equivalents*, which are so useful in reactions, related to our theoretical units of moles?

If we compare the equivalent weights listed in Table X and Table XI with the molecular weights of the substances, we will find that the molecular weights are *always* some simple multiple of the equivalent weights. This is shown in Table XII.

TABLE XII
SOME EQUIVALENT AND MOLECULAR WEIGHTS

Substance	Equivalent Weight (g./eq.)	Molecular Weight (g./mole)	Ratio of Mol. Wt./Eq. Wt.
Oxygen (O)	8.000	16.00	2
Carbon (C)	3.00	12.00	4
Calcium (Ca)	20.00	40.00	2
Nitrate (NO_3)	62.00	62.00	1
Sulfate (SO_4)	48.00	96.0	2
Calcium sulfate ($CaSO_4$)	68.0	136.0	2

This ratio of the molecular weight of an element or group to the equivalent weight of the same element or group has the units of equivalents per mole and tells us how many equivalent weights or combining powers are present in one mole of the element or group.

$$\text{Ratio of molecular weight divided by equivalent weight} = \frac{\text{Grams/Mole}}{\text{Grams/Equivalent}} = \frac{\text{Equivalents}}{\text{Mole}}$$

Because of the standards used for oxygen (1 eq. $O = 8$ g. O; 1 mole $O = 16$ g. O), it turns out that this ratio is never less than 1 and always turns out to be a whole number. This number is called the *valence* of the element or group, and we see now the precise meaning of the term:

Definition: Valence is the number of equivalents of an element or compound present in 1 mole of the compound.

or

$$\boxed{\text{Valence} = \frac{\text{Equivalents}}{\text{Mole}}}$$

The valence of an element or group is thus a quantity which measures the capacity of the element or group for chemical combination.

When we say that oxygen (O) has a valence of 2 and hydrogen (H) has a valence of 1, we mean that the combining power of 1 mole of O is twice as great as the combining power of 1 mole of H, and, in particular, 1 mole of O can combine with 2 moles of H.

6. Valence and Chemical Formulae

If we know the valences of elements or radicals, we can write chemical formulae for the compounds they form. Thus the valence of aluminum (Al) is 3, that of chlorine (Cl) is 1. Then, 1 mole of aluminum can combine with 3 moles of chlorine and the compound aluminum chloride will have the formula, $AlCl_3$. Similarly the valence of sulfate (SO_4) is 2. Then 2 moles of Al will combine with 3 moles of SO_4, since 2 moles of Al have a combining power of 6, and 3 moles of SO_4 have a combining power of 6. The formula is then $Al_2(SO_4)_3$. From a table of valences the student can write the formula for any combination of elements and radicals shown. (*Note:* This is, however, no guarantee that the compound written exists. If it does, however, the formula will be correct.)

Similarly, if we know the formula (from analysis) of a compound and the valence of one of the elements, we can always deduce the valence of the other.

Example: The formula of chromic sulfate is $Cr_2(SO_4)_3$. What is the valence of chromium? The valence of SO_4 is 2.

Answer: The SO_4 group has a valence of 2. Three SO_4 groups represent 6 equivalents. There must be 6 equivalents of Cr combined with this. Since there are 2 moles of Cr, each mole of Cr must contain 3 equivalents. Thus the valence of Cr is 3.

Do problem 10 at the end of the chapter.

7. Calculation of Equivalent Weights

Because it is much simpler to remember the valences of elements and radicals rather than their combining weights, not much use is made of the Table of Equivalent Weights. Instead the equivalent weights of elements and radicals are calculated from the molecular weights and the known valences. For this purpose the definition of valence is used:

Definition:

$$\text{Equivalent weight} = \frac{\text{Molecular weight}}{\text{Valence}}$$

Example: The molecular weight of tin (Sn) is 118.7 g./mole. Its valence is 4. What is its equivalent weight?

Answer:

$$\text{Eq. wt. Sn} = \frac{118.7 \text{ g./mole}}{4 \text{ eq./mole}} = 29.68 \text{ g./eq.}$$

Similar calculations can be made for radicals.

Example: The molecular weight of orthosilicate (SiO_4) is 92 g./mole. Its valence is 4 eq./mole. What is its equivalent weight?

Answer:

$$\text{Eq. wt. SiO}_4 = \left(\frac{92 \text{ g.}}{\text{mole}}\right) \times \left(\frac{1 \text{ mole}}{4 \text{ eq.}}\right)$$
$$= 23 \text{ g./eq.}$$

Observe that the property of valence provides a conversion factor to convert from equivalents to moles. With these rules it is also possible to compute the equivalent weight of a compound from its molecular weight. Thus 1 mole of calcium chloride $(CaCl_2)$ will weigh

111.0 g. and contain 2 equivalents of Ca and 2 equivalents of Cl. One-half of a mole will contain 1 equivalent of each group, and so the equivalent weight of $CaCl_2$ is 55.5 g./eq.

Table XIII shows some compounds and their equivalent weight:

TABLE XIII
EQUIVALENT WEIGHTS OF SOME COMPOUNDS

Compound	Molecular Weight (grams)	Number of Equivalents in 1 mole	Equivalent Weight (grams)
NaCl	58.5	1	58.5
Na_2SO_4	142	2	71
$ZnCl_2$	136.4	2	68.2
$ZnSO_4$	161.4	2	80.7
$AlCl_3$	133.5	3	44.5
$AlPO_4$	122	3	40.7
$Al_2(SO_4)_3$	342	6	57

8. Some Complications—Multivalence

Having thus developed what seems to be a super-elegant way of doing calculations of chemical reactions, a way that avoids the need for balanced equations, we must now raise the disappointing specter of complication. It is unfortunate, but true, that many, actually a majority, of the elements display the property of multivalence. That is, they may have one valence in a given set of reactions and another valence in a different set of reactions.

Even our standard-bearer, oxygen, has the valence of 2 in water (H_2O) but can form another compound with hydrogen in which it has the valence of 1, namely hydrogen peroxide (H_2O_2). Nitrogen can form five different oxides, each showing a different valence.

This means that we shall have to exercise due care in discussing equivalents and equivalent weights, since we must be sure of the particular valence state that is involved. This complication is almost great enough to cause us to discard the concept of equivalence entirely. However, its usefulness is so great that it has persisted, and so we shall continue to apply it but be warned of the confusion and ambiguity that may arise.

9. Summary

1. *The equivalent weight of an element or radical is that weight which combines with 8.000 g. of oxygen.*

2. *The unit, equivalent, is defined as the equivalent weight in grams.*

3. *The law of combining weights states that 1 equivalent weight of any element will combine with precisely 1 equivalent weight of another element or compound.*

4. *By the equivalent weight of a compound we shall mean that weight which contains 1 equivalent of each element or radical.*

5. *The valence of a radical or element is defined as the number of equivalent weights present in 1 mole of the element or radical. It has the units of equivalents per mole and may be used as a property conversion factor to relate equivalents and moles.*

6. *The equivalent weight of an element or radical may be calculated from its molecular weight and its valence.*

$$Equivalent \; weight \; = \; Molecular \; weight/Valence$$

7. *From the principle of reacting equivalence contained in the law of combining weights we can say that, when elements or compounds react, equal numbers of equivalents will always react with each other to produce equal numbers of equivalents of each product. This allows us to perform calculations without the use of balanced equations.*

8. *The property of multivalence exhibited by most elements indicates that caution be used in dealing with the above properties.*

10. Problems

1. 4.25 g. of an element X combines with oxygen to form 5.40 g. of an oxide. What is the equivalent weight of X?

2. 1.08 g. of a metal oxide, on heating, decomposes to give the pure metal and 56.0 cc. STP of O_2 gas. What is the equivalent weight of the metal?

3. 2.94 g. of nickel (valence = 2) combines with an element X to form 4.49 g. of a compound. What is the equivalent weight of X?

4. Using the Table of Atomic Weights and known valences, make the following conversions:

    (a) 2 moles of $FeCl_3$ to equivalents.

    (b) 25.6 g. of zinc to equivalents.

    (c) 13 mmoles of Pb to milliequivalents.

    (d) 6.5 g. of $CaSO_4$ to equivalents.

    (e) 10 l. STP of gaseous CCl_4 to equivalents.

    (f) 0.45 eq. of H_2S to moles.

    (g) 0.64 eq. of $AlBr_3$ to grams.

    (h) 0.20 eq. of $CuSO_4$ to grams.

    (i) 340 cc. STP of oxygen gas (O_2) to equivalents.

    (j) 1.4 meq. of Cl_2 gas to cubic centimeters STP.

5. Using the principle of equivalence, calculate (without chemical equations):

    (a) How many grams of $CuSO_4$ will react with 2.4 g. of Na_2S to produce CuS and Na_2SO_4?

    (b) How many grams of NaOH will react with 30 g. of $Al_2(SO_4)_3$?

    (c) How many grams of $Ca_3(PO_4)_2$ can be made from 20 g. of $Ca(NO_3)_2$ by the reaction with H_3PO_4?

(d) How many grams of sulfuric acid (H_2SO_4) are needed to react with 20 g. of NaOH?

(e) How many grams of Zn will react with 11 g. of NaOH to produce hydrogen and sodium zincate?

6. 14.2 g. of an unknown acid X are neutralized by precisely 12.0 g. of NaOH. What is the equivalent weight of the acid?

7. 24.5 mmoles of $Ca(OH)_2$ will exactly neutralize 1.37 g. of an acid. What is the equivalent weight of the acid?

8. When 18.7 g. of an unknown acid react with zinc metal, exactly 800 cc. STP of H_2 gas are evolved. What is the equivalent weight of the acid?

9. When 3.5 g. of an unknown metal react with an acid, exactly 250 cc. STP of H_2 gas are produced. What is the equivalent weight of the metal?

10. Given the valence of oxygen as 2, calculate the valence of the other element in each of the following compounds:

(a) N_2O.   (e) SO_3.   (i) Tl_2O_3.
(b) NO_2.   (f) CO.   (j) PtO_2.
(c) N_2O_3.   (g) Mn_2O_7.   (k) Fe_3O_4.
(d) P_2O_5.   (h) ClO_2.

CHAPTER VIII

Measurement of Solutions

1. Solutions—Concentration Units

It is generally clumsy to carry out reactions between solids or gases. First, it is difficult to mix the solids adequately; and second, it is difficult to handle gases in the laboratory without a great deal of equipment. On the other hand, liquids mix quite readily, are easily handled, and can be measured out accurately and quickly by volumetric equipment.

For these reasons it is always preferable to carry out chemical reactions in the liquid state. But many substances are solids or gases! This difficulty is circumvented by finding a liquid capable of dissolving them. Thus sodium chloride is most frequently used in chemical reactions in the form of a solution of sodium chloride in water. The liquid is called the *solvent*. The substance dissolved in the liquid is called the *solute*. (This distinction sometimes appears quite arbitrary as when, for example, alcohol, itself a liquid, is dissolved in an equal volume of water. Either substance could then be called the solute.)

In order to do quantitative work with solutions, if we are going to measure the solution in terms of volume, we must know the amount of solute contained per unit of volume of solution. This property is known as the concentration of the solution.

There are a number of different units employed in specifying the concentration of solute present in a given quantity of solution. These are listed in Table XIV.

Do problems 1 and 2 at the end of the chapter.

2. Conversion of Units

It can be seen that there are two types of units for expressing the concentration of a solution. One is in units of the weight of the solution and requires that the solution be weighed when dispensing (e.g., molality, weight per cent). This type of unit is used only in

TABLE XIV

UNITS USED IN EXPRESSING CONCENTRATION OF A SOLUTION

Name	Definition	Most Frequently Used Units	Property of Solution Measured When Dispensing
Weight percent $\frac{M}{M}$	Weight units of solute contained in 100 weight units of solution	$\dfrac{\text{Grams of solute}}{100 \text{ grams of solution}}$	Weight of solution
Weight concentration $\frac{M}{V}$	Weight of solute contained in a unit volume of solution	$\dfrac{\text{Grams of solute}}{\text{Liters of solution}}$	Volume of solution
Molarity (M) $\frac{moles}{V}$	Number of moles of solute contained in 1 l. of solution	$\dfrac{\text{Moles of solute}}{\text{Liters of solution}}$	Volume of solution
Normality (N) $\frac{Eq. wt}{V}$	Number of equivalents of solute contained in 1 l. of solution	$\dfrac{\text{Equivalent of solute}}{\text{Liters of solution}}$	Volume of solution
Molality $\frac{moles}{M}$	Number of moles of solute per kilogram of solvent	$\dfrac{\text{Moles of solute}}{\text{Kilograms of solvent}}$	Weight of solution

experiments requiring great accuracy. The second type of unit is in terms of the volume of the solution and is in much more common usage.

Before proceeding to the analysis of problems, let us first say a word about the relations between the three concentration units which refer to volume of solutions and are most popular.

The three units—for weight concentration, for molarity, and for normality—all have reference to the quantity of solute per liter of solution. We can use the appropriate conversion factors to convert from any one of these to the other.

Example: The concentration of a solution is given as 40.0 g. of NaCl per liter of solution (abbreviation: 40.0 g. NaCl/l.). Convert this to units of molarity and normality.

Answer: To convert to units of molarity, we use the relation:

$$1 \text{ mole NaCl} = 58.5 \text{ g. NaCl}$$

Then:

$$\frac{40.0 \text{ g. NaCl}}{1.} = \left(\frac{40.0 \text{ g. NaCl}}{1.}\right) \times \left(\frac{1 \text{ mole NaCl}}{58.5 \text{ g. NaCl}}\right)$$

$$= \frac{0.684 \text{ mole NaCl}}{1.} \text{ or } 0.684 \; M \text{ NaCl}$$

For normality we need the relation:

$$58.5 \text{ g. NaCl} = 1 \text{ mole NaCl} = 1 \text{ eq. NaCl}$$

Then:

$$\frac{40.0 \text{ g. NaCl}}{1.} = \left(\frac{40.0 \text{ g. NaCl}}{1.}\right) \times \left(\frac{1 \text{ eq. NaCl}}{58.5 \text{ g. NaCl}}\right)$$

$$= \frac{0.684 \text{ eq. NaCl}}{1.} \text{ or } 0.684 \; N \text{ NaCl}$$

Example: A solution of $ZnSO_4$ has a concentration of 0.70 mole $ZnSO_4$ per liter of solution (abbreviation: 0.70 M $ZnSO_4$). Express this in units of weight concentration and normality. $W.C = \frac{a}{V}$ $Nom. = \frac{E.W.}{V}$

Answer:

(A)
$$\frac{0.70 \text{ mole ZnSO}_4}{1.} = \left(\frac{0.70 \text{ mole ZnSO}_4}{1.}\right) \times \left(\frac{161.4 \text{ g. ZnSO}_4}{1 \text{ mole ZnSO}_4}\right)$$

$$= \frac{113.0 \text{ g. ZnSO}_4}{1.}$$

(B)
$$\frac{0.70 \text{ mole ZnSO}_4}{1.} = \left(\frac{0.70 \text{ mole ZnSO}_4}{1.}\right) \times \left(\frac{2 \text{ eq. ZnSO}_4}{1 \text{ mole ZnSO}_4}\right)$$

$$= \frac{1.40 \text{ eq. ZnSO}_4}{1.} \text{ or } 1.40 \; N \text{ ZnSO}_4$$

Do problem 3 at the end of the chapter.

3. Interpretation of Concentration Units

Concentration is an intensive property of a solution and in many respects is similar to density. Just as the density of a substance expresses a relation between the property of mass and the property of volume for the particular substance, so concentration expresses a relation between the property, the mass of the solute (present in a given quantity of the solution), and the property of the volume of the solution.

We can use concentration units to give conversion factors between these two properties. This is perhaps most easily seen from the definition in algebraic form:

Definition: Molarity $(M) = \dfrac{\text{Moles of solute}}{\text{Volume of solution}}$

Definition: Normality $(N) = \dfrac{\text{Equivalents of solute}}{\text{Volume of solution}}$

Definition: Weight concentration $(C) = \dfrac{\text{Grams of solute}}{\text{Volume of solution}}$

Each equation relates three properties. If we know two of these we can always solve for the third. However, the method of conversion factors is so much simpler that we shall use it to illustrate problems:

Example: How many moles of HCl are there in 1.5 l. of a 2.0 M solution?   How many grams of HCl?
Answer:

(A) 1.5 l. soln. $= 1.5 \text{ l. soln.} \times \left(\dfrac{2.0 \text{ moles HCl}}{1 \text{ l. soln.}} \right)$

$= 3.0$ moles HCl

(B) 1.5 l. soln. $= 1.5 \text{ l. soln.} \times \left(\dfrac{2.0 \text{ moles HCl}}{1 \text{ l. soln.}} \right) \times \left(\dfrac{36.5 \text{ g. HCl}}{1 \text{ mole HCl}} \right)$

$= 109.5$ g. HCl

Example: What volume of a 0.64 N solution of H_2SO_4 will contain 13.0 g. of H_2SO_4?   What volume will contain 0.25 mole of H_2SO_4?
Answer:

(A) 13.0 g. $H_2SO_4 = 13.0 \text{ g. } H_2SO_4 \times \left(\dfrac{1 \text{ mole } H_2SO_4}{98 \text{ g. } H_2SO_4} \right) \times \left(\dfrac{2 \text{ eq. } H_2SO_4}{1 \text{ mole } H_2SO_4} \right)$

$\times \left(\dfrac{1 \text{ l. soln.}}{0.64 \text{ eq. } H_2SO_4} \right)$

$= \dfrac{13.0 \times 2}{98 \times 0.64}$ l. soln.

$= 0.414$ l. soln.

Note the logic of our procedure. We were given the property of mass in grams and asked to find the property of volume of solution, being also given the concentration in equivalents per liter. As indicated by the successive conversions, we converted mass to moles, moles to equivalents, and, finally, equivalents to liters of solution.

(B) 0.25 mole $H_2SO_4 = 0.25 \text{ mole } H_2SO_4 \times \left(\dfrac{2 \text{ eq. } H_2SO_4}{1 \text{ mole } H_2SO_4} \right)$

$\times \left(\dfrac{1 \text{ l. soln.}}{0.64 \text{ eq. } H_2SO_4} \right)$

$= 0.781$ l. soln.

Example: How would you make 300 cc. of a 2.2 M solution of $AlCl_3$?
Answer:

$$300 \text{ cc. soln.} = 300 \text{ cc. soln.} \times \left(\frac{2.2 \text{ moles } AlCl_3}{1 \text{ l. soln.}}\right) \times \left(\frac{1 \text{ l.}}{1000 \text{ cc.}}\right)$$

$$\times \left(\frac{133.5 \text{ g. } AlCl_3}{1 \text{ mole } AlCl_3}\right)$$

$$= 88.1 \text{ g. } AlCl_3$$

Thus we would take 88.1 g. of $AlCl_3$ and add water until the total volume of the solution was 300 cc.

Do problems 4–10 at the end of the chapter.

4. Dilution

In laboratory practice we quite frequently are given stock solutions of certain concentrations and are required to make dilute solutions from them. In addition, in the course of reactions we will mix two solutions. This will result in diluting the concentration of each solution. It is, therefore, of interest to see how these changes, which are changes in volume, affect the concentration.

Example: A laboratory bottle is labeled 12.0 M HCl. How would you make from this 20 cc. of a 3.0 M HCl solution?
Answer: It is well to visualize first the procedure we must follow. We are going to take a certain volume of the concentrated 12.0 M HCl solution and add to it enough water to make 20 cc. of the 3.0 M solution. Thus we want to know how many cubic centimeters of the 12.0 M solution to start with.
In 20 cc. of 3.0 M HCl there are

$$20 \text{ cc. soln.} = 20 \text{ cc. soln.} \times \left(\frac{3.0 \text{ moles HCl}}{1 \text{ l. soln.}}\right) \times \left(\frac{1 \text{ l.}}{1000 \text{ cc.}}\right)$$

$$= 0.060 \text{ mole HCl}$$

In order to get 0.060 mole HCl we need to take

$$0.060 \text{ mole HCl} = 0.060 \text{ mole HCl} \times \left(\frac{1 \text{ l. soln.}}{12.0 \text{ moles HCl}}\right) \times \left(\frac{1000 \text{ cc.}}{1 \text{ l.}}\right)$$

$$= 5.0 \text{ cc. solution.}$$

Thus if we take 5.0 cc. of the stock solution and add enough water (about 15 cc.) to make 20 cc. of solution we will have a concentration of 3.0 M HCl.
Note that both parts of this problem could have been combined as a single series of conversions.

Example: How would you make 24 cc. of a 0.25 M solution of H_2SO_4, starting with 6.0 M H_2SO_4?

Answer: Let us label these solutions A and B to avoid confusion.

$$24 \text{ cc. soln. A} = 24 \text{ cc. soln. A} \times \left(\frac{0.25 \text{ mole } H_2SO_4}{1000 \text{ cc. soln. A}}\right) \times \left(\frac{1000 \text{ cc. soln. B}}{6.0 \text{ moles } H_2SO_4}\right)$$

$$= 1.00 \text{ cc. solution B}$$

Thus we take 1.00 cc. of solution B (6.0 M H_2SO_4) and dilute to 24 cc. with water.

Example: 50 cc. of a 3.0 M solution of HCl is mixed with 70 cc. of a 4.0 M solution of KNO_3. What is the final concentration of HCl and KNO_3 in the mixture? (Assume no contraction of volume on mixing.*)

Answer: Let us label the mixture solution C. Its volume is $50 + 70 = 120$ cc. By definition:

$$\text{Molarity of HCl in mixture} = \frac{\text{moles HCl}}{\text{l. soln. C}} = \frac{50 \text{ cc. soln. A} \times \left(\frac{3.0 \text{ moles HCl}}{1 \text{ l. soln. A}}\right) \times \left(\frac{1 \text{ l.}}{1000 \text{ cc.}}\right)}{120 \text{ cc. soln. C} \times \left(\frac{1 \text{ l.}}{1000 \text{ cc.}}\right)}$$

$$= \frac{1.25 \text{ moles HCl}}{\text{l. soln. C}} = 1.25 \ M \text{ HCl}$$

$$\text{Molarity of } KNO_3 \text{ in mixture} = \frac{\text{moles } KNO_3}{\text{l. soln. C}}$$

$$= \frac{70 \text{ cc. soln. B} \times \left(\frac{4.0 \text{ moles } KNO_3}{1 \text{ l. soln. B}}\right) \times \left(\frac{1 \text{ l.}}{1000 \text{ cc.}}\right)}{120 \text{ cc. soln. C} \left(\frac{1 \text{ l.}}{1000 \text{ cc.}}\right)}$$

$$= 2.33 \frac{\text{moles } KNO_3}{\text{l. soln. C}} = 2.33 \ M \ KNO_3$$

* Note that on dilution of a solution the original concentration is diminished in the ratio of the initial to the final volume. In the above example the final M HCl $= \frac{50}{120} \times$ (original M HCl).

Do problems 11–17 at the end of the chapter.

5. Chemical Reactions Involving Solutions

In Chapter IV we discussed the method of solving problems involving chemical reactions. The problems discussed, however, involved only the reaction of pure substances. How may we extend the methods to include solutions? The answer is that we will follow the same procedure but now add to it the methods just discussed for converting from volume of a solution to quantity of solute present.

Example:

$$3Cu + 8HNO_3 \rightarrow 3Cu(NO_3)_2 + 2NO\uparrow + 4H_2O$$

How many grams of copper may be dissolved in 150 cc. of 4 N HNO₃?

Answer:

$$150 \text{ cc. soln.} = 150 \text{ cc. soln.} \times \left(\frac{1 \text{ l.}}{1000 \text{ cc.}} \right) \times \left(\frac{4 \text{ eq. HNO}_3}{1 \text{ l. soln.}} \right)$$

$$\times \left(\frac{1 \text{ mole HNO}_3}{1 \text{ eq. HNO}_3} \right) \times \left(\frac{3 \text{ moles Cu}}{8 \text{ moles HNO}_3} \right) \times \left(\frac{63.6 \text{ g. Cu}}{1 \text{ mole Cu}} \right)$$

$$= \frac{150 \times 4 \times 63.6 \times 3}{1000 \times 8} = 14.3 \text{ g. Cu}$$

Example:

$$3Cl_2 + 6NaOH \rightarrow 5NaCl + NaClO_3 + 3H_2O$$

How many liters STP of Cl₂ gas will react with 75 cc. of 1.6 M NaOH?

Answer:

$$75 \text{ cc. soln.} = 75 \text{ cc. soln.} \times \left(\frac{1 \text{ l.}}{1000 \text{ cc.}} \right) \times \left(\frac{1.6 \text{ moles NaOH}}{1 \text{ l. soln.}} \right)$$

$$\times \left(\frac{3 \text{ moles Cl}_2}{6 \text{ moles NaOH}} \right) \times \left(\frac{22.4 \text{ l. STP Cl}_2}{1 \text{ mole Cl}_2} \right)$$

$$= \frac{75 \times 1.6 \times 3 \times 22.4}{6 \times 1000} \text{ l. STP Cl}_2$$

$$= 1.34 \text{ l. STP Cl}_2$$

6. Reactions between Solutions—Principle of Equivalence

If we are dealing with the reaction between two solutions, we may use the procedure outlined in section 5.

Example:

$$2FeCl_3 + 3Ag_2SO_4 \rightarrow 6AgCl\downarrow + Fe_2(SO_4)_3$$

How many cubic centimeters of 0.20 M Ag₂SO₄ will react with 68 cc. of 0.65 M FeCl₃?

Answer: Label the FeCl₃ solution A and the Ag₂SO₄ solution B.

$$68 \text{ cc. soln. A} = 68 \text{ cc. soln. A} \times \left(\frac{1 \text{ l.}}{1000 \text{ cc.}} \right) \times \left(\frac{0.65 \text{ mole FeCl}_3}{1 \text{ l. soln. A}} \right)$$

$$\times \left(\frac{3 \text{ moles Ag}_2SO_4}{2 \text{ moles FeCl}_3} \right) \times \left(\frac{1 \text{ l. soln. B}}{0.20 \text{ mole Ag}_2SO_4} \right) \times \left(\frac{1000 \text{ cc.}}{1 \text{ l.}} \right)$$

$$= \frac{68 \times 0.65 \times 3 \times 1000}{1000 \times 2 \times 0.20} \text{ cc. soln. B} = 331 \text{ cc. soln. B}$$

However, when dealing with solutions we can also use the much more powerful methods outlined in the section dealing with equivalents (Chapter VII). The principle of equivalence tells us that equal volumes of solutions having the same normality will have the same capacity for chemical reaction since they will have equal numbers of equivalents in equal volumes.

Thus, in dealing with reactions between two solutions, if we convert their concentrations to normalities, we can dispense with a balanced chemical equation.

To illustrate this let us consider the previous example:

Example: How many cubic centimeters of 0.20 M Ag_2SO_4 will react with 68 cc. of 0.65 M $FeCl_3$?

Answer:

$$0.65 \ M \ FeCl_3 = \left(\frac{0.65 \ \text{mole } FeCl_3}{1. \ \text{soln.}} \right) \times \left(\frac{3 \ \text{eq. } FeCl_3}{1 \ \text{mole } FeCl_3} \right)$$

$$= \frac{1.95 \ \text{eq. } FeCl_3}{1. \ \text{soln.}} = 1.95 \ N \ FeCl_3$$

Similarly:

$$0.20 \ M \ Ag_2SO_4 = 0.40 \ N \ Ag_2SO_4$$

Then:

$$68 \ \text{cc. soln. A} = 68 \ \text{cc. soln. A} \times \left(\frac{1 \ l.}{1000 \ cc.} \right) \times \left(\frac{1.95 \ \text{eq. } FeCl_3}{1 \ l. \ \text{soln. A}} \right)$$

$$\times \left(\frac{1 \ \text{eq. } Ag_2SO_4}{1 \ \text{eq. } FeCl_3} \right) \times \left(\frac{1 \ l. \ \text{soln. B}}{0.40 \ \text{eq. } Ag_2SO_4} \right) \times \left(\frac{1000 \ \text{cc.}}{1 \ l.} \right)$$

$$= \frac{68 \times 1.95 \times 1000}{1000 \times 0.40} \ \text{cc. soln. B}$$

$$= 331 \ \text{cc. soln. B}$$

Thus by means of the principle of equivalence we have achieved the same result without a balanced equation. Note that in the above example we could have combined the conversion of concentrations units with the other steps.

The student will probably by now have noticed that we generally deal in the laboratory with cubic centimeters (or milliliters) of solutions rather than with such large quantities as liters. Also, we are much more apt to use millimoles or milliequivalents of material rather than such large amounts as moles. Is it not possible to use these smaller units for calculations? The answer is, of course, yes, and it can easily be seen that a concentration of 1 mole/l. is the same as

1 millimole/milliliter (1 mmole/ml.).   Similarly, a 2 N solution may be taken to mean 2 equivalents/liter (2 eq./l.) or 2 milliequivalents/milliliter (2 meq./ml.).

These latter units are more convenient than the other units and consequently widely used for most laboratory work.   (*Note:* 1 ml. may be taken as equal to 1 cc.)

Example: How many milliliters of a 3.4 M solution of $Ba(NO_3)_2$ will react with 60 ml. of a 2.4 M solution of Na_3PO_4?

Answer: We will use the principle of equivalence and combine all steps: Call the $Ba(NO_3)_2$ solution A, and the Na_3PO_4 solution B.

$$60 \text{ ml. soln. B} = 60 \text{ ml. soln. B} \times \left(\frac{2.4 \text{ mmoles } Na_3PO_4}{1 \text{ ml. soln. B}} \right) \times \left(\frac{3 \text{ meq. } Na_3PO_4}{1 \text{ mmole } Na_3PO_4} \right)$$

$$\times \left(\frac{1 \text{ meq. } Ba(NO_3)_2}{1 \text{ meq. } Na_3PO_4} \right) \times \left(\frac{1 \text{ mmole } Ba(NO_3)_2}{2 \text{ meq. } Ba(NO_3)_2} \right) \times \left(\frac{1 \text{ ml. soln. A}}{3.4 \text{ mmole } Ba(NO_3)_2} \right)$$

$$= \frac{60 \times 2.4 \times 3}{2 \times 3.4} \text{ ml. soln. A}$$

$$= 63.5 \text{ ml. soln. A}$$

Do problems 18, 19, and 20 at the end of the chapter.

7. Titration of Acids and Bases

One of the most important of the general reactions in chemistry is the reaction of an acid and base to produce a salt and water.   These reactions may be performed in solution, using a colored dye to indicate when neutralization has been achieved.   When such neutralizations are performed extremely accurately, with burettes to measure volumes they are referred to as titrations.   We may apply the methods of the preceding chapter to such calculations.

Example: How many milliliters of 0.3 N H_2SO_4 are required to neutralize 40 ml. of 0.6 N NaOH?

Answer: Call the acid A, and the base solution B.

$$40 \text{ ml. soln. B} = 40 \text{ ml. soln. B} \times \left(\frac{0.6 \text{ meq. } NaOH}{1 \text{ ml. soln. B}} \right) \times \left(\frac{1 \text{ meq. } H_2SO_4}{1 \text{ meq. } NaOH} \right)$$

$$\times \left(\frac{1 \text{ ml. soln. A}}{0.3 \text{ meq. } H_2SO_4} \right)$$

$$= \frac{40 \times 0.6}{0.3} \text{ ml. soln. A}$$

$$= 80 \text{ ml. acid}$$

If the concentrations are given in terms of molarities, we may first convert to normalities or combine the conversions with the problem.

Example: How many milliliters of 0.46 M H_3PO_4 are needed to neutralize 60 ml. of 0.62 N NaOH?

Answer:

$$60 \text{ ml. soln. B} = 60 \text{ ml. soln. B} \times \left(\frac{0.62 \text{ meq. NaOH}}{1 \text{ ml. soln. B}}\right) \times \left(\frac{1 \text{ meq. } H_3PO_4}{1 \text{ meq. NaOH}}\right)$$

$$\times \left(\frac{1 \text{ mmole } H_3PO_4}{3 \text{ meq. } H_3PO_4}\right) \times \left(\frac{1 \text{ ml. soln. A}}{0.46 \text{ mmole } H_3PO_4}\right)$$

$$= \frac{60 \times 0.62}{3 \times 0.46} \text{ ml. soln. A}$$

$$= 26.9 \text{ ml. acid}$$

It is interesting to observe that in all such problems we can from the principle of equivalence compute the quantity of each substance produced in the reaction. Thus, if we titrate an acid with a base we will produce a salt and water. For each milliequivalent of acid we will require 1 meq. equivalent of base and we will produce 1 meq. of salt and 1 meq. of water (considered as H—OH; 18 g./eq.).

Example: In the preceding example, the neutralization of 60 ml. of 0.62 N NaOH by 0.46 M H_3PO_4, how many equivalents of salt (Na_3PO_4) are produced? What is its weight?

Answer: Using the principle of equivalence to convert NaOH to Na_3PO_4:

$$60 \text{ ml. soln. B} = 60 \text{ ml. soln. B} \times \left(\frac{0.62 \text{ meq. NaOH}}{1 \text{ ml. soln. B}}\right) \times \left(\frac{1 \text{ meq. } Na_3PO_4}{1 \text{ meq. NaOH}}\right)$$

$$= 37.2 \text{ meq. } Na_3PO_4$$

To convert to weight we first convert to millimoles and then to weight units:

$$= 37.2 \text{ meq. } Na_3PO_4 \times \left(\frac{1 \text{ mmole } Na_3PO_4}{3 \text{ meq. } Na_3PO_4}\right)$$

$$\times \left(\frac{164 \text{ mg. } Na_3PO_4}{1 \text{ mmole } Na_3PO_4}\right) \times \left(\frac{1 \text{ g.}}{1000 \text{ mg.}}\right)$$

$$= 2.03 \text{ g. } Na_3PO_4$$

Do problems 21–24 at the end of the chapter.

8. Density and Specific Gravity

In industrial operation, composition of solutions is frequently measured by their density. The reason for this is that it is very simple to measure the density of a solution by means of the depth to which a hollow-stemmed, weighted bob will sink in it. Such an instrument is known as a hydrometer.

Thus the attendant in a gasoline station can tell very quickly and very accurately the condition of a car's storage battery by measuring with a hydrometer the density of the sulfuric acid in the battery. In order to make use of such a measurement, the relation between density and composition must be known. Such relations must be obtained by experiment. Many chemical handbooks contain tables giving the density of common solutions as functions of their composition. With such information available it is always possible to translate such data into the other concentration units discussed.

Example: A bottle of commercial sulfuric acid (H_2SO_4) is labeled 86% sulfuric acid: density, 1.787 g./cc. What is the molarity of this solution?

Answer: We want to find the number of moles of H_2SO_4 in 1 l. of this solution (i.e., molarity). The student should check the origin of the conversion factors.

$$1 \text{ l. soln.} = 1 \text{ l. soln.} \times \left(\frac{1000 \text{ cc.}}{1 \text{ l.}} \right) \times \left(\frac{1.787 \text{ g. soln.}}{1 \text{ cc. soln.}} \right) \times \left(\frac{86 \text{ g. } H_2SO_4}{100 \text{ g. soln.}} \right)$$

$$\times \left(\frac{1 \text{ mole } H_2SO_4}{98 \text{ g. } H_2SO_4} \right) = \frac{1000 \times 1.787 \times 86}{100 \times 98} \text{ moles } H_2SO_4$$

$$= 15.69 \text{ moles } H_2SO_4$$

The concentration is thus 15.69 *M*.

Density, as we have used it, is always expressed in units of mass divided by volume. It is frequently valuable to have instead of an absolute density scale a relative density scale. In a relative density scale we would express the density of a substance by saying how many times more dense or less dense it was than another substance.

Such a relative density scale is in common use industrially, and the units are known as specific gravity. It is defined with respect to the density of water at 4°C.

$$\text{Specific gravity of a substance} = \frac{\text{Density of the substance}}{\text{Density of water at } 4°C}.$$

Water is thus the standard for such a scale. When we say that the specific gravity of a substance is 2, we mean that it is 2 times as dense as water at 4°C. If we wish to find the absolute density of the substance we then multiply its specific gravity by the density of water at 4°C.   Since the density of water at 4°C. is 1.000 g./cc., as far as the metric system is concerned the numerical value of the specific gravity will be the same as the density in grams per cubic centimeter. In other scales we do not have this simple relation.

Example: The specific gravity of concentrated sulfuric acid (96%) at 20°C. is 1.836.   What is its density in grams per cubic centimeter? in pounds per cubic foot?

Answer: From the above, the density must be also 1.836 g./cc.   To find the density in pounds per cubic foot we can make our usual conversion, or we can find out the density of water in pounds per cubic foot.   Since the latter is 62.4 lb./ft.^{3}:

$$\text{Density of sulfuric acid} = 1.836 \times 62.4 \text{ lb./ft.}^3 = 114.6 \text{ lb./ft.}^3$$

9. Problems

1. If the concentration of a solution is known in weight per cent, what property of the solution should be measured in dispensing it?   What if the concentration were expressed as molarity?

2. Of a solution whose normality is known, 100 g. are weighed out.   What additional property must be known to compute the amount of solute dispensed?

3. Make the following conversions:

    (*a*) 3 *M* H_2SO_4 to normality.
    (*b*) 0.1 *N* $Ca(OH)_2$ to molarity.
    (*c*) 5 g. Na_2SO_4/l. to molarity.
    (*d*) 20 mg. $CuSO_4$/ml. to molarity.
    (*e*) 3 *N* $Al_2(SO_4)_3$ to millimole $Al_2(SO_4)_3$/ml.
    (*f*) 0.46 mmole K_3PO_4/ml. to g. K_3PO_4/l.
    (*g*) 2.4 mg. $CaCl_2$/ml. to normality.
    (*h*) 5% NaCl solution to moles NaCl/kg. solvent (molality).
    (*i*) 1 Molal solution NaCl to weight per cent.

4. How many moles of $Al_2(SO_4)_3$ are there in 20 cc. of a 3.0 *M* solution?

5. How many grams of $Ca(OH)_2$ are there in 800 cc. of a 0.12 *N* solution? How many millimoles?   How many milliequivalents?

6. How many equivalents of $Al_2(CrO_4)_3$ are there in 60 ml. of a solution having a concentration of 20 mg. $Al_2(CrO_4)_3$/ml.?   How many millimoles?   How many grams?

7. A reaction requires 12 g. of H_2SO_4.   How many cubic centimeters of a 3.0 *M* solution should you use?

8. A reaction requires 3.4 mmoles of Na_3PO_4.   How many milliliters of a 1.8 *N* solution should you use?

9. How would you prepare 150 ml. of a 3.5 *N* solution of $Ca(NO_3)_2$?

10. How would you prepare 240 ml. of a solution of Na_2CO_3 containing 3.8 g. Na_2CO_3/l.?

11. How would you prepare 25 ml. of a 1.2 *M* solution of KCl from a stock solution which is 3.0 *M*?

12. How would you prepare 15 cc. of a 0.45 *N* solution of $CuSO_4$ from a stock solution which is 2.4 *M*?

13. 150 cc. of 3 M K_2SO_4 is mixed with 80 cc. of 2 M $NaNO_3$. What is the concentration of each salt in the final solution?

14. A stock solution of $CuSO_4$ is 1 M. How would you make from this 80 cc. of a solution containing 20 mg. $CuSO_4$/ml.?

15. How many grams of Cu are there in 100 ml. of a 0.5 M solution of $CuSO_4$? How many millimoles?

16. How would you make a solution containing 5 mg. Cu/ml. from a stock solution which is 0.80 M $Cu(NO_3)_2$?

17. How many millimoles of Zn are there in 5 ml. of a solution which is 2.4 M $ZnCl_2$?

18. $2Al + 3Zn(NO_3)_2 \rightarrow 2Al(NO_3)_3 + 3Zn$. How many grams of Al will react with 50 ml. of a 0.4 M solution of $Zn(NO_3)_2$?

19. $BaCl_2 + H_2SO_4 \rightarrow 2HCl + BaSO_4\downarrow$. How many grams of $BaCl_2$ are needed to react with 90 ml. of a 0.48 N solution of H_2SO_4.? How many grams of $BaSO_4$ will be produced?

20. How many cubic centimeters STP of HCl *gas* are needed to neutralize 40 ml. of a 0.8 M solution of KOH. How many millimoles of KCl will be formed?

21. How many milliliters of 3.0 M H_2SO_4 are needed to neutralize 200 ml. of 0.34 N $Ca(OH)_2$? How many milliequivalents of $CaSO_4$ are formed?

22. How many milliliters of 1.4 N NaOH will completely neutralize 80 ml. of 0.72 M H_3PO_4? How many grams of Na_3PO_4 are formed?

23. 40 ml. of 0.56 N NaOH just neutralize 1.75 g. of an unknown acid. What is the equivalent weight of the acid?

24. 60 ml. of a 0.75 N solution of KOH neutralize 44 ml. of a solution of H_2SO_4. What is the molarity of the acid?

25. The concentrated ammonia solution in laboratories is a 26.0% solution of NH_3. If its density is 0.904 g./cc. what is its molarity? its normality? its specific gravity?

26. Concentrated hydrochloric acid is 37% by weight HCl and has a specific gravity of 1.184. What is its molarity? its normality? its molality?

27. Laboratory nitric acid is 68% by weight with a density of 1.405 g./cc. How many milliliters of this acid are needed to neutralize 800 ml. of 0.04 M $Ca(OH)_2$ solution?

CHAPTER IX

The Physical Properties of Solutions

1. Properties of Ideal Solutions

Pure substances may be characterized by their physical properties. They have very sharp melting points, very sharp boiling points (at 1 atm. pressure), definite densities, definite vapor pressures, etc. Thus pure water has a melting point of 0°C., a boiling point of 100°C. (at 1 atm. pressure), density of 1.000 g./cc. (at 20°C.), a vapor pressure of 17.36 mm. Hg (at 20°C.), etc.

These properties can provide a reliable means of identifying a pure substance. It is of some interest to know how such physical properties are affected when a solution of two pure substances is made. In general we might expect that the physical properties of the solution (mixture) will be intermediate between the properties of the two components of the mixture. Thus we might reasonably expect that a 50% by volume mixture of two liquids might have a density intermediate between the densities of the individual liquids, and similarly for other properties.

Investigations have shown that this is approximately true for large numbers of solutions. A solution for which it would be exactly borne out is called an *ideal solution*. In practice there are very few ideal solutions. But many solutions are almost ideal, especially when very dilute (i.e., containing only a small amount of solute).

We use the term *colligative* to describe those properties of a solution which may be calculated by taking simple arithmetic averages of the properties of solute and solvent. As we shall see, the colligative properties of solutions can give us much valuable information about the properties of the solute if the properties of the solvent are known.

2. Vapor Pressure of Solutions—Raoult's Law

When a non-volatile solute, (e.g., sugar) is added to a volatile solvent (e.g., water), it is found that the vapor pressure of the solvent is reduced. In dilute solutions it is found that the reduction is proportional to the molecular concentration of the solvent. Or, conversely, the vapor pressure of the solution is proportional to the molecular fraction of the solvent present in it.

Thus if we take 10 molecules of sugar and 990 molecules of water to make a solution, the vapor pressure of the water in the solution will be $990/1000$ of what it was before the sugar was dissolved in it. This observation, which will hold true for other substances besides sugar and other solvents besides water, is known as Raoult's law. In terms of molar units:

Raoult's Law: The vapor pressure of a volatile solvent in a dilute solution is proportional to its mole fraction.

Definition:

VP ⠂

$SOLVENT$

$IN SOLUTION$

$$\text{Mole fraction of a substance } A \text{ in a mixture of substances} = \frac{\text{Number of moles } A}{\text{Total number of moles of all substances}}$$

Example: 1 mole of sugar ($C_6H_{12}O_6$) is added to 19 moles of water at 30°C. If the vapor pressure of pure water at 30°C. is 31.51 mm. Hg, what will the vapor pressure of the mixture be?

Answer: From Raoult's Law:

Vapor pressure of solution = Mole fraction of water × Vapor pressure of pure water

On substitution, since the mole fraction of H_2O is $19/20$:

$$\text{V.P. soln.} = \frac{19}{20} \times 31.51 \text{ mm. Hg} = 29.93 \text{ mm. Hg}$$

---

3. Molecular Weight of Solute—Vapor Pressure Lowering

It can be seen that Raoult's law provides a very useful method of measuring molecular weights of substances that are not capable of being vaporized. Thus, if we find that when we add 60 g. of an unknown compound to 9 moles of water the vapor pressure of the water is lowered by 10%, we can see that we must have added 1 mole of solute and we can conclude that its molecular weight is 60 g.

Example: It is found that the addition of 20 g. of a solid to 160 g. of water lowers the vapor pressure at 25°C. from 23.52 mm. Hg to 22.80 mm. Hg. What is the molecular weight of the solid?

Answer: From Raoult's Law:

Vapor pressure of solution = Mole fraction of water × Vapor pressure of pure water

$$VP_{sol} = MF_w \cdot VP_w$$

$$MF_w = \frac{VP_{sol}}{VP_w}$$

Solving this equation for the mole fraction of water we find:

$$\text{Mole fraction } H_2O = \frac{\text{V.P. soln.}}{\text{V.P. pure } H_2O} = \frac{22.80}{23.52}$$

$$= 0.969$$

But the mole fraction by definition $= \dfrac{\text{Moles of } H_2O}{\text{Moles of solute } + \text{ Moles of } H_2O} = 0.969.$

Solving this equation for moles of solute:

$$\text{Moles solute} = \left(\frac{\text{Moles } H_2O}{0.969}\right) - (\text{Moles } H_2O) = \frac{0.031}{0.969} \times (\text{Moles } H_2O)$$

$$= \frac{0.031}{0.969} \times 160 \text{ g. } H_2O \times \left(\frac{1 \text{ mole } H_2O}{18 \text{ g. } H_2O}\right)$$

$$= 0.284$$

Then:

$$\text{Molecular weight solute} = \frac{20 \text{ g.}}{0.284 \text{ mole}} = 70 \text{ g./mole}$$

Do problems 1, 2, and 3 at the end of the chapter.

4. Molecular Weight of Solute—Boiling Point Elevation

It is a much simpler procedure to measure the elevation in boiling point of a solvent (at constant pressure) than to measure the change in vapor pressure (at constant temperature). It can be shown (by not too simple reasoning) that the addition of a non-volatile solute to a volatile solvent will raise its boiling point by an amount which is proportional to the number of moles of solute added. That is, 1 mole of any solute added to the same quantity of solvent will always produce the same elevation of the boiling point.

For each solvent, measurements have been made of the number of degrees C. increase in boiling point produced by adding 1 mole of non-volatile solute to 1000 g. of solvent (1 kg. of solvent). This number is known as the *molal boiling point constant* ($K_{B.P.}$) and can be used to calculate the molecular weights of solutes from laboratory experiments. This constant ($K_{B.P.}$) has the unit of °C.-kg. solvent/ mole solute.

Example: The addition of 42.5 g. of a solid, X, to 800 g. of water produces an increase in boiling point of 0.34°C. If $K_{B.P.}$ for water is 0.52°C.-kg. H_2O/mole solute, what is the molecular weight of the solute, X?

Answer: We want to know the number of moles of X in 42.5 g. X. From the increase in boiling point we can calculate how many moles of X have been added:

$$0.34°C. = 0.34°C. \times \left(\frac{1 \text{ mole } X}{0.52°C.\text{-kg. } H_2O}\right) \times \left(\frac{1 \text{ kg.}}{1000 \text{ g.}}\right) \times 800 \text{ g. } H_2O$$

$$= \frac{0.34 \times 800}{0.52 \times 1000} \text{ mole } X = 0.523 \text{ mole } X$$

Then:

$$\text{Molecular weight } X = \frac{42.5 \text{ g. } X}{0.523 \text{ mole } X} = 81.3 \text{ g./mole}$$

Do problems 4, 5, and 6 at the end of the chapter.

5. Molecular Weight of Solute—Freezing Point Depression

It is found that the addition of a solute to a solvent will lower its freezing point by an amount which depends only on the number of moles of solute which have been added and not on other properties of the solute. Thus we can use the observed lowering of the freezing point of a solvent to obtain the molecular weight of the solute dissolved in it. The tabulated value of the known depression of the freezing point in degrees C. of a solvent containing 1 mole of solute per kilogram of solvent is known as the *molal freezing point* constant $(K_{F.P.})$ and has the unit of °C.-kg. solvent/mole solute.

Example: The addition of 30.0 g. of a solute, X, to 650 g. of water lowers its freezing point by 0.82°C. If the $K°_{F.P.}(H_2O)$ is 1.86°C.-kg. H_2O/mole solute, what is the molecular weight of X?

Answer: As before, we must determine the number of moles of X in 30.0 g. X. The ratio of the two will be the molecular weight of X. The following shows how all steps may be combined in one:

$$\text{Molecular weight X} = \frac{\text{Grams X}}{\text{Moles X}}$$

$$= \frac{30.0 \text{ g. X}}{0.82°C. \times \left(\frac{1 \text{ mole X}}{1.86°C.\text{-kg. } H_2O}\right) \times \left(\frac{1 \text{ kg.}}{1000 \text{ g.}}\right) \times 650 \text{ g. } H_2O}$$

$$= \frac{30.0 \text{ g. X}}{\frac{0.82 \times 650}{1.86 \times 1000} \text{ moles X}} = \frac{30.0 \times 1.86 \times 1000}{0.82 \times 650} \text{ g./mole}$$

$$= 105 \text{ g./mole}$$

Do problems 7 and 8 at the end of the chapter.

6. Molecular Weight of Solute—Osmotic Pressure

If a solution containing a solute is enclosed in a membrane (i.e., a cellophane bag) which is immersed in a pure solvent (see Figure 2), the natural tendency of the system will be for the solute to distribute itself equally between the solution inside the bag and the solvent outside.

If, however, the pores of the membrane are such that solute molecules cannot pass through the walls of the membrane, then the solution will exact a pressure against these walls which can be measured by a manometer. It is called *osmotic pressure*. Figure 2 illustrates a simple apparatus for measuring osmotic pressure.

The osmotic pressure is independent of the solvent and, in dilute solutions, depends only on the temperature (T), the volume (V) enclosed by the membrane, and the number of moles of solute therein. It is found experimentally that the osmotic pressure (abbreviated by the Greek letter, π) is related to these other properties, just as though the solute were acting as a gas. The pressure, π, is given by the ideal gas law: $\pi \times V = nRT$. (See Chapter VI.) R is the ideal gas constant, 82.1 cc.-atm./mole-°K.; T is the absolute temperature; and n is the number of moles of solute.

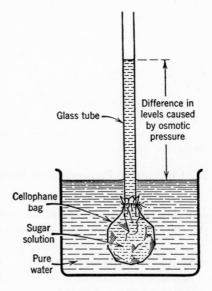

FIG. 2.   Apparatus for demonstrating osmotic pressure.

Since osmotic pressure can be quite high (many atmospheres) and pressure is easily measured, the measurement of osmotic pressure provides a convenient method for obtaining the molecular weights of very large molecules, such as proteins.

Since n/V = Moles/Liter = Concentration (c), we can express the osmotic pressure in units of concentration: $\pi = cRT$. In this equation c is the molarity of the solution.

Example: A solution containing 30 g. of protein per liter exerts an osmotic pressure of 9.4 mm. Hg at 25°C. What is the molecular weight of the protein?

Answer: Solving the osmotic pressure equation for the concentration:

$$c = \frac{\pi}{RT}$$

Substituting, we find:

$$c = \frac{9.4 \; \text{mm. Hg} \times \left(\dfrac{1 \; \text{atm.}}{760 \; \text{mm. Hg}} \right)}{0.0821 \; \dfrac{\text{l.-atm.}}{\text{mole-°K.}} \times 298°\text{K.}}$$

$$= \frac{9.4}{760 \times 0.0821 \times 298} \; \frac{\text{mole}}{\text{l.}} = 5.1 \times 10^{-4} \; \frac{\text{mole}}{\text{l.}}$$

Thus 30 g. protein/l. is equivalent to 5.1×10^{-4} mole/l.

$$\text{Molecular weight} = \frac{\text{Grams}}{\text{Moles}} = \frac{30 \; \text{g.}}{5.1 \times 10^{-4} \; \text{mole}} = 5.9 \times 10^4 \; \text{g./mole}$$

$$= 59{,}000 \; \text{g./mole}$$

---

7. Colligative Properties of Ionic Solutions

Many substances are not made of molecules but rather of ions, notably the class of compounds referred to as salts. When a formula weight of these compounds is placed in water, the change in freezing point, boiling point, and vapor pressure is usually close to some simple multiple of the expected change.

Thus, 1 mole of NaCl/kg. H_2O will show an increase in boiling point of $2 \times 0.52°C.$, and a lowering of freezing point of $2 \times 1.86°C.$* Similarly, 1 mole of $CaCl_2$/kg. H_2O will have three times as great changes in properties.

The explanation for this behavior is quite simple. Sodium chloride (NaCl) is not made up of NaCl molecules but rather of Na ions and Cl ions. When we dissolve 1 mole of NaCl in water we are in reality dissolving a mixture of 1 mole of Na ions and 1 mole of Cl ions. Thus our solution contains not one solute (NaCl) but two solutes (Na ions and Cl ions). Consequently, we have two moles of solute and twice the expected change in properties. Similarly, 1 mole of $CaCl_2$ is actually 3 moles of solute—1 mole of Ca ion and 2 moles of Cl ion.

When dealing with salts which are in reality mixtures of ions, we must treat each ion as an individual and separate quantity.

---

* These values are approximate. The true values are somewhat lower, owing to the electrical forces of interaction between the ions (see section on activities).

8. Problems

1. Calculate the mole fraction and the molality of the solutes in each of the following solutions:

    (a) 50 g. of ethyl alcohol (C_2H_6O) in 400 g. of water (H_2O).

    (b) 70 g. of benzene (C_6H_6) in 180 g. of acetone (C_3H_6O).

    (c) 28 g. of NaCl in 280 g. of H_2O.

    (d) 13 g. of H_2SO_4 in 90 g. of H_2O.

2. The vapor pressure of ethyl alcohol at 20°C. is 43.9 mm. Hg. What is the vapor pressure of a solution at 20°C. containing 50 g. of ethyl alcohol (C_2H_6O) and 14 g. of phenol (C_6H_6O)?

3. The vapor pressure of water at 60°C. is 149.4 mm. Hg. What is the vapor pressure of a solution containing 25 g. of glucose ($C_6H_{12}O_6$) in 150 g. of water at 60°C.?

4. What concentration of glucose ($C_6H_{12}O_6$) in water is needed to raise its boiling point by 1.3°C.? $K_{B.P.}(H_2O)$ = 0.52°C.-kg. H_2O/mole solute.

5. If 25.0 g. of an unknown compound, X, dissolved in 340 g. of benzene raises its boiling point by 1.38°C., what is the molecular weight of X? $K_{B.P.}(C_6H_6)$ = 2.53°C.-kg. C_6H_6/mole solute.

6. It is found that, when 32.0 g. of a compound, X, are dissolved in 450 g. of CCl_4, the boiling point is raised by 6.21°C. Calculate the molecular weight of X. $K_{B.P.}(CCl_4)$ = 5.03°C.-kg. CCl_4/mole solute.

7. How many grams of diethylene glycol ($C_4H_{10}O_3$) should be added to 400 g. of water to give a solution which will not freeze at −10°C.? $K_{F.P.}(H_2O)$ = −1.86°C.-kg. H_2O/mole solute.

8. When 8.7 g. of a substance, X, are dissolved in 60 g. of benzene, the freezing point is depressed by 6.3°C. If $K_{F.P.}(C_6H_6)$ = 4.9°C.-kg. C_6H_6/mole solute, calculate the molecular weight of X.

9. What is the osmotic pressure of a 1.0 M solution of sucrose ($C_{12}H_{22}O_{11}$) at 20°C.?

10. A solution containing 4.5 g./l. of an unknown compound, X, exerts an osmotic pressure of 30 mm. Hg at 15°C. What is the molecular weight of X?

11. What is the freezing point lowering of a 0.3 molal solution of $CaCl_2$ in water?

12. What is the boiling point elevation of a 0.20 molal solution of $Al_2(SO_4)_3$?

CHAPTER X

Chemical Equilibrium

1. Reversible Reactions

A great many chemical reactions are reversible. That is, the products of the reaction may themselves react chemically to reform the original reactants. As a result of this ambidextrousness, such reactions do not generally go to completion. At 400°C., hydrogen (gas) and iodine (gas) will react to produce hydrogen iodide (gas). However, hydrogen iodide molecules simultaneously react with each other to form the initial reactants, hydrogen and iodine. Such reactions are designated by the use of a double arrow:

$$H_2 \ (g) + I_2 \ (g) \rightleftarrows 2HI \ (g)$$

If 1 mole of hydrogen and 1 mole of iodine are put into a 100-l. flask at a temperature of 400°C., the reaction will proceed until about 1.60 moles of HI have been produced and 0.20 mole each of H_2 and I_2 remain. Thereafter no further changes occur. If 2 moles of HI are placed in the same flask, it will decompose until 0.20 mole each of H_2 and I_2 are produced and 1.60 moles of HI remain. The reaction in each instance is said to have reached equilibrium, and the concentrations of the different species at the equilibrium point are known as the equilibrium concentrations. In this particular experiment they are 1.6×10^{-2} mole/l. of HI and 2.0×10^{-3} mole/l. of H_2 and I_2.

It is clear that at the equilibrium point no further changes occur because the rates of the forward and backward reactions are equal.

2. Le Châtelier's Principle

One of the most important laws governing the behavior of such reversible systems is known as Le Châtelier's principle. It enables us to predict qualitatively the way in which the equilibrium concentrations will change when external changes are made in the equilibrium system.

Le Châtelier's Principle: When a system is in equilibrium, a change in the properties of the system will cause the equilibrium concentration to shift in that direction which will tend to absorb the effect of the change.

The changes which we shall consider are temperature, total pressure, and addition or removal of one of the reacting species.

3. Effect of Temperature Changes on Equilibrium

Let us write the previous equilibrium to include the heat of the reaction:

$$H_2 + I_2 \rightleftarrows 2HI + 12 \text{ kcal.}$$

Consider the flask containing equilibrium concentrations of H_2, I_2, and HI. What will happen to the equilibrium concentrations if the temperature is raised? Note that the volume is constant.

Le Châtelier's principle tells us that the equilibrium point will shift in a direction to absorb the effect of the increase in temperature. To increase temperature, we must add heat energy. If some of the HI molecules decompose, they will absorb energy from their surroundings since this reverse reaction is endothermic.

Thus we can answer the question by saying that if the temperature is increased (at constant volume) the concentration of HI will decrease and the concentrations of H_2 and I_2 will increase.

Conversely, if the temperature is lowered the reverse will happen. However, we cannot from Le Châtelier's principle predict the extent of the change.

4. Effect of Changing Concentrations

Suppose some I_2 is added to our equilibrium mixture. How will this affect the concentrations?

Again, reasoning from Le Châtelier's principle, the system can absorb this stress if some hydrogen reacts with the iodine to produce more HI.

Or, in general, if we increase the concentration of any of the materials, the equilibrium point will be shifted in that direction that will use up this material. Again we cannot say how great the change will be from Le Châtelier's principle.

5. Effect of Pressure Changes

To illustrate the effect of pressure changes let us consider the Haber process for the production of ammonia (NH_3).

$$N_2 \ (g) + 3H_2 \ (g) \rightleftarrows 2NH_3 \ (g) + 34 \text{ kcal.}$$

Suppose we have an equilibrium mixture of N_2, H_2, and NH_3 in a cylinder fitted with a piston, and we compress the mixture by lowering the piston. How is the equilibrium affected? (*Note:* the temperature is to be kept constant.)

We are dealing here with a gas reaction. Gases are quite compressible. If all the N_2 and H_2 were to react, the system would occupy only 2 gas volumes. If all the NH_3 were decomposed, the system would occupy 4 gas volumes. Thus, as the N_2 and H_2 react to produce NH_3, there is a reduction in volume occupied by the gases. This gives us our answer. If the pressure is increased the system will accommodate itself by moving in that direction which will occupy a smaller volume. By occupying a smaller volume it will reduce its pressure. Thus an increase in pressure will increase the concentration of NH_3 and decrease that of N_2 and H_2.

Not all systems behave in this manner. In the previous illustration of $H_2 \ (g) + I_2 \ (g) \rightleftarrows 2HI \ (g)$, both products and reactants occupy the same gas volume and changing the pressure will have no affect on the equilibrium point.

In reactions involving solids or liquids only, since these are almost incompressible, changing pressure has practically no effect on the equilibrium point.

In systems involving solids or liquids and gases we need pay attention only to the gases involved.

Example: Consider the equilibrium:

$$PtO_2 \ (s) + 2Cl_2 \ (g) \rightleftarrows PtCl_4 \ (s) + O_2 \ (g) + 1 \text{ kcal.}$$

If we increase the pressure, how is the equilibrium affected?

Answer: Since the molar volumes of the solids are very small compared to the gases, consider only the gas volumes. Two moles of Cl_2 occupies twice the volume of 1 mole of O_2 at the same temperature and volume.

Thus, increasing the pressure will increase the equilibrium concentration of O_2 and decrease Cl_2.

Do problem 1 at the end of the chapter.

6. Law of Mass Action—Equilibrium Constants

It has been found that there is a quantitative relation between the equilibrium concentrations present in a system at equilibrium. This relation is known as the law of mass action.

Law of Mass Action: If the product of the concentrations of *all* of the products are divided by the product of the concentrations of *all* the reactants, the ratio formed is a constant under all changes except that of temperature.*

Consider the equilibrium,

$$H_2 (g) + I_2 (g) \rightleftarrows 2HI (g)$$

Then by the law of mass action the ratio:

$$\frac{C_{HI} \times C_{HI}}{C_{H_2} \times C_{I_2}} = \frac{C^2_{HI}}{C_{H_2} \times C_{I_2}} \text{ is a constant} = K_{eq.}(HI)$$

These equilibrium constants can be measured at each temperature and can be changed only by changing the temperature. They will have complex units depending on the units used to measure the concentrations. In the above case the units for $K_{eq.}(HI)$ are (moles HI)^2 per (moles H_2) $\times$ (moles I_2), if the units representing the concentrations are moles per liter. Generally this is so and values are listed for $K_{eq.}$ without stating units, it being understood that concentrations are in moles per liter.

Example: Write the equilibrium constant for:

$$N_2 + 3H_2 \rightleftarrows 2NH_3$$

Answer:

$$K_{eq.} = \frac{C^2_{NH_3}}{C_{N_2} \times C^3_{H_2}}$$

Units are $\dfrac{(\text{Moles } NH_3)^2 - \text{Liter}^2}{(\text{Moles } N_2) \times (\text{Moles } H_2)^3}$

The equilibrium constant is a defined quantity, and the student should observe the rules of the definition. If this is accepted, then the equations given become regular algebraic equations wherein we simply substitute numbers when we want an answer.

The utility of the law of mass action is that it gives us a method of calculating precisely how the equilibrium concentrations change when there is a change in the external conditions (except for temperature).

Do problem 2 at the end of the chapter.

* This must be clarified by the understanding that, if a certain substance appears in the balanced equation with a coefficient 3, then the ratio must contain its concentration multiplied threefold (i.e., the cube power).

7. Calculation of Equilibrium Constants

We can calculate $K_{eq.}$ for a given equilibrium if we know the equilibrium concentrations. Thus if we return to section 1 we will find that at 400°C. the concentrations of H_2, I_2, and HI in equilibrium are 2×10^{-3} mole H_2/l., 2×10^{-3} mole I_2/l., and 1.6×10^{-2} mole HI/l. From these we can calculate the equilibrium constant:

$$K_{eq.} = \frac{C^2_{HI}}{C_{H_2} \times C_{I_2}} = \frac{(1.60)^2 \times 10^{-4}}{(0.20)(0.20) \times 10^{-4}} = \frac{2.56}{0.040} = 64 \quad \text{(at 400°C.)}$$

We have followed general practice in omitting mention of units although they may be inserted if desired.

Similarly, it is found that for the reaction

$$2SO_2\ (g) + O_2\ (g) \rightleftarrows 2SO_3\ (g) + \text{Heat}$$

a set of equilibrium concentrations at 527°C. are found to be

$$C_{SO_3} = 4 \text{ moles/l.}; \quad C_{O_2} = 0.5 \text{ mole/l.}; \quad C_{SO_2} = 0.2 \text{ mole/l.}$$

We can write

$$K_{eq.} = \frac{C^2_{SO_3}}{C^2_{SO_2} \times C_{O_2}} = \frac{4^2}{(0.2)^2 \times (0.5)} = \frac{16}{0.04 \times 0.5}$$

or

$$K_{eq.} = 800 \qquad \text{(at 527°C.)}$$

Do problem 3 at the end of the chapter.

8. Calculation of Equilibrium Concentrations

If we know $K_{eq.}$ and have sufficient additional information, we can always calculate the equilibrium concentrations at a given set of conditions.

Example:
$$2SO_2 + O_2 \rightleftarrows 2SO_3$$

$K_{eq.} = 800$ at 527°C. If the concentrations of SO_2 and SO_3 are 2.0 moles SO_2/l. and 10 moles SO_3/l., what is the C_{O_2}?

Answer: Solving the K_{eq} for C_{O_2} we have

$$C_{O_2} = \frac{C^2_{SO_3}}{C^2_{SO_2} \times K_{eq.}}$$

and on substitution:

$$C_{O_2} = \frac{(10)^2}{(2)^2 \times 800} = \frac{100}{4 \times 800} = 0.031 \text{ mole } O_2/l.$$

Example:

$$H_2 + I_2 \rightleftarrows 2HI$$

If $K_{eq.} = 64$ at 400°C., calculate the equilibrium concentration when 2 moles of H_2 and 2 moles of I_2 are put into a 10-l. flask at 400°C.

Answer: Let us make a table of starting concentrations and equilibrium concentrations. Let X be the number of moles per liter of H_2 used up.

	Starting Concentration	Equilibrium Concentration
H_2	0.2 mole/l.	$0.2 - X$
I_2	0.2 mole/l.	$0.2 - X$
HI	0	$2X$

(*Note:* From X moles of H_2 we make $2X$ moles of HI and use up X moles of I_2.)
Then, by definition:

$$K_{eq} = \frac{C^2_{HI}}{C_{H_2} \times C_{I_2}}$$

Now substitute from the table:

$$64 = \frac{(2X)^2}{(0.2 - X)(0.2 - X)} = \frac{(2X)^2}{(0.2 - X)^2}$$

This equation may be solved by taking the square roots of both sides:

$$8 = \frac{2X}{0.2 - X}$$

Solving for X we find:

$$1.6 - 8X = 2X \quad \text{or} \quad 10X = 1.6 \quad \text{or} \quad X = 0.16 \text{ mole/l.}$$

The equilibrium concentrations are thus:

$$C_{H_2} = 0.04 \text{ mole/l.}; \ C_{I_2} = 0.04 \text{ mole/l.}; \ C_{HI} = 0.32 \text{ mole/l.}$$

Note that the equation would be more difficult to solve if the starting concentrations of H_2 and I_2 had been different. We shall tackle these more complicated equations when we discuss ionic equilibria.

9. Heterogeneous Equilibria—Concentrations of Solids and Liquids

We have thus far discussed equilibria in which all the reacting substances were distributed uniformly throughout the volume of the reacting systems. These are called *homogeneous equilibria*. How shall we treat systems in which this is not the case?

If we put 1 g. of $BaCO_3$ into a quartz bulb and heat it to 900°C. we shall find the following equilibrium:

$$BaCO_3 \ (s) \rightleftarrows BaO \ (s) + CO_2 \ (g) - \text{Heat}$$

But the $BaCO_3$ and BaO are solids and will occupy only a small part of the total volume of the quartz bulb. The CO_2 gas which is dispersed throughout will react with BaO only when the two are in contact. Such systems in which there are more than one phase present are called *heterogeneous systems.*

The answer to the problem of calculating concentrations in such systems is as follows. The concentration of a substance is equal to the mass (in grams or moles) divided by the *volume occupied just by that substance!*

Thus if we put 2 g. of ice into a 12-l. bulb along with some gases, the concentration of water (in the form of ice) is not 2 g. $H_2O/12$ l. but 2 g. $H_2O/2.2$ cc. $= 0.9$ g. H_2O/cc. (the density of ice being 0.9 g./cc.). In fact, the reader will observe that if we put in 20 g. of ice its concentration is still 0.9 g. H_2O/cc. (or 50 moles H_2O/l. by conversion).

This consideration leads us to an important conclusion. The concentration of *pure* solids taking part in an equilibrium can be calculated from the density of the solid and do not depend on the volume of the vessel used! Furthermore, their concentrations are not affected by other substances we may add or remove or by changes in pressure.

We can thus combine these concentrations with the number representing the equilibrium constant, which is also a constant. The result will be a new equilibrium constant which expresses a simple relation between the concentrations of those materials which do change their concentrations with changes in external conditions.

Example:

$$BaCO_3 \ (s) \rightleftarrows BaO \ (s) + CO_2 \ (g)$$

Write the equilibrium constant.

Answer:

$$K_{eq} = \frac{C_{BaO} \times C_{CO_2}}{C_{BaCO_3}}$$

But $BaCO_3$ and BaO are pure solids, and so their concentrations are constant and will not change. Rearranging the equation we find:

$$\frac{K_{eq.} \times C_{BaCO_3}}{C_{BaO}} = \boxed{C_{CO_2} = K'_{eq.}} \quad \text{(the new equilibrium constant)}$$

since $\dfrac{K_{eq.} \times C_{BaCO_3}}{C_{BaO}}$ is itself a constant.

We can conclude in this case that at equilibrium the concentration of CO_2 is constant and does not depend on the amounts of BaO or $BaCO_3$ in the system!

Example:

$$CuO\ (s) + CO\ (g) \rightleftarrows Cu\ (s) + CO_2\ (g)$$

What is the equilibrium constant?
  Answer:

$$K_{eq.} = \frac{C_{Cu} \times C_{CO_2}}{C_{CuO} \times C_{CO}}$$

But again, since Cu and CuO are pure solids with constant concentrations, we simplify:

$$K'_{eq.} = \frac{K_{eq.} \times C_{CuO}}{C_{Cu}} = \frac{C_{CO_2}}{C_{CO}}$$

Whenever we have heterogeneous equilibria we shall omit the concentrations of pure solids and write the simpler expression involving only the concentrations that can be changed.

10. Problems

1. Predict from Le Châtelier's principle the effect of temperature increase and pressure increase, for each of the following equilibria: *inc T inc P*
  (a) $4HCl\ (g) + O_2\ (g) \rightleftarrows 2Cl_2\ (g) + 2H_2O\ (g)$ − Heat
  (b) $CO\ (g) + H_2O\ (g) \rightleftarrows CO_2\ (g) + H_2\ (g)$ − Heat
  (c) $CO\ (g) + H_2\ (g) \rightleftarrows C\ (s) + H_2O\ (g)$ + Heat
  (d) $N_2O_4\ (g) \rightleftarrows 2NO_2\ (g)$ − Heat
  (e) $Fe_3O_4\ (s) + 4H_2\ (g) \rightleftarrows 3Fe\ (s) + 4H_2O\ (g)$ + Heat
  (f) $NH_4HS\ (s) \rightleftarrows NH_3\ (g) + H_2S\ (g)$ − Heat
  (g) $2O_3 \rightleftarrows 3O_2$ + Heat

2. Write expressions for the equilibrium constants of all the equilibria in problem 1.

3. The equilibrium constant for reaction 1(b) above at 800°C. is 1.2. Calculate the concentrations of all substances when 2.0 moles each of CO and H_2O are put into a 5-l. flask at 800°C.

4. At 21°C., $K_{eq.}$ for the dissociation of N_2O_4 [reaction 1(d) above] is 0.48 (mole NO_2)^2-l./moles N_2O_4. Calculate the concentration of NO_2 in equilibrium with 0.36 mole N_2O_4/l. at 21°C.

5. $PCl_3\ (g) + Cl_2\ (g) \rightleftarrows PCl_5\ (g)$ − Heat. What is the equilibrium constant for this reaction, given that an equilibrium mixture in a 12-l. flask contains 0.42 mole of PCl_5, 1.76 moles of Cl_2, and 0.10 mole of PCl_3?

6. At 400°C., calculate the concentrations of H_2, I_2, and HI that will be in equilibrium [given $K_{eq.}$(HI) = 64 at 400°C.] if 1.4 moles of HI is put in a 20-l. flask and allowed to come to equilibrium.

7. At any temperature ice may be in equilibrium with water vapor:

$$H_2O\ (s) \rightleftarrows H_2O\ (g)\ \text{−\ Heat}$$

Write the equilibrium constant. What can you conclude about the concentration of water vapor if more ice is added to the system?

8. What is the concentration of solid $CaCO_3$ (density = 2.711 g./cc.)? Will this be very different at 20 atm. pressure?

9. Given the following equilibrium between carbon tetrachloride liquid and its vapor:

$$CCl_4 \ (l) \rightleftarrows CCl_4 \ (g) - \text{Heat}$$

(*a*) Write the equilibrium constant.

(*b*) What is the concentration of CCl_4 (*l*) (density = 1.59 g./cc.)?

(*c*) What happens to the equilibrium concentration of CCl_4 (*g*) as the temperature is lowered? if some of the liquid CCl_4 is removed?

CHAPTER XI

Electrical Properties of Ionic Solutions

1. Classification of Compounds by Electrical Properties

We can classify compounds into two categories, depending on whether or not they will conduct an electric current when placed in water solution.

1. **Electrolytes:** Those compounds whose water solutions will conduct an electric current (e.g., NaCl, CuSO$_4$, HCl, H$_2$SO$_4$).
2. **Non-Electrolytes:** Those compounds whose water solutions will not conduct an electric current (e.g., sugar, alcohol, acetone).

We can further divide class 1, the electrolytes, into two categories:

True Electrolytes: Electrolytes that will conduct an electric current in the pure, molten state (e.g., NaCl, CuSO$_4$).
Pseudo-Electrolytes: Electrolytes that will not conduct an electric current in the pure, molten state (e.g., all acids, SnCl$_2$, AlCl$_3$).

The present chapter is concerned with the chemical reactions that occur when an electric current is passed through a solution of an electrolyte, a phenomenon referred to as electrolysis.

2. Reactions Occurring during Electrolysis

When the terminals of a battery or any other source of direct current are connected to metal wires and the wires inserted into a water solution of an electrolyte, current will flow through the solution. As a result of this passage of current, chemical reactions take place at the surfaces of the electrodes dipping into the solution.

Negatively charged electrons move from the battery to its negative terminal (cathode). This cathode becomes electrically charged (negative), and the electrons on it react with the materials surrounding it.

At the positively charged terminal (anode), the materials in the

111

solution react with it, giving up their electrons to it.   These electrons can now return to the battery, completing the electric circuit.

Electrolysis is thus a set of reactions at the anode ($+$) and cathode ($-$) which involve the transfer of electrons between the materials in solution and the electrodes.   Such electron-transfer reactions are referred to as oxidations (loss of electrons) or reduction (gain of electrons), and the two always occur together.

During electrolysis three possible types of reactions may occur at the electrodes:

The electrode reacts: The material of which the electrode is made (e.g., zinc, copper, carbon) may react with the solution.

The solvent reacts: The water which is always present may gain or lose electrons, itself being broken up into products.

The solute reacts: One or more of the ions present in the solute material will gain or lose electrons at the electrode and be deposited or transformed.

It is possible to predict which of these three possible reactions takes place under given conditions if we know the relative tendencies of the different alternative reactions.   These may be predicted from the electromotive series (see Chapter XV).

Under certain conditions two or more of the possible reactions may occur simultaneously.

3. Reactions at the Cathode

The cathode is negatively charged.   Positive ions in the solution will migrate towards it, and negative ions will be repelled.   If the positive ion of a fairly inactive metal (e.g., copper, silver, lead, zinc) is present, then this ion will combine with the electrons present on the cathode and be deposited as free metal.

Case I.   Inactive Metals.   If we electrolyze a solution of $CuCl_2$, the reaction at the cathode may be written:

$$Cu^{+2} + 2e^{-1} \rightarrow Cu^0 \quad \text{(reduction at cathode)}$$

These equations must be electrically balanced as well as chemically balanced.   The exponents refer to the units of charge present in the particle.

The copper ion (Cu^{+2}) with 2 plus charges combines with 2 electrons (e^{-1}), each bearing 1 negative charge, and is deposited as neutral copper metal (Cu^0).   This reaction representing a gain in electrons by Cu^{+2} ions is called reduction (since the positive charge of the Cu^{+2} ions is reduced).

Case II.   Active Metals. If, on the other hand, we pass a current through a solution of NaCl, the Na^{+1} ions will not readily combine with an electron and, instead, water molecules are preferentially decomposed, liberating hydrogen gas.

$$2H_2O + 2e^{-1} \rightarrow 2OH^{-1} + \underline{H_2\uparrow} \qquad \text{(reduction)}$$

It is seldom that the cathode ever reacts with the solution.

4. Reactions at the Anode

The anode is positively charged and attracts negative ions and repels positive ions. If the negative ion has little attraction for electrons, it will lose them to the anode and be deposited or transformed. If the negative ion has a strong attraction for electrons, then water will be decomposed, losing electrons and producing oxygen gas. If the anode itself is composed of an active metal, then it will go into solution in the form of positive metal ions, leaving the electrons behind.

Case I.   Deposition of Anions. If an electric current is passed through a solution of $CuCl_2$, the Cl^{-1} ions will react:

$$2Cl^{-1} \rightarrow \underline{Cl_2{}^0\uparrow} + 2e^{-1} \qquad \text{(oxidation at anode)}$$

This process of loss of electrons (by Cl^{-1} ions) is called oxidation. Oxidation always takes place at the anode.

Case II.   Reaction of the Anode Metal. If the anode is made of a metal which is more easily oxidized than the anion, then it will react. Thus, if a copper anode had been used in the electrolysis of a solution such as $ZnSO_4$, the Cu is more easily oxidized than the $SO_4{}^{-2}$ ion and the reaction that occurs is

$$Cu^0 \rightarrow Cu^{+2} + 2e^{-1} \qquad \text{(oxidation at anode)}$$

Case III.   Decomposition of Water at Anode. If the metal anode is inert (e.g., platinum) and the anion more difficult to oxidize than water, then the water is preferentially decomposed as follows:

$$2H_2O \rightarrow \underline{O_2{}^0\uparrow} + 4H^{+1} + 4e^{-1} \qquad \text{(oxidation at anode)}$$

We will defer a discussion of which of these types of reactions occur until Chapter XV. However, the student should practice writing these ion-electron equations and should familiarize himself with their balancing.

5. Quantitative Relations—Faraday's Law

We can state Faraday's law as follows:

Faraday's Law:

1. The amount of chemical reaction that takes place at each electrode is directly proportional to the total amount of electricity that has passed through the solution.
2. The number of equivalents of reaction that takes place at the cathode is exactly equal to the number of equivalents of reaction at the anode. (This is understandable from our knowledge of electricity. For every electron that enters the solution at the cathode, an equal number must leave at the anode to complete the circuit.)

To employ these laws for quantitative work we must first define some practical units.

Definition: One equivalent of electricity is that amount of charge (electrons) needed to release 1 equivalent of cation at the cathode (and simultaneously 1 equivalent of anion at the anode). It is called the *faraday.*

By experiment we find that 1 equivalent of electricity (i.e., 1 mole of electrons) is equal to 96,500 coulombs:

$$1 \text{ eq. electricity} = 1 \text{ faraday} = 1 \text{ mole electron}   \text{(definition)}$$

$$1 \text{ faraday} = 96,500 \text{ coulombs}   \text{(experiment)}$$

Since 1 ampere of current is defined as 1 coulomb/sec., we can calculate the total number of coulombs of electricity passing through a solution by multiplying the current by the time:

$$\text{Coulombs} = \text{Amperes} \times \text{Seconds}$$

Example: One equivalent of electricity is passed through a solution of sulfuric acid. What are the products of the reaction?
Answer: At the cathode:

$$1 \text{ eq. hydrogen} = 1 \text{ g. } H_2 = 11.2 \text{ l. STP } H_2$$

At the anode:

$$1 \text{ eq. oxygen} = 8 \text{ g. } O_2 = 5.6 \text{ l. STP } O_2$$

Example: 20 amp. are passed through a concentrated solution of sodium chloride for 50 sec. What are the products of the reaction?

Answer:

20 amp. $\times$ 50 sec. = 1000 coulombs = 1000 ~~coulombs~~ $\times \left(\dfrac{1 \text{ eq. elec.}}{96,500 \text{ ~~coulombs~~}} \right)$

$$= 0.0104 \text{ eq.}$$

At the cathode:

$$0.0104 \text{ ~~eq. H$_2$~~} \times \left(\frac{11.2 \text{ l. STP H}_2}{1 \text{ ~~eq. H$_2$~~}} \right) = 0.116 \text{ l. STP H}_2$$

At the anode:

$$0.0104 \text{ eq. Cl}_2 = 0.369 \text{ g. Cl}_2 = 0.0104 \text{ ~~eq. Cl$_2$~~} \times \left(\frac{11.2 \text{ l. STP Cl}_2}{1 \text{ ~~eq. Cl$_2$~~}} \right)$$

$$= 0.116 \text{ l. STP Cl}_2$$

Note: It will turn out that the valence of an ion is equal numerically to the number of charges on it. This is helpful in calculating the equivalent weights of ions.

6. Problems

1. Write balanced ion-electron equations for each of the following:
   (a) The deposition of Cr^{+3} ions at the cathode.
   (b) The reaction of Zn metal anode to give Zn^{+2} ions.
   (c) The anode and cathode reactions occurring during the electrolysis of $AgNO_3$ with inert electrodes.
   (d) The anode and cathode reactions occurring during the electrolysis of NH_4Cl with inert electrodes.

2. Make the following conversions:
   (a) 480 coulombs to faradays.
   (b) 5×10^{10} electrons to coulombs.
   (c) 1.4 moles of electrons to coulombs.
   (d) 0.680 faraday to coulombs.
   (e) 0.20 equivalent of electricity to coulombs.
   (f) 80 amp.-min. to coulombs.
   (g) 8500 coulombs to ampere-hours.

3. A current of 12 amp. is passed through a solution of $CrCl_3$ for 40 min. How many grams of Cr and how many liters STP of Cl_2 gas are produced?

4. A current of 2 amp. is passed through HNO_3 solution for 40 sec. How many millimoles of H_2 and O_2 gas, respectively, are formed?

5. How long must a silver plater allow a current of 20 amp. to run through a $AgNO_3$ bath to deposit 40 g. of Ag? How many moles of O_2 gas will be formed?

CHAPTER XII

Simple Equilibria in Ionic Solutions

1. What Is Present in an Ionic Solution?

Before discussing equilibria in ionic solutions, let us first restate some of the properties of ionic substances.

An ionic compound (such as NaCl) is different from non-ionic substances in that it is in reality a mixture of two species, the Na^{+1} ion and the Cl^{-1} ion. When placed in a water solution, these two ions exist separately and have their own individual existences. They may also react independently. A 1 M solution of NaCl should thus be looked upon as a solution containing two solutes, 1 mole of Na^{+1} ions and 1 mole of Cl^{-1} ions. Similarly, a 1 M solution of $Al_2(SO_4)_3$ contains 2 moles of Al^{+3} ions and 3 moles of SO_4^{-2} ions.

When we mix a solution of NaCl with a solution of KNO_3, the resulting solution does not contain either NaCl or KNO_3 molecules. Instead it contains Na^{+1} ions, K^{+1} ions, Cl^{-1} ions, and NO_3^{-1} ions. The same result may be obtained by mixing $NaNO_3$ solution with KCl solution.

2. The Solubility of Ionic Compounds

If we add some sodium chloride to water it will dissolve. If we keep adding the solid salt, we eventually reach a point at which no more will dissolve. The solution is then said to be *saturated* with sodium chloride. Such a system is also in equilibrium; in fact, it represents a *heterogeneous equilibrium* between the solid sodium chloride and the Na^{+1} ions and the Cl^{-1} ions present in the solution. We can represent the equilibrium by an equation:

$$NaCl \ (s) \rightleftarrows Na^{+1} \ (aq) + Cl^{-1} \ (aq)$$

The symbol (aq) indicates that the ions exist in the aqueous solution, as distinct from the NaCl (s) which is present as pure solid. We shall generally omit the symbol (aq), it being understood from the equation.

For such a heterogeneous equilibrium we can write an equilibrium constant:

$$K_{eq.} = \frac{C_{Na^{+1}} \times C_{Cl^{-1}}}{C_{NaCl}}$$

However, since the NaCl is present as pure solid its concentration is constant, and this expression may be simplified by combining $K_{eq.}$ with C_{NaCl} (see Chapter X):

$$K_{eq.} \times C_{NaCl} = C_{Na^{+1}} \times C_{Cl^{-1}} = K_{S.P.}$$

The simplified relation thus obtained states that in an *equilibrium system* containing pure, *solid NaCl* and *dissolved Na^{+1} and Cl^{-1} ions*, the product of the concentrations of the Na^{+1} ions and Cl^{-1} ions is equal to a constant which is called the *solubility product constant* ($K_{S.P.}$).

3. The Solubility Product Constant

The significance of the solubility product relation is of some interest. In the case of NaCl, mentioned above, the relation predicts that, if we add to the saturated solution some substance containing Na^{+1} ions (e.g., $NaNO_3$), then in order to maintain the product of $C_{Na^{+1}}$ and $C_{Cl^{-1}}$ constant the Cl^{-1} ions must decrease. This occurs when some of the Cl^{-1} ions in the solution react with some of the Na^{+1} ions to form more pure, solid NaCl. From the numerical value of the solubility product constant we can predict exactly how much solid will form and what the final concentration will be.

Before discussing such calculations in detail, let us see how the constants should be written for more complex salts. The following list gives a representative set of such salts and the algebraic expressions for their solubility product constants:

Salt	Solubility Product*
Ag_2CrO_4	$K_{S.P.}(Ag_2CrO_4) = C^2_{Ag^{+1}} \times C_{CrO_4^{-2}}$
$CaSO_4$	$K_{S.P.}(CaSO_4) = C_{Ca^{+2}} \times C_{SO_4^{-2}}$
CaF_2	$K_{S.P.}(CaF_2) = C_{Ca^{+2}} \times C^2_{F^{-2}}$
Bi_2S_3	$K_{S.P.}(Bi_2S_3) = C^2_{Bi^{+3}} \times C^3_{S^{-2}}$

* The name solubility product is misleading. Although it is true that a small value of $K_{S.P.}$ for a particular salt means that the salt is not very soluble, and vice versa, nevertheless the $K_{S.P.}$ *is not proportional* to the solubility of the salt. This is true even though we shall see that it is possible to calculate the solubility of a salt if we know its $K_{S.P.}$ and, conversely, we may calculate $K_{S.P.}$ for a salt if we know its solubility.

By common agreement the units for the concentrations in these expressions are always moles per liter.

Do problem 1 at the end of the chapter.

4. Measurement of the Solubility Product Constant

From the definition of $K_{\text{S.P.}}$ we see that it may be calculated if we are given the values of the concentration of the ions of the salt that are present in an equilibrium solution.

The most straightforward method of obtaining such information is to take a solution containing the ions in equilibrium with the solid salt and analyze the *solution* to see what the ionic concentrations are.

The simplest of such procedures is to take the salt itself and shake it up with a large volume of water until a saturated solution is formed. This can then be filtered, 1 l. of the clear solution taken, the water evaporated, and the total amount of salt measured by weighing the solid residue.

Example: When 1 l. of a saturated solution of $CaCO_3$ is evaporated to dryness, the residue is found to weigh 7.0 mg. What is the $K_{\text{S.P.}}(CaCO_3)$?

Answer: The saturated solution contained 7.0 mg. $CaCO_3$ dissolved in it. This is

$$7.0 \times 10^{-3} \text{ g. } CaCO_3 \times \left(\frac{1 \text{ mole } CaCO_3}{100 \text{ g. } CaCO_3} \right) = 7.0 \times 10^{-5} \text{ mole } CaCO_3$$

Since there were no other substances present, this means that the saturated solution contained 7.0×10^{-5} mole Ca^{+2} ions/l. and 7.0×10^{-5} mole CO_3^{-2} ions/l. By definition, the solubility product is

$$K_{\text{S.P.}}(CaCO_3) = C_{Ca^{+2}} \times C_{CO_3^{-2}}$$

On substitution we have

$$K_{\text{S.P.}}(CaCO_3) = (7.0 \times 10^{-5})(7.0 \times 10^{-5})$$

$$= 49 \times 10^{-10} = 4.9 \times 10^{-9}$$

Example: At 20°C. a saturated solution of $PbCl_2$ is found to contain 4.50 g. of $PbCl_2$ per liter dissolved in it. What is $K_{\text{S.P.}}(PbCl_2)$?

Answer:

$$4.50 \text{ g. } PbCl_2/l. = \left(\frac{4.50 \text{ g. } PbCl_2}{l.} \right) \times \left(\frac{1 \text{ mole } PbCl_2}{278 \text{ g. } PbCl_2} \right)$$

$$= 1.62 \times 10^{-2} \text{ mole } PbCl_2/l.$$

But 1.62×10^{-2} mole $PbCl_2/l.$ in solution will produce 1.62×10^{-2} mole Pb^{+2} ions/l. and $2 \times 1.62 \times 10^{-2}$ mole Cl^{-1} ions/l. = 3.24 moles $Cl^{-1}/l.$ By definition:

$$K_{\text{S.P.}}(PbCl_2) = C_{Pb+2} \times C^2_{Cl-1}$$

and on substitution:

$$K_{S.P.} = (1.62 \times 10^{-2}) \times (3.24 \times 10^{-2})^2$$
$$= 1.62 \times 10^{-2} \times 10.5 \times 10^{-4}$$
$$= 1.70 \times 10^{-5}$$

If from other measurements we know the value of the $K_{S.P.}$ for a salt at a given temperature, then it is possible to calculate the solubility of the salt in water at that temperature.*

Example: The $K_{S.P.}$(AgCl) is known to be 1.6×10^{-10} at 20°C. Calculate from this the solubility of AgCl in water at 20°C.

Answer: By definition:

$$K_{S.P.} = C_{Ag^{+1}} \times C_{Cl^{-1}}$$

If we have a saturated solution of AgCl, then let us call the solubility of AgCl X moles/l. However, if X moles/l. of AgCl is dissolved, the solution will contain X moles/l. of Ag^{+1} ions and X moles/l. of Cl^{-1} ions. We can now substitute these values and solve for X.

Then

$$K_{S.P.} = (X)(X) = 1.6 \times 10^{-10}$$

$$X^2 = 1.6 \times 10^{-10}$$

$$X = 1.26 \times 10^{-5} \text{ mole/l.}$$

Example: The $K_{S.P.}$ for $PbBr_2$ is 6.3×10^{-6} at 20°C. What is the solubility of $PbBr_2$ at 20°C.?

Answer: By definition:

$$K_{S.P.} = C_{Pb^{+2}} \times (C_{Br^{-1}})^2$$

Let us set X = the solubility of $PbBr_2$ in moles per liter. But X moles $PbBr_2$/l. will produce X moles Pb^{+2}/l. and $2X$ moles Br^{-1}/l. On substitution and solving for X we find:

$$K_{S.P.}(PbBr_2) = (X)(2X)^2 = 6.3 \times 10^{-6}$$

or

$$4X^3 = 6.3 \times 10^{-6}$$

Then

$$X^3 = 1.58 \times 10^{-6}$$

$$X = 1.17 \times 10^{-2} \text{ mole/l.}$$

Do problems 2–5 at the end of the chapter.

* The algebraic expression for $K_{S.P.}$ is given by definition as a certain product of concentrations of ions raised to certain powers. In problems dealing with this relation, the student must decide what the concentrations of the ions are and then substitute as required into the equation. Once the concentrations are decided on, the rest is pure arithmetic.

5. Use of the Solubility Product Constant—Common Ion Effect

We have thus far discussed the solubility product relation for solutions containing only the ions of the pure salt. However, in most laboratory experiments a salt is made to precipitate in the presence of other ions as well, and the simple relations between the concentrations of the positive and negative ions which we obtain from the formula no longer hold.

Thus we can prepare a saturated solution of AgCl (containing Ag^{+1} ions and Cl^{-1} ions) by dissolving solid AgCl in water. In this solution, because all the Ag^{+1} and Cl^{-1} ions come from AgCl, their concentrations are equal. However, it is possible to make a saturated solution of AgCl by adding a small amount of $AgNO_3$ to a large amount of a solution of NaCl. Ag^{+1} ions will unite with Cl^{-1} ions (if enough of each are present), and a white precipitate of AgCl will form. The solution will contain Na^{+1} ions, NO_3^{-1} ions, a large excess of Cl^{-1} ions, and a small amount of Ag^{+1} ions. Because of the method of preparation, the concentrations of Ag^{+1} and Cl^{-1} are no longer equal. Nevertheless, despite all these complications, the system is an equilibrium system and the solubility product relation holds true: $K_{S.P.} = C_{Ag^{+1}} \times C_{Cl^{-1}}$. If we know $K_{S.P.}$ and either the $C_{Ag^{+1}}$ or $C_{Cl^{-1}}$, this equation permits us to solve for the unknown concentration.

Example: A few drops of a solution of $AgNO_3$ are added to a large amount of a 0.01 M solution of NaCl and a ppt. of AgCl is formed. On analysis it is found that the solution contains 0.010 moles/l. of Cl^{-1} ions. If $K_{S.P.}$ (AgCl) = 1.6 × 10^{-10}, calculate the $C_{Ag^{+1}}$ left in the solution.

Answer: By definition:

$$K_{S.P.} \text{ (AgCl)} = C_{Ag^{+1}} \times C_{Cl^{-1}}$$

But we are given:

$$K_{S.P.} = 1.6 \times 10^{-10}; \quad C_{Cl^{-1}} = 1.0 \times 10^{-2}$$

Then on solving for $C_{Ag^{+1}}$ ions and substituting:

$$C_{Ag^{+1}} = \frac{K_{S.P.}(\text{AgCl})}{C_{Cl^{-1}}} = \frac{1.6 \times 10^{-10}}{1.0 \times 10^{-2}} = 1.6 \times 10^{-8} \text{ mole/l.}$$

Example: What concentration of Ag^{+1} ions will be in equilibrium with a saturated solution containing a ppt. of Ag_2CrO_4 and a CrO_4^{-2} ion concentration of 0.40 mole/l.?

$$K_{S.P.} \text{ (Ag}_2\text{CrO}_4) = 1.1 \times 10^{-11}$$

Answer: By definition:

$$K_{S.P.} \text{ (Ag}_2\text{CrO}_4) = C^2_{Ag^{+1}} \times C_{CrO_4^{-2}}$$

We are given

$$C_{CrO_4^{-2}} = 0.40; \quad K_{S.P.} = 1.1 \times 10^{-11}$$

Solving for $C_{Ag^{+1}}$ and substituting:

$$C^2_{Ag^{+1}} = \frac{K_{S.P.}}{C_{CrO_4^{-2}}} = \frac{1.1 \times 10^{-11}}{0.40} = 2.75 \times 10^{-11}$$

$$C^2_{Ag^{+2}} = 27.5 \times 10^{-12}$$

and taking square roots:

$$C_{Ag^{+1}} = 5.2 \times 10^{-6} \text{ mole/l.}$$

The solubility product relation may be used to answer the following types of questions:

1. When will precipitates form?
2. How much excess of one reagent is needed to reduce the concentration of a certain ion to a given value? (Or, in another form: How far towards completion can we drive ionic reactions?)

Example: A solution contains a concentration of Pb^{+2} ions of 2×10^{-3} mole/l. To this is added enough solid NaCl to bring the Cl^{-1} ion concentration to 3×10^{-2} mole/l. Will a ppt. of $PbCl_2$ form, given that $K_{S.P.}(PbCl_2) = 1.7 \times 10^{-5}$? (Ignore volume change.)

Answer: By definition:

$$K_{S.P.}(PbCl_2) = C_{Pb^{+2}} \times C^2_{Cl^{-1}}$$

This relation holds true only in a solution saturated with $PbCl_2$. If the solution is not saturated (i.e., more $PbCl_2$ can be dissolved in it) then the product of the $C_{Pb^{+2}} \times C^2_{Cl^{-1}}$ will be less than the $K_{S.P.}(PbCl_2)$. (No solution may contain so many Pb^{+2} ions and Cl^{-1} ions that $C_{Pb^{+2}} \times C^2_{Cl^{-1}}$ is greater than $K_{S.P.}(PbCl_2)$ unless the solution is *supersaturated*.) In the problem given:

$$C_{Pb^{+2}} \times C^2_{Cl^{-1}} = (2 \times 10^{-3})(3 \times 10^{-2})^2$$

$$= 2 \times 10^{-3} \times 9 \times 10^{-4}$$

$$= 18 \times 10^{-7} = 1.8 \times 10^{-6}$$

But 1.8×10^{-6} is clearly a smaller number than 1.7×10^{-5} which is $K_{S.P.}(PbCl_2)$, and so the solution is not saturated, and no ppt. of $PbCl_2$ will form.

Example: A solution is contaminated with Pb^{+2} ions. By adding Na_2SO_4, $PbSO_4$ may be made to ppt. What concentration of SO_4^{-2} ions is needed to reduce the $C_{Pb^{+2}}$ ions to 2×10^{-6} mole/l.? Given:

$$K_{S.P.}(PbSO_4) = 1.8 \times 10^{-8}$$

Answer:

$$K_{S.P.}(PbSO_4) = C_{Pb^{+2}} \times C_{SO_4^{-2}}$$

Solving for $C_{SO_4^{-2}}$ ions:

$$C_{SO_4^{-2}} = \frac{K_{S.P.}}{C_{Pb^{+2}}}$$

Substituting:

$$C_{SO_4^{-2}} = \frac{1.8 \times 10^{-8}}{2 \times 10^{-6}} = 0.9 \times 10^{-2} = 9 \times 10^{-3} \text{ mole/l.}$$

Do problems 6–14 at the end of the chapter.

6. Limitation on the Use of the Solubility Product Relation

A. Temperature. The solubility of salts usually increases with increasing temperature. Thus the $K_{S.P.}$ for a salt will also increase with increasing temperature. Therefore values of $K_{S.P.}$ must be known for each individual temperature for which it is proposed to use the relation. This is illustrated in the table for $PbCl_2$.

Temperature	20°C.	60°C.	90°C.
Solubility (moles $PbCl_2$/l.)	0.033	0.065	0.100
$K_{S.P.}(PbCl_2)$	1.5×10^{-4}	12×10^{-4}	40×10^{-4}

B. Salt Effect—Activities. As the concentration of ions in the solution increases, the ions are hampered in their motion; that is, they move less freely. This is due mostly to the fact that positive ions will attract to themselves negative ions in preference to other positive ions. This crowd of ions of negative charge will hamper the mobility of the positive ions, and the same is true for the effect of positive ions on the mobility of negative ions.

Thus in a 1.00 M solution of NaCl both the Na^{+1} and Cl^{-1} ions will be considerably less mobile than the Na^{+1} and Cl^{-1} ions in a solution of NaCl which is less concentrated, for example, 0.001 M NaCl. The result of this crowding on the properties of the Na^{+1} and Cl^{-1} ions is to make it appear as though their concentrations were lower. That is, they will react more slowly in the concentrated solutions. This seemingly smaller concentration can be observed experimentally and is called the "effective" or "active" concentration of ions.

When the effective or active concentrations of the ions are used to calculate the $K_{S.P.}$ for a solution, this corrected solubility product constant is called the *activity product constant*. The effect of this crowding can be as much as 10% or 20% in more concentrated solutions.

As an example, the solubility of AgCl is increased by some 10% by adding 1 mole/l. of KNO_3 to water. The K^{+1} and NO_3^{-1} ions impede the motions of the Ag^{+1} and Cl^{-1} ions and thus decrease their tendency to form solid AgCl.

For these reasons the $K_{S.P.}$ relation may be in error by as much as 20% or even higher if the solution contains large concentrations of salts. The relation is likewise very inaccurate when applied to salts like NaCl which are quite soluble, because a saturated solution of NaCl will contain almost 1 mole/l. of NaCl.

As a rough rule of thumb, the $K_{S.P.}$ relation is used only for salts whose solubilities are 1×10^{-2} mole/l. or less. Also, it is not very accurate even for these salts if the solution contains large concentrations of other dissolved salts.

It should be noted, however, that, if the concentration of other salts is known and the "activities" of the ions are known, then the corrected ion activity product may be used instead of the $K_{S.P.}$. This is, however, quite involved, and we shall not discuss it further.

7. Incomplete Ionization—Weak Electrolytes

True salts are solids whose crystal lattices are made up of positive and negative ions. These are completely ionized in the solid state. When dissolved in water they remain 100% ionized. There are no molecules of such salts (e.g., all salts of the alkali metals, etc.)!

There is a large class of compounds which are not true salts although they display salt-like properties. They are characterized by the property of not conducting the electric current in the molten state but conducting the electric current when dissolved in water solution. Such substances are called pseudo-electrolytes. They are molecular, not ionic, in structure. The ability of their water solutions to conduct the electric current is due to a reversible, chemical reaction of their molecules with molecules of water to produce ions. *All acids* and most salts of the amphoteric metals belong to this category of pseudo-electrolytes.

In a water solution of a pseudo-electrolyte there will exist positive ions, negative ions, and undissociated molecules of the pseudo-electrolyte. These will all be in equilibrium, and the equilibrium may be represented by balanced chemical equations:

$$HCl + H_2O \rightleftarrows H_3O^{+1} + Cl^{-1}$$

$$HC_2H_3O_2 + H_2O \rightleftarrows H_3O^{+1} + C_2H_3O_2^{-1}$$

$$FeCl_3 + 6H_2O \rightleftarrows Fe(H_2O)_6^{+3} + 3Cl^{-1}$$

We can divide these pseudo-electrolytes into two classes. Class I are known as strong electrolytes. Class II are known as weak electrolytes. Strong electrolytes are those which are almost 100% ionized in water solution. (HCl; HNO_3; H_2SO_4; HBr; HI; $HClO_4$ are the only common acids which are strong electrolytes.) Weak electrolytes are those which are only ionized to a small extent in water solution (acetic acid, $HgCl_2$, HClO, H_2S, H_2CO_3).

8. Ionization Constants

The reversible reaction of water with the molecules of weak electrolytes to produce ions is a *homogeneous equilibrium* and, as such, we can apply to it the law of mass action and write an equilibrium constant expression.

Thus, for the ionization of acetic acid (abbreviated, HAc; Ac represents the acetate group $C_2H_3O_2$):

$$HAc + H_2O \rightleftarrows H_3O^{+1} + Ac^{-1}$$

$$K_{eq.} = \frac{C_{H_3O^{+1}} \times C_{Ac^{-1}}}{C_{H_2O} \times C_{HAc}} \quad \text{(by definition of equilibrium constant)}$$

Now for the reasons discussed previously this relation is fairly accurate only if the concentrations of the ions are low and the solution is not too concentrated with respect to other ions. But in solutions which are more dilute than 1 M, the main part of the solution is made up of water, and the water concentration of these solutions is not very different from pure water (55.5 moles H_2O/l.). To the extent of accuracy of our expression then, we can combine the almost constant concentration of water C_{H_3O} with the constant $K_{eq.}$ and write a simplified expression:

$$K_{eq.} \times C_{H_2O} = \frac{C_{H_3O^{+1}} \times C_{Ac^{-1}}}{C_{HAc}} = K_{ion} \text{ (HAc)}$$

This new constant is known as the ionization constant and is abbreviated K_{ion}.

For weak electrolytes that may ionize in several steps there will be a different chemical equation for each step, and a K_{ion} can be written for each step   Or, if desired, the steps may be combined into a single step representing the overall ionization and a third K_{ion} written for this equilibrium. The relations used in any given problem will depend on which species we are interested in. This is illustrated for the weak electrolyte H_2S as follows:

Step I: $H_2S + H_2O \rightleftarrows H_3O^{+1} + HS^{-1}$

Step II: $HS^{-1} + H_2O \rightleftarrows H_3O^{+1} + S^{-2}$

If our interest is only in the amount of sulfide ion (S^{-2}) that is present in the solution, we can add both equations together and obtain the direct equilibrium between this ion and the H_2S.

Overall Equilibrium: $H_2S + 2H_2O \rightleftarrows 2H_3O^{+1} + S^{-2}$

The ionization constants for these different steps can each be written separately. (*Note:* In a given problem we would use the ionization constant which relates those ions and molecules in which we are interested.)

Step I: $\dfrac{(C_{H_3O^{+1}}) \cdot (C_{HS^{-1}})}{(C_{H_2S})} = K_{ion}(H_2S)$ (first ionization)

$= 1 \times 10^{-7}$ at 20°C.   (by experiment)

Step II: $\dfrac{(C_{H_3O^{+1}}) \cdot (C_{S^{-2}})}{(C_{HS^{-1}})} = K_{ion}(HS^{-1})$ (second ionization)

$= 1 \times 10^{-15}$ at 20°C.   (by experiment)

The ionization constant for the overall ionization into sulfide ion may be obtained from the third equation above (overall equilibrium):

$\dfrac{(C_{H_3O^{+1}})^2 \cdot (C_{S^{-2}})}{(C_{H_2S})} = K_{ion}(H_2S)$ (overall ionization)

$= 1 \times 10^{-22}$ at 20°C.   (by experiment)

Note that mathematically the products of the ionization constants for steps I and II are equal to the overall ionization constant.

Problem: Write the three equilibrium equations for the step-wise ionization of phosphoric acid (H_3PO_4). Write also the overall equation for the second ionization, and the overall equation for the third ionization. Write the ionization constant equations for each of these five equilibria.

The student should work this out by himself, following the scheme outlined above. Look up the experimental values for these steps in any textbook or in the *Handbook of Chemistry and Physics*.

The smaller the ionization constant of a weak electrolyte, the fewer ions will it give in solution and thus the weaker will it be as an electrolyte. $K_{ion}(HCN) = 4.0 \times 10^{-10}$ at 20°C.; $K_{ion}(HC_2H_3O_2) = 1.8 \times 10^{-5}$ at 20°C. Comparing these values we see that K_{ion} is greater for acetic acid, and so we can conclude that acetic acid is a stronger acid than hydrocyanic acid.

Do problem 15 at the end of the chapter.

9. Relation between Per Cent Ionization and Ionization Constant

The ionization constant expression relates the concentrations of ions of a weak electrolyte and the concentrations of undissociated molecules. If all these concentrations are known, the value of K_{ion} may be calculated. Conversely, if K_{ion} is known, then the concentrations of the ions and the molecules may be calculated.

Example: A 0.40 M solution of HAc is found to be 0.67% ionized. Calculate the concentrations of all ions and molecules present in the solution and the $K_{ion}(HAc)$.

Answer: Since 0.67% of the HAc is ionized, 99.33% is left in the form of HAc. The concentrations are:

$$C_{HAc} = 99.33\% \text{ of } 0.40 \text{ mole HAc/l.} = 0.9933 \times 0.4 \ M$$
$$= 0.397 \ M$$

Every molecule of HAc that ionizes produces 1 H_3O^{+1} ion and 1 Ac^{-1} ion. Thus their concentrations are equal and given by

$$C_{Ac^{-1}} = C_{H_3O^{+1}} = 0.67\% \text{ of } 0.40 \text{ mole HAc/l.} = 0.0067 \times 0.4 \ M$$
$$= 0.00268 \text{ mole/l.} = 2.68 \times 10^{-3} \ M$$

By definition:

$$K_{ion}(HAc) = \frac{(C_{H_3O^{+1}}) \cdot (C_{Ac^{-1}})}{(C_{HAc})}$$

Then, on substitution:

$$K_{ion}(HAc) = \frac{(2.68 \times 10^{-3})(2.68 \times 10^{-3})}{0.397} = \frac{7.20 \times 10^{-6}}{0.397}$$
$$= 1.8 \times 10^{-5}$$

Example:

$$K_{ion}(HF) \text{ at } 20°C. = 7.2 \times 10^{-4}$$

Calculate the concentrations of H_3O^{+1}, F^{-1}, and HF in a 0.60 M solution of HF. Calculate the per cent ionization of HF.

Answer: Let X = the number of moles HF/l. that have dissociated. Then the concentration left will be:

$$C_{HF} = 0.60 - X$$

But since every HF that ionizes produces $1H_3O^{+1}$ and $1F^{-1}$:

$$C_{F^{-1}} = C_{H_3O^{+1}} = X$$

By definition:

$$K_{ion}(HF) = \frac{C_{H_3O^{+1}} \times C_{F^{-1}}}{C_{HF}}$$

On substituting the given information and concentrations:

$$7.2 \times 10^{-4} = \frac{(X)(X)}{0.60 - X} = \frac{X^2}{0.6 - X}$$

This relation, if solved for X, would give a quadratic equation which we could solve by means of a formula. However, we can simplify our task by making an approximation.

HF is a weak acid since K_{ion} is small (7.2×10^{-4}). This means that X is small. If this is so, then it will not be making much of an error to set $C_{HF} = 0.60$ instead of $(0.60 - X)$. That is, we ignore the X compared to 0.60. The equation now becomes:

$$7.2 \times 10^{-4} = \frac{X^2}{0.6}$$

or

$$X^2 = 0.6 \times 7.2 \times 10^{-4} = 4.32 \times 10^{-4}$$

and

$$X = 2.1 \times 10^{-2} \text{ mole/l.}$$

Thus our answer is:

$$C_{F^{-1}} = C_{H_3O^{+1}} = 0.021 \text{ mole/l.}$$

$$C_{HF} = 0.579 \text{ mole/l.}$$

and

$$\text{Per cent ionization} = \frac{\text{Amount of HF ionized}}{\text{Original amount of HF}} \times 100 = \frac{0.021}{0.60} \times 100 = 3.5\%$$

Note: The approximation is justified since X did turn out to be a small number. If an exact calculation is made, the answer still turns out to be $X = 0.021$. Such approximations will be used constantly.

Do problems 16 and 17 at the end of the chapter.

10. Use of the Ionization Constant—Common Ion Effect

Although we have thus far illustrated the ionization constant relation by using weak acids, the same methods apply to the dissociation of weak bases and weak salts. This is illustrated in the following table:

Substance	Equilibria	K_{ion}
Ammonia (NH_3)	$NH_3 + H_2O \rightleftarrows NH_4^{+1} + OH^{-1}$	$\dfrac{(C_{NH_4^{+1}}) \times C_{OH^{-1}}}{C_{NH_3}}$
Methyl amine (CH_3NH_2)	$CH_3NH_2 + H_2O \rightleftarrows CH_3NH_3^{+1} + OH^{-1}$	$\dfrac{C_{CH_3NH_3^{+1}} \times C_{OH^{-1}}}{C_{CH_3NH_2}}$
Mercuric chloride ($HgCl_2$)	$HgCl_2 \rightleftarrows HgCl^{+1} + Cl^{-1}$	$\dfrac{C_{HgCl^{+1}} \times C_{Cl^{-1}}}{C_{HgCl_2}} = K_I$
	$HgCl^{+1} \rightleftarrows Hg^{+2} + Cl^{-1}$	$\dfrac{C_{Hg^{+2}} \times C_{Cl^{-1}}}{C_{HgCl^{+1}}} = K_{II}$

In the discussion thus far we have limited ourselves to examples in which both ions came only from the weak electrolyte. However, it is far more frequent in the laboratory to have other salts present in the solution which may have ions in common with the weak electrolyte. Then we no longer have the simple relationship between the concentrations of the ions and the un-ionized weak electrolyte.

Example: To a solution of 0.2 M HAc, some HCl (g) is added until the concentration of HCl is 0.3 M. What substances are now present in the solution, and what are their concentrations?

$$K_{ion}(HAc) = 1.8 \times 10^{-5}$$

Answer: HCl is a strong electrolyte. We may consider it completely dissociated into 0.3 M H_3O^{+1} ions and 0.3 M Cl^{-1} ions. On adding it to the weakly dissociated acetic acid (HAc) and applying Le Châtelier's principle we will see that the H_3O^{+1} ions from the HCl will cause the HAc equilibrium to be shifted towards lesser dissociation.

Let X = number of moles of HAc/l. that are still dissociated. Then there are present in the solution:

$$C_{Cl^{-1}} = 0.3 \ M$$
$$C_{H_3O^{+1}} = 0.3 + X$$
$$C_{Ac^{-1}} = X$$
$$C_{HAc} = 0.2 - X$$

By definition:

$$K_{ion}(HAc) = \frac{C_{H_3O^{+1}} \times C_{Ac^{-1}}}{C_{HAc}}$$

On substitution:

$$1.8 \times 10^{-5} = \frac{(0.3 + X)(X)}{0.2 - X}$$

This equation can be solved exactly for X. However, to simplify our work, let us make an approximation. X will be very small, since HAc is a weak acid. We can thus replace $0.3 + X$ by 0.3 and, similarly, $0.2 - X$ by X. The equation now becomes:

$$1.8 \times 10^{-5} = \frac{(0.3)(X)}{(0.2)} = 1.5X$$

Then

$$X = \frac{1.8 \times 10^{-5}}{1.5} = 1.2 \times 10^{-5} \text{ mole}/l.$$

Note: This justifies our approximation, since $X = 1.2 \times 10^{-5}$, which is indeed small compared to 0.3 or 0.2.

Our answer is:

$$C_{Cl^{-1}} = 0.3 \ M$$
$$C_{H_3O^{+1}} = 0.3 \ M$$
$$C_{Ac^{-1}} = 1.2 \times 10^{-5} \ M$$
$$C_{HAc} = 0.2 \ M$$

Example: A solution contains 0.4 *M* HAc and 0.2 *M* NaAc. What ions and molecules are present in it, and what are their concentrations?

$$K_{ion}(HAc) = 1.8 \times 10^{-5}$$

Answer: From the completely ionized NaAc we get 0.2 *M* Na^{+1} ions and 0.2 *M* Ac^{-1} ions. Let X = moles HAc/l. that dissociate. Then we have

$$C_{Na^{+1}} = 0.2 \ M$$
$$C_{Ac^{-1}} = 0.2 + X$$
$$C_{H_3O^{+1}} = X$$
$$C_{HAc} = 0.4 - X$$

Again:

$$K_{ion}(HAc) = \frac{C_{Ac^{-1}} \times C_{H_3O^{+1}}}{C_{HAc}}$$

and on substitution:

$$1.8 \times 10^{-5} = \frac{(0.2 + X)(X)}{(0.4 - X)}$$

and, making the approximation that X is small compared to 0.2 or 0.4:

$$1.8 \times 10^{-5} = \frac{(0.2)(X)}{0.4} = \frac{X}{2}$$

Thus

$$X = 2 \times 1.8 \times 10^{-5} = 3.6 \times 10^{-5} \ mole/l.$$

and

$$C_{Ac^{-1}} = 0.2 \ M$$
$$C_{H_3O^{+1}} = 3.6 \times 10^{-5} \ M$$
$$C_{HAc} = 0.4 \ M$$

Do problems 18–20 at the end of the chapter.

11. Buffer Solutions

When an ion is present in a solution in small concentrations, a small amount of another substance that will react with it may almost completely remove it. Quite frequently it is important to have an ion present in small concentrations and yet have reserves of other compounds present such that, if a small amount of it is removed, these others will act to replenish it, that is, bring back the original concentration. An ion whose concentration may be low but stabilized in this way is said to be buffered, and the solution containing such an ion is called a *buffer solution.*

A buffer solution of any ion may be made by mixing a weak electrolyte containing that ion together with a large amount of a salt containing the other ion of the weak electrolyte.

Thus a mixture of HAc and NaAc constitute a buffer solution for the H^+ ion (actually H_3O^{+1}). Similarly a mixture of HAc and HCl are a buffer solution for the Ac^{-1} ion.

The behavior of these solutions is indicated by the following:

$$
\text{A solution of HAc} \atop \text{and NaAc} \quad \xleftrightarrow{\text{contains}} \quad
\begin{cases}
1. & \text{A large amount of } Ac^{-1} \text{ ions} \\
2. & \text{A large amount of HAc molecules} \\
3. & \text{A small amount of } H_3O^{+1} \text{ ions}
\end{cases}
$$

(*Note:* We omit the Na^{+1} ions which do not concern us. KAc would work just as well.)

If we add to this solution something that contains H_3O^{+1} ions (e.g., HCl), part of the reservoir of Ac^{-1} ions will react with it to form more HAc, thus tending to restore the original concentration of H_3O^{+1}.

If, on the other hand, we add to the solution something that removes H_3O^{+1} (such as NaOH which neutralizes it), part of the large reservoir of HAc molecules will ionize to restore the original concentration.

These restorative mechanisms are indicated by the equilibrium between H_3O^{+1} ions and the reservoirs:

$$
\boxed{HAc + H_2O} \; \rightleftarrows \; \boxed{Ac^{-1}} \; + \; \boxed{H_3O^{+1}}
$$

By varying the concentrations of weak acid and salt we can fix the concentration of H_3O^{+1} within broad limits. The concentration of the buffered ion, H_3O^{+1}, can be calculated by the methods outlined in the preceding paragraph on the common ion effect.

Example: What concentration of NaAc and HAc would you use to make a buffered solution in which $C_{H_3O^{+1}} = 1 \times 10^{-4}$?

Answer: Let $C_{NaAc} = X$ and $C_{HAc} = Y$; 1×10^{-4} = concentration of HAc that dissociates. Then we will have in the solution:

$$C_{Na^{+1}} = X$$

$$C_{Ac^{-1}} = X + 1 \times 10^{-4}$$

$$C_{H_3O^{+1}} = 1 \times 10^{-4}$$

$$C_{HAc} = Y - 1 \times 10^{-4}$$

$$K_{ion}(HAc) = 1.8 \times 10^{-5} = \frac{C_{H_3O^{+1}} \times C_{Ac^{-1}}}{C_{HAc}}$$

On substitution:

$$1.8 \times 10^{-5} = \frac{(1 \times 10^{-4})(X + 1 \times 10^{-4})}{(Y - 1 \times 10^{-4})}$$

But note again that 1×10^{-4} will be small compared to X and Y, so we can approximate:

$$1.8 \times 10^{-5} = \frac{(1 \times 10^{-4})(X)}{(Y)}$$

Solving for the ratio:

$$\frac{X}{Y} = \frac{1.8 \times 10^{-5}}{1 \times 10^{-4}} = 1.8 \times 10^{-1} = 0.18$$

Thus any concentrations of NaAc and HAc that are in the ratio $C_{NaAc}/C_{HAc} = 0.18$ will provide a buffer solution in which $C_{H_3O^{+1}} = 1 \times 10^{-4}$. The following combinations are taken as illustrations:

$$C_{NaAc} = 0.18 \ M; \quad C_{HAc} = 1 \ M$$

$$C_{NaAc} = 0.018 \ M; \quad C_{HAc} = 0.1 \ M$$

Will $C_{NaAc} = 1.8 \times 10^{-4}$; $C_{HAc} = 10 \times 10^{-4}$ work? Why not?

12. Problems

1. Write $K_{S.P.}$ for each of the following salts:

   (a) AgI. $K_{SP} = C_{Ag} \times C_I$ (d) $Mg(OH)_2$.
   (b) CuS. $C_{Cu} \times C_S$ (e) Sb_2S_3.
   (c) $Ca_3(PO_4)_2$. $(C_{Ca})^3 \times (C_{PO_4})^2$ (f) $Fe_4[Fe(CN)_6]_3$.

2. $K_{S.P.}(BaCrO_4) = 2 \times 10^{-10}$ at 20°C. Calculate the molar solubility of $BaCrO_4$ in water at 20°C.

3. $K_{S.P.}(PbF_2) = 3.7 \times 10^{-8}$ at 20°C. Calculate the molar solubility of PbF_2 at 20°C.

4. $K_{S.P.}[Al(OH)_3] = 1.9 \times 10^{-33}$ at 20°C. Calculate the molar solubility of $Al(OH)_3$ at 20°C.

5. For each of the following salts, whose solubility is given at 20°C., calculate the value of $K_{S.P.}$:

   (a) Solubility of AgBr is 5.8×10^{-7} mole/l.
   (b) Solubility of $BaCO_3$ is 7×10^{-5} mole/l.
   (c) Solubility of $Pb(OH)_2$ is 4.2×10^{-6} mole/l.
   (d) Solubility of Bi_2S_3 is 1.7×10^{-15} mole/l.

6. $K_{S.P.}(BaCrO_4) = 2 \times 10^{-10}$. (a) What is the solubility of $BaCrO_4$ in 0.040 M $BaCl_2$? (b) What is its solubility in 0.25 M K_2CrO_4?

7. $K_{S.P.}(PbF_2) = 3.7 \times 10^{-8}$. (a) What is the solubility of PbF_2 in 0.050 M $Pb(NO_3)_2$? (b) What is its solubility in 0.020 M NaF?

8. $K_{S.P.}[Mg(OH)_2] = 5.5 \times 10^{-12}$. (a) What is the solubility of $Mg(OH)_2$ in 0.0010 M NaOH? (b) What concentration of OH^{-1} ions in a solution will ensure that $C_{Mg^{+2} \ ion}$ is less than $4 \times 10^{-8} \ M$?

9. $K_{S.P.}(CuCl) = 1.8 \times 10^{-7}$. A solution contains a concentration of Cu^{+1} ions $= 2 \times 10^{-4} \ M$. Solid NaCl is added until $C_{Cl^{-1}}$ is $1 \times 10^{-2} \ M$. Was this high enough to cause a ppt. of CuCl to form? (Neglect volume change.)

10. $K_{S.P.}(PbI_2) = 8.7 \times 10^{-9}$. To a solution in which $C_{Pb^{+2}} = 3 \times 10^{-3} \ M$, solid NaI is added until $C_{I^{-1}}$ is $1 \times 10^{-4} \ M$. Will a ppt. of PbI_2 form?

11. If 50 cc. of solution in which $C_{Ag^{+1}} = 3 \times 10^{-4}\ M$ is added to 100 cc. of a solution in which $C_{Cl^{-1}} = 2 \times 10^{-6}\ M$, will a ppt. of AgCl form? $K_{S.P.}(AgCl) = 1.7 \times 10^{-10}$. (*Note:* volume change is important.)

12. A solution contains $1 \times 10^{-2}\ M\ Cl^{-1}$ ions and $1 \times 10^{-3}\ M\ I^{-1}$ ions. $K_{S.P.}(AgCl) = 1.7 \times 10^{-10}$. $K_{S.P.}(AgI) = 8.5 \times 10^{-17}$.

    (a) If a salt of Ag^{+1} ion is added dropwise to this, which ppt. forms first, AgCl or AgI?

    (b) What is the largest $C_{Ag^{+1}\ ion}$ which may exist in this solution without pptg. AgCl?

    (c) When this concentration is reached, what will the $C_{I^{-1}}$ be?

13. To a solution containing 0.04 $M\ Cd^{+2}$ ions and 0.3 $M\ Zn^{+2}$ ions some S^{-2} ions are added. $K_{S.P.}(ZnS) = 4.5 \times 10^{-24}$. $K_{S.P.}(CdS) = 1.4 \times 10^{-28}$.

    (a) What is the largest $C_{S^{-2}}$ ion that can exist in this solution without pptg. ZnS?

    (b) What will the $C_{Cd^{+2}}$ ion be at this point?

From your answer, what can you conclude regarding the possibility of using S^{-2} ions to make a quantitative separation of Zn^{+2} and Cd^{+2} ions?

14. A solution contains 0.02 $M\ Ca^{+2}$ ions and 0.003 $M\ Ba^{+2}$ ions. Could you make a separation of Ba^{+2} ions and Ca^{+2} ions by using SO_4^{-2} to ppt. one of them? Explain. $K_{S.P.}(CaSO_4) = 2.4 \times 10^{-5}$; $K_{S.P.}(BaSO_4) = 9.9 \times 10^{-11}$.

15. Write K_{ion} expressions for each of the following weak electrolytes:

    (a) HCN.

    (b) HClO.

    (c) H_2SO_3 (first ionization).

    (d) HCO_3^{-1} ions.

    (e) $PbAc_2$ (first ionization).

    (f) $PbAc^{+1}$ ions.

    (g) $SnCl_2$ (overall ionization).

    (h) $Fe(OH)^{+1}$ ions.

16. Given the percentage of ionization of each of the following solutions, calculate the concentration of ions and molecules present in the solution and the K_{ion} of the weak electrolyte.

    (a) 0.5 $M\ HNO_2$ is 3.0% ionized.

    (b) 0.04 M HF is 13.4% ionized.

    (c) 0.08 $M\ NH_3$ solution is 1.5% ionized.

    (d) 0.003 $M\ H_2S$ solution is 0.6% ionized (consider first ionization only).

    (e) 0.060 $M\ H_2CO_3$ solution is 0.27% ionized (consider first ionization only).

17. From the known ionization constants of the following weak electrolytes, calculate the concentrations of all ions and molecules present in the solutions given and the percentage of ionization:

    (a) 0.20 M HClO; $K_{ion}(HClO) = 5.6 \times 10^{-8}$.

    (b) 0.020 $M\ H_2CO_3$; $K_{ion}(H_2CO_3) = 4.3 \times 10^{-7}$ (first ionization).

    (c) 0.004 M HAc; $K_{ion}(HAc) = 1.8 \times 10^{-5}$.

    (d) 0.45 $M\ NH_3$ solution; $K_{ion}(NH_3) = 1.8 \times 10^{-5}$.

    (e) 0.65 $M\ H_2PO_4^{-1}$ ions; $K_{ion}(H_2PO_4^{-1}) = 6.2 \times 10^{-8}$ (only one ionization).

18. What concentration of Ac^{-1} ions will reduce $C_{H_3O^{+1}}$ ion to $2 \times 10^{-4}\ M$ in a 0.40 M solution of HAc? $K_{ion}(HAc) = 1.8 \times 10^{-5}$?

19. What concentration of H_3O^{+1} ions will reduce $C_{S^{-2}}$ ion to $2 \times 10^{-18}\ M$ in a 0.10 M solution of H_2S? $K_{ion}(H_2S) = 1 \times 10^{-22}$ (overall ionization).

20. What concentration of H_3O^{+1} ions will reduce $C_{HS^{-1}}$ ion to $2 \times 10^{-6}\ M$ in a 0.10 M solution of H_2S? $K_{ion}(H_2S) = 1 \times 10^{-7}$ (first ionization).

21. What mixtures would provide buffer solutions for each of the following ions?

(a) H_3O^{+1}.

(b) OH^{-1}.

(c) F^{-1}.

(d) NO_2^{-1}.

(e) Pb^{+2}.

(f) HS^{-1}.

(g) HCO_3^{-1}.

(h) CO_3^{-2}.

22. How would you make a buffer solution from NaAc and HAc in which the $C_{H_3O^{+1}}$ was $2 \times 10^{-5}\ M$? $K_{ion}(HAc) = 1.8 \times 10^{-5}$.

23. How would you make a buffer solution from HCl and HAc in which the $C_{Ac^{-1}\ ion}$ was $4 \times 10^{-4}\ M$? $K_{ion}(HAc) = 1.8 \times 10^{-5}$.

24. What are the units of $K_{S.P.}(AgCl)$? of $K_{S.P.}(PbCl_2)$?

25. What are the units of $K_{ion}(HAc)$? of $K_{ion}(HF)$?

26. Convert $K_{S.P.}(AgCl)$ in which the units of concentration are expressed in moles per liter to the $K_{S.P.}$ when the units of concentration are expressed in grams per liter. $K_{S.P.}(AgCl) = 1.7 \times 10^{-10}$.

27. Convert $K_{ion}(HAc)$ to the K_{ion} in which all concentrations are expressed in grams per liter. $K_{ion}(HAc) = 1.8 \times 10^{-5}$.

CHAPTER XIII

The Ionization of Water—Hydrolysis

1. Ionization of Water

To the processes going on in water solutions of ions, which we have already discussed, we must now add the following complication. Water is itself a weak electrolyte, owing to the process of self-ionization. The equilibrium of this weak electrolyte may be represented by the following equation:

$$H_2O + H_2O \rightleftarrows H_3O^{+1} + OH^{-1}$$

This self-ionization occurs in every solution containing water! Thus all water solutions always contain some H_3O^{+1} ions and some OH^{-1} ions. Only when these two concentrations are equal, as they are in pure water, can we say that the solution is neutral. In acid solution we will still have some OH^{-1} ions. The solution is said to be acid only because $C_{H_3O^{+1}}$ ion is greater than $C_{OH^{-1}}$, and conversely for basic solutions.

We can apply the law of mass action to this equilibrium:

$$K_{eq.} = \frac{C_{H_3O^{+1}} \times C_{OH^{-1}}}{(C_{H_2O})^2}$$

But since the C_{H_2O} is very nearly the same, either in pure water or dilute solutions (namely, about 55 moles $H_2O/l.$), we can combine this concentration with the $K_{eq.}$ and write a simplified expression:

$$K_{eq.} \times (C_{H_2O})^2 = C_{H_3O^{+1}} \times C_{OH^{-1}} = K_{ion}(H_2O)$$

This new constant $K_{ion}(H_2O)$ has been measured experimentally and found to be equal to 1×10^{-14} at 25°C. It is found to increase as the temperature increases, being 56×10^{-14} at 100°C. We shall generally use the value at 25°C. unless otherwise indicated.

This expression for K_{ion} of water tells us that in every water solution at 25°C. the product of the concentrations of OH^{-1} and H_3O^{+1} ions is equal to 1×10^{-14}. If we know one of these, we can always calculate the other.

Example: What substances are present in a 0.020 M solution of NaOH? What are their concentrations?

Answer: NaOH is an ionic salt (base). A 0.020 M solution of NaOH will have 0.020 M Na^{+1} ions and 0.020 M OH^{-1} ions. However, we will also get some OH^{-1} ions and H_3O^{+1} ions from the ionization of water itself. These amounts will be small, since water is such a weak electrolyte. Since $C_{OH^{-1}}$ from NaOH is large (2×10^{-2} M) we can neglect the added OH^{-1} ions from the water. To calculate the H_3O^{+1} ions:

$$K_{ion}(H_2O) = C_{OH^{-1}} \times C_{H_3O^{+1}}$$

Solving for $C_{H_3O^{+1}}$:

$$C_{H_3O^{+1}} = \frac{K_{ion}(H_2O)}{C_{OH^{-1}}}$$

and substituting:

$$C_{H_3O^{+1}} = \frac{1 \times 10^{-14}}{2 \times 10^{-2}} = 5 \times 10^{-13} \ M$$

Note: Our approximation that the amounts of OH^{-1} and H_3O^{+1} ions from the ionization of water are small is certainly justified.

Summarizing:

$$C_{Na^{+1}} = 2 \times 10^{-2} \ M$$

$$C_{OH^{-1}} = 2 \times 10^{-2} \ M$$

$$C_{H_3O^{+1}} = 5 \times 10^{-13} \ M$$

$$C_{H_2O} \simeq 55 \ M$$

The approximation adopted above will be generally applicable Almost any solute that contributes OH^{-1} ions (like a base) or H_3O^{+1} (like an acid) will suppress the ionization of water immensely, and we can neglect the additional ions contributed by this ionization.

Do problems 1 and 2 at the end of the chapter.

2. Neutrality of Solutions

The simultaneous existence of H_3O^{+1} and OH^{-1} ions in all water solutions forces us to adopt a new definition of neutrality.

Definition: A *neutral solution* is one in which

$$C_{OH^{-1}} = C_{H_3O^{+1}}$$

Since the product of these concentrations is 1×10^{-14} [K_{ion} (H_2O)] at 25°C., their concentrations in a neutral solution at 25°C. are

Neutral solution at 25°C.:

$$C_{OH^{-1}} = C_{H_3O^{+1}} = 1 \times 10^{-7} \ M$$

Thus, in an acid solution $C_{H_3O^{+1}}$ is greater than $1 \times 10^{-7} M$. Similarly, in a basic solution $C_{OH^{-1}}$ is greater than $1 \times 10^{-7} M$ (at 25°C.).

3. Logarithmic Units—The p Scale—pH

Science is always seeking abbreviations and shorthand to enable it to express briefly and compactly its facts and its theories. To avoid the inconvenience of writing exponentials (powers of 10), it has been found useful to express very large and small numbers in logarithmic units. For this purpose the following definition is employed:

Definition:

$$p\mathrm{H} = -\log C_{H_3O^{+1}}$$

In general, a negative logarithm or p scale has been adopted with the following interpretation. When a quantity is preceded by the letter p the combination means -1 times the logarithm of the quantity following the letter p, e.g.:

$$pK_{\mathrm{ion}} \text{ means } (-\log K_{\mathrm{ion}})$$

$$p\mathrm{OH} \text{ means } (-\log C_{OH^{-1}})$$

$$pK_{\mathrm{S.P.}} \text{ means } (-\log K_{\mathrm{S.P.}})$$

A pH of 2 means that $-\log C_{H_3O^{+1}} = 2$ or, changing the minus sign from left to right, $\log C_{H_3O^{+1}} = -2$. Since the logarithm of 10^{-2} is -2, we see that a pH of 2 signifies a concentration of hydrogen ion equal to 10^{-2} mole/l.

The following table shows the relation between the p scale and the normal concentration units in the case of pH.

RELATION BETWEEN pH AND CONCENTRATION OF HYDROGEN IONS

pH	-2	-1	0	1	2	3	4	...	11	...	16
$C_{H_3O^{+1}}$	100	10	1	0.1	0.01	1×10^{-3}	1×10^{-4}	...	1×10^{-11}	...	1×10^{-16}

Example: The concentration of hydrogen ion in a certain solution is $3 \times 10^{-4} M$. What is the pH of the solution?

Answer:

$$p\mathrm{H} = -\log C_{H_3O^{+1}} = -\log (3 \times 10^{-4})$$

$$= -(\log 3 + \log 10^{-4})$$

$$= -[0.48 + (-4)] = -(0.48 - 4)$$

$$= -(-3.52) = 3.52$$

Note: It is always possible to check the answer to such a problem, at least approximately. Note that 3×10^{-4} is larger than 10^{-4} and smaller than 10^{-3}. Since the pH of the former is 4 and the pH of the latter is 3, we see that the correct pH must be between 3 and 4.

Example: The pH of a solution is 4.65.   What is the concentration of hydrogen ion in the solution?

Answer: (Note first that, since 4.65 is between 4 and 5, the hydrogen ion concentration must lie between 10^{-4} and 10^{-5} M.)

$$p\text{H} = - \log C_{\text{H}_3\text{O}^{+1}} = 4.65$$

Therefore

$$\log C_{\text{H}_3\text{O}^{+1}} = -4.65$$

In looking up antilogarithms we must break up the number into two parts; a positive decimal (the mantissa) which can then be found in logarithm tables or on a slide rule, and a whole number (the characteristic), either positive or negative, which will appear as a power of 10 in the answer.

$$\log C_{\text{H}_3\text{O}^{+1}} = -4.65 = -5.00 + 0.35$$

Therefore

$$C_{\text{H}_3\text{O}^{+1}} = (10^{-5}) \cdot (2.24)$$

$$= 2.24 \times 10^{-5} \ M$$

Check: 2.24×10^{-5} is between 10^{-4} and 10^{-5}.

Note: If the student lacks familiarity with logarithms he should consult the Appendix or a suitable textbook.

Do problems 3 and 4 at the end of the chapter.

4. A Paradox—When Is the Ionization of Water Significant?

We have thus far used the $K_{\text{ion}}(\text{H}_2\text{O})$ relation to compute the concentration of either OH^{-1} or H_3O^{+1} if one of these is known.   In doing this we ignored the contribution of ions from water to the given concentration.   Is such a procedure always justified?

Let us take an example of when it is not.   Let us compute the concentration of ions in a 1×10^{-8} M solution of HCl.   Proceeding as usual we write $C_{\text{Cl}^{-1}} = 1 \times 10^{-8}$ M; $C_{\text{H}_3\text{O}^{+1}} = 1 \times 10^{-8}$ M, and, calculating $C_{\text{OH}^{-1}\text{ion}}$,

$$C_{\text{OH}^{-1}\text{ion}} = \frac{K_{\text{ion}}(\text{H}_2\text{O})}{C_{\text{H}_3\text{O}^{+1}}} = \frac{1 \times 10^{-14}}{1 \times 10^{-8}} = 1 \times 10^{-6}$$

Thus we find that in an acid solution of 1×10^{-8} M HCl $C_{\text{OH}^{-1}\text{ion}}$ is greater than $C_{\text{H}_3\text{O}^{+1}\text{ion}}$!   That is, the solution is basic!   The error is easy to detect.   In pure water $C_{\text{H}_3\text{O}^{+1}} = 1 \times 10^{-7}$ M.   By adding

HCl (1×10^{-8} mole/l.) we can only increase this.   But in the example chosen the amount of added H_3O^{+1} was less than the amount already present from the ionization of water.

Whenever the amount of added OH^{-1} ions or H_3O^{+1} ions is about the same or less than 10^{-7} M, then we cannot ignore the amounts arising from the ionization of water!   The given problem must be solved as follows:

Let X = concentration of H_3O^{+1} and OH^{-1} from ionization of water.   Then

$$C_{OH^{-1}} = X; \quad C_{H_3O^{+1}} = X + 1 \times 10^{-8}$$

$$K_{ion}(H_2O) = 1 \times 10^{-14} = (X)(X + 1 \times 10^{-8}) = X^2 + X \cdot 10^{-8}$$

This quadratic equation can be solved accurately to give X.   However, a quick way to get an approximate answer is as follows: Since neutral water contains $C_{H_3O^{+1}} = 1 \times 10^{-7}$, let us add to this the amount obtained from the acid ($1 \times 10^{-8} = 0.1 \times 10^{-7}$).   Their sum is $1 \times 10^{-7} + 0.1 \times 10^{-7} = 1.1 \times 10^{-7}$.   But this is too large, since the addition of the acid suppresses the ionization of water.   If we take the average of these two estimates, 1×10^{-7} and 1.1×10^{-7}, namely, 1.05×10^{-7}, we will be very close to the correct answer.   The reader can check the accuracy of this answer by solving the quadratic for X.   It gives $X = 9.5 \times 10^{-8}$.   But $C_{H_3O^{+1}} = X + 1 \times 10^{-8} = 10.5 \times 10^{-8} = 1.05 \times 10^{-7}$, which checks well!

Do problem 5 at the end of the chapter.

5. Hydrolysis

Acids and bases are not the only substances that will upset the balance of OH^{-1} and H_3O^{+1} ions in water.   When certain salts are placed in water it is found that the solution may become acidic or basic.   This process is termed *hydrolysis*.

Etymologically, hydrolysis means "to dissolve in water."   Technically, with special regard to ionic equilibria, the term represents the following process:

If a salt contains ions of a weak electrolyte, when it is placed in water solution those ions will react reversibly with the water molecules to form the *undissociated weak electrolyte* and either hydrogen or hydroxide ions.

If the ion is the ion of a weak base, then the product of hydrolysis will be the unionized weak base plus hydrogen ions and the solution will be acidic.   If it is the ion of a weak acid, then the products will be the molecules of the weak acid plus hydroxide ions and the solution will be basic. In this sense, hydrolysis may be thought of as the reverse reaction to neutralization.

Example: What will happen when sodium acetate is dissolved in water?

Answer: The acetate ion, being the ion of a weak acid, will react with water molecules to form un-ionized molecules of acetic acid and hydroxide ions. Thus the solution will be basic. The sodium ion is unaffected:

$$C_2H_3O_2^{-1} + H_2O \rightleftarrows HC_2H_3O_2 + OH^{-1}$$

Example: What ions and molecules will be present in a 0.2 M solution of sodium cyanide (NaCN)? If the salt is 2% hydrolyzed, what are their concentrations?

Answer: Note: 2% hydrolyzed does not mean 2% ionized! NaCN is a true salt and as such is 100% ionized in solution. However, the cyanide ion (CN^{-1}) is the ion of a weak acid, HCN, and so the hydrolysis refers to the reaction of this ion with water. Because of the hydrolysis of this ion, the solution will contain HCN molecules and excess OH^{-1} and therefore will be basic. The sodium ion is not the ion of a weak base and will be totally unaffected.

$$C_{Na^{+1}} = 0.2 \ M$$

$$C_{CN^{-1}} = 98\% \text{ of } 0.2 \ M = 0.98 \times 0.2 = 0.196 \ M$$

$$C_{HCN} = C_{OH^{-1}}$$

(since these are produced in equal amounts by the hydrolysis)

$$= 2\% \text{ of } 0.2 \ M = 0.02 \times 0.2 = 0.004 \ M$$

$$= 4 \times 10^{-3} \ M$$

$$C_{H_3O^{+1}} = \frac{1 \times 10^{-14}}{4 \times 10^{-3}} = 2.5 \times 10^{-12} \ M$$

$$C_{H_2O} = 55 \ M$$

To determine whether or not a given salt will undergo hydrolysis, we must look at the individual ions of the salt. Only ions of either weak acids or weak bases will undergo hydrolysis.

Do problems 7–9 at the end of the chapter.

6. Calculation of the Extent of Hydrolysis—Hydrolysis Constants

We can always determine qualitatively which ions will undergo the greatest hydrolysis. The weaker the acid or base, the greater the extent of hydrolysis of its ions. Thus CN^{-1} ions will hydrolyze more completely than Ac^{-1} ions since $K_{ion}(HCN) = 4 \times 10^{-10}$ whereas $K_{ion}(HAc) = 1.8 \times 10^{-5}$.

The extent of hydrolysis may be calculated quantitatively if the

K_{ion} of the weak acids and bases are known. Let us do this for the hydrolysis of the Ac^{-1} ion in a 0.04 M solution of NaAc. The equation for the hydrolysis is

$$Ac^{-1} + H_2O \rightleftarrows HAc + OH^{-1}$$

We can apply the law of mass action to this equilibrium:

$$K_{eq.} = \frac{C_{HAc} \times C_{OH^{-1}}}{C_{H_2O} \times C_{Ac^{-1}}}$$

Following the usual approximation we combine $K_{eq.}$ with the practically constant C_{H_2O} and obtain the simplified expression:

$$K_{eq.} \times C_{H_2O} = \frac{C_{HAc} \times C_{OH^{-1}}}{C_{Ac^{-1}}} = K_{hyd.}(Ac^{-1})$$

This $K_{hyd.}(Ac^{-1})$ is, however, related to $K_{ion}(HAc)$ and $K_{ion}(H_2O)$.

$$K_{ion}(H_2O) = C_{H_3O^{+1}} \times C_{OH^{-1}}$$

$$K_{ion}(HAc) = \frac{C_{Ac^{-1}} \times C_{H_3O^{+1}}}{C_{HAc}}$$

If we divide the first equation by the second we obtain

$$\frac{K_{ion}(H_2O)}{K_{ion}(HAc)} = \frac{C_{H_3O^{+1}} \times C_{OH^{-1}}}{C_{Ac^{-1}} \times C_{H_3O^{+1}}} \times C_{HAc} = \frac{C_{HAc} \times C_{OH^{-1}}}{C_{Ac^{-1}}}$$

We have thus derived a very important relation:

$$\boxed{K_{hyd.}(Ac^{-1}) = \frac{K_{ion}(H_2O)}{K_{ion}(HAc)}}$$

Thus the $K_{hyd.}$ for any given ion can be obtained by dividing $K_{ion}(H_2O)$ by the ionization constant of the acid. The same formula can be derived for the hydrolysis of basic ions. Thus, for the hydrolysis of NH_4^{+1}, the ion of the weak base NH_3:

$$\boxed{K_{hyd.}(NH_4^{+1}) = \frac{K_{ion}(H_2O)}{K_{ion}(NH_3)} = \frac{C_{H_3O^{+1}} \times C_{NH_3}}{C_{NH_4^{+1}}}}$$

the equation being

$$NH_4^{+1} + H_2O \rightleftarrows NH_3 + H_3O^{+1}$$

We can now return to our original problem of the hydrolysis of

0.04 M NaAc. Let X = moles Ac^{-1} per liter that hydrolyze. Then $0.04 - X = C_{Ac^{-1}}$ that is left. Since each mole of Ac^{-1} hydrolyzing produces 1 mole of OH^{-1} ions and 1 mole of HAc, these concentrations must be equal to each other.

$$C_{HAc} = C_{OH^{-1}} = X$$

We can now substitute into the hydrolysis constant relation since $K_{ion}(HAc) = 1.8 \times 10^{-5}$ and $K_{ion}(H_2O) = 1 \times 10^{-14}$.

$$K_{hyd.}(Ac^{-1}) = \frac{K_{ion}(H_2O)}{K_{ion}(HAc)} = \frac{1 \times 10^{-14}}{1.8 \times 10^{-5}} = \frac{C_{OH^{-1}} \times C_{HAc}}{C_{Ac^{-1}}}$$

or

$$5.5 \times 10^{-10} = \frac{(X)(X)}{0.04 - X} = \frac{X^2}{0.04 - X}$$

But X will be small since $K_{hyd.}$ is small, and we can neglect X compared to 0.04. This approximation results in

$$5.5 \times 10^{-10} = \frac{X^2}{0.04}$$

Solving for X we find

$$X^2 = 0.04 \times 5.5 \times 10^{-10} = 22 \times 10^{-12}$$

Thus

$$X = 4.7 \times 10^{-6} \text{ mole/l.} = C_{OH^{-1}} = C_{HAc}$$

To calculate the percentage of hydrolysis:

$$\% \text{ hydrolysis} = \frac{\text{Amount of } Ac^{-1} \text{ hydrolyzed}}{\text{Original amount of } Ac^{-1}} \times 100$$

$$= \frac{4.7 \times 10^{-6} M}{4.0 \times 10^{-2}} \times 100$$

$$= 1.18 \times 10^{-2} \%$$

If we make other calculations we will find quite generally that the percentage of hydrolysis will be small. It will be large only when $K_{hyd.}$ is large, or (since this is the ratio of $K_{ion}(H_2O)$ to K_{ion} for the weak acid or base) when K_{ion} (acid or base) is close to 10^{-14} or less. This is the case for K_{ion} of the HS^{-1} ion, the HPO_4^{-2} ion, and a very few other common acids or bases. Thus S^{-2} and PO_4^{-3} ions in solution may be almost completely hydrolyzed, depending on the concentrations.

Do problem 10 at the end of the chapter.

7. Salts of Weak Acids and Weak Bases

An interesting case in hydrolysis arises when we consider the behavior of a salt which contains ions of both a weak acid and a weak base. NH_4Ac, NH_4CN, $AlAc_3$, and MgF_2 are examples of such combinations. (*Note:* the student should write separate equations for each of these the weak acid and the weak base—for Mg^{+2} it is $Mg(OH)^{+1}$—that is, only the first hydrolysis step need be considered.)

If we know the ionization constants of the acid and the base, we can decide qualitatively which hydrolysis will proceed farther. Thus, since HCN is a weaker acid ($K_{ion} = 4 \times 10^{-10}$) than NH_3 is a base ($K_{ion} = 1.8 \times 10^{-5}$), when NH_4CN is dissolved the CN^{-1} ion will hydrolyze to a greater extent than the NH_4^{+1} ion and the solution will be basic.

In the unusual case of NH_4Ac, both acid and base are equally weak and the solution is neutral.

However, even when the dissociation constants of the acid and base differ considerably, there is another mechanism which tends to prevent them from hydrolyzing to different extents. In NH_4CN, the CN^{-1} ion would normally hydrolyze as follows:

$$CN^{-1} + H_2O \rightleftarrows HCN + OH^{-1} \qquad (A)$$

However, the NH_4^{+1} ion which hydrolyzes only to a slight extent in neutral solution will immediately react with this excess OH^{-1} ion:

$$NH_4^{+1} + OH^{-1} \rightleftarrows NH_3 + H_2O \qquad (B)$$

By removing the OH^{-1} ions, this second reaction tends to cause still more of the CN^{-1} ions to hydrolyze, and the final result is to bring about a great deal more hydrolysis of both the CN^{-1} and the NH_4^{+1} than would normally occur if each existed in a separate solution. The net result of these two reactions can be seen by adding them.

$$CN^{-1} + NH_4^{+1} \rightleftarrows NH_3 + HCN \qquad (H_2O \text{ and } OH^{-1} \text{ cancel}) \quad (C)$$

That is, the anions and cations tend to reverse the normal neutralization process and form undissociated acid and base. This tendency so far outweighs the differences in acid and base strength that, as a first approximation, we can always consider that the anions and cations hydrolyze to an equal extent.

In making calculations, no great error will be made if equation C is used as the basis of the calculation rather than the individual hydrolyses A and B The slight differences in hydrolysis of anions and cations which do exist and are responsible for the solution being either acidic or basic may then be calculated rather simply.

Example: Compute the hydrolysis of a 0.2 M solution of NH_4CN.

$$K_{ion}(HCN) = 4 \times 10^{-10}; \quad K_{ion}(NH_3) = 1.8 \times 10^{-5}$$

Answer: The CN^{-1} ion will ionize more extensively, and hence the solution will be basic. Let us make the approximation that CN^{-1} and NH_4^{+1} hydrolyze about equally. Let X = the number of moles of each that hydrolyze. Then we have

Reaction: $CN^{-1} + NH_4^{+1} \rightleftarrows NH_3 + HCN$

Concentration: $(0.3 - X)$ $(0.3 - X)$ (X) (X)

For this equilibrium we can write, using the law of mass action:

$$K_{eq.} = \frac{C_{NH_3} \times C_{HCN}}{C_{NH_4^+} \times C_{CN^{-1}}} = \frac{(X)(X)}{(0.3 - X)(0.3 - X)} = \frac{X^2}{(0.3 - X)^2}$$

If we know $K_{eq.}$ we can calculate X. However, the reader will observe that this $K_{eq.}$ is related to $K_{ion}(NH_3)$, $K_{ion}(HCN)$, and $K_{ion}(H_2O)$. Thus:

$$K_{ion}(NH_3) = \frac{C_{NH_4^{+1}} \times C_{OH^{-1}}}{C_{NH_3}}; \quad K_{ion}(HCN) = \frac{C_{H_3O^{+1}} \times C_{CN^{-1}}}{C_{HCN}}$$

If we multiply these two together we have

$$K_{ion}(NH_3) \times K_{ion}(HCN) = \frac{C_{NH_4^{+1}} \times C_{CN^{-1}} \times C_{H_3O^{+1}} \times C_{OH^{-1}}}{C_{NH_3} \times C_{HCN}}$$

But $K_{ion}(H_2O) = C_{H_3O^{+1}} \times C_{OH^{-1}}$. If we divide this equation by the preceding one, we obtain

$$\frac{K_{ion}(H_2O)}{K_{ion}(NH_3) \times K_{ion}(HCN)} = \frac{C_{NH_3} \times C_{HCN}}{C_{NH_4^{+1}} \times C_{CN^{-1}}}$$

But this is precisely $K_{eq.}$ for the joint hydrolysis. We can thus say that, for the joint hydrolysis of both ions, the $K_{eq.}$ is given by

$$K_{eq.} = \frac{K_{ion}(H_2O)}{K_{ion}(acid) \times K_{ion}(base)}$$

In the particular problem this is

$$K_{eq.} = \frac{1 \times 10^{-14}}{(4 \times 10^{-10}) \times (1.8 \times 10^{-5})} = 1.39$$

We can now return to our expression for X and solve.

$$\frac{X^2}{(0.3 - X)^2} = 1.39$$

or, taking square roots of both sides:

$$\frac{X}{0.3 - X} = 1.18$$

and, solving for X:

$$X = 0.354 - 1.18X \quad \text{or} \quad 2.18X = 0.354 \quad \text{or} \quad X = 0.162$$

Thus the salt is $(0.162/0.300) \times 100 = 54\%$ hydrolyzed.

Now to calculate the OH^{-1} concentration: Since we have already decided that the solution is basic, we use the relation for $K_{hyd.}(CN^{-1})$:

$$K_{hyd.}(CN^{-1}) = \frac{K_{ion}(H_2O)}{K_{ion}(HCN)} = \frac{C_{HCN} \times C_{OH^{-1}}}{C_{CN^{-1}}}$$

On substitution:

$$\frac{1 \times 10^{-14}}{4 \times 10^{-10}} = 2.5 \times 10^{-5} = \frac{(0.162)C_{OH^{-1}}}{0.138}$$

Solving for $C_{OH^{-1}}$:

$$C_{OH^{-1}} = \frac{0.138}{0.162} \times 2.5 \times 10^{-5} = 2.1 \times 10^{-5} \ M$$

From $K_{ion}(H_2O)$ we find

$$C_{H_3O^{+1}} = \frac{K_{ion}(H_2O)}{C_{OH^{-1}}} = \frac{1 \times 10^{-14}}{2.1 \times 10^{-5}} = 4.8 \times 10^{-10} \ M$$

These answers are necessarily approximate since we have assumed that CN^{-1} and NH_4^{+1} are equally hydrolyzed. An exact algebraic solution is very difficult to derive, but it will give almost the same answer.

---

8. Summary of Hydrolysis Calculations

If M represents the concentration of an ion of a weak acid or base and X represents the concentration of this ion that hydrolyzes, then:

A. For Anions of Weak Acid

$$K_{hyd.} = \frac{K_{ion}(H_2O)}{K_{ion}(acid)} \qquad \text{(exact)}$$

$$X = \sqrt{M \times K_{hyd.}} = \sqrt{\frac{M \times K_{ion}(water)}{K_{ion}(acid)}} \quad \text{(approximate)}$$

$$\% \text{ hydrolysis} = \frac{X}{M} \times 100 = \left(\sqrt{\frac{K_{ion}(water)}{M \times K_{ion}(acid)}} \right) \times 100$$

B. For Cations of Weak Base

$$K_{hyd.} = \frac{K_{ion}(H_2O)}{K_{ion}(base)} \qquad \text{(exact)}$$

$$X = \sqrt{M \times K_{hyd.}} = \sqrt{\frac{M \times K_{ion}(water)}{K_{ion}(base)}} \quad \text{(approximate)}$$

$$\% \text{ hydrolysis} = \frac{X}{M} \times 100 = \left(\sqrt{\frac{K_{ion}(water)}{M \times K_{ion}(base)}} \right) \times 100$$

C. For Simultaneous Hydrolysis of Anions and Cations

$$K_{\text{hyd.}} = \frac{K_{\text{ion}}(H_2O)}{K_{\text{ion}}(\text{acid}) \times K_{\text{ion}}(\text{base})} \qquad \text{(approximate)}$$

$$X_{\text{anion}} = X_{\text{cation}} = \frac{M \sqrt{K_{\text{hyd.}}}}{1 + \sqrt{K_{\text{hyd.}}}} \qquad \text{(approximate)}$$

$$\% \text{ hydrolysis} = \frac{X}{M} \times 100 = \left(\frac{\sqrt{K_{\text{hyd.}}}}{1 + \sqrt{K_{\text{hyd.}}}}\right) \times 100$$

$$C_{H_3O^{+1}} = \sqrt{\frac{K_{\text{ion}}(H_2O)K_{\text{ion}}(\text{acid})}{K_{\text{ion}}(\text{base})}} \qquad \text{(approximate)}$$

$$C_{OH^{-1}} = \frac{K_{\text{ion}}(H_2O)}{C_{H_3O^{+1}}} = \sqrt{\frac{K_{\text{ion}}(H_2O)K_{\text{ion}}(\text{base})}{K_{\text{ion}}(\text{acid})}}$$

9. Titration of Weak Acids and Bases

When we titrate an acid or base we add equal numbers of equivalent of acid and base and form a salt and water. If the acid and base are both strong, the salt formed does not hydrolyze and the final solution will be neutral. That is, its pH will be 7.

If, however, either the acid of the base is weak, the final salt solution is hydrolyzed and not neutral. (A titration cannot be performed successfully if both acid and base are weak.)

The pH of the final salt solution may be estimated from the methods developed in the previous paragraphs on hydrolysis.

However, a good rule of thumb is: the pH of the final solution can be obtained by adding or subtracting from 7, $\frac{1}{2}$ pK_{ion} of the acid or base.

Titration of Weak Acid: pH of salt = $7 + \frac{1}{2}pK_{\text{ion}}(\text{acid})$

Titration of Weak Base: pH of salt = $7 - \frac{1}{2}pK_{\text{ion}}(\text{base})$

Thus, if we are titrating HAc with NaOH, the pH at the endpoint will be the pH of NaAc (the salt formed) and is roughly $7 + \frac{1}{2}[pK_{\text{ion}}(\text{HAc})] = 7 + \frac{1}{2}(4.74) = 9.37$. This result depends slightly on the concentration of the solutions used, and the accurate answer may be obtained from the equations developed previously (see section on hydrolysis).

For the titration of NH_3 with HCl, the pH at the endpoint will be 4.63.

These results are important since we shall want to choose indicators for these titrations that change color at the proper pH values, not at 7.

10. Problems

1. (a) What are the units of $K_{ion}(H_2O)$?
   (b) What would the value of $K_{ion}(H_2O)$ be if concentrations were expressed in grams per liter?

2. What ions are present in each of the following solutions, and what are their concentrations?

   (a) 0.0050 M HCl.   (d) 0.75 M NaOH.
   (b) 0.34 M NaCl.   (e) 3×10^{-5} M KOH.
   (c) 0.60 M K_2SO_4.   (f) $2 = 10^{-4}$ M $ZnCl_2$ (ignore hydrolysis of Zn^{+2}).

3. What is the pH and the pOH of each of the following solutions:

   (a) 0.0010 M HCl.   (e) 0.06 M H_2SO_4.
   (b) 0.0010 M H_2SO_4.   (f) 0.53 M KOH.
   (c) 1.0×10^{-4} M NaOH.   (g) 0.034 M $Ca(OH)_2$.
   (d) 3.4×10^{-4} M HCl.   (h) 0.03 M HAc (if it is 2.4% ionized).

4. Make the following conversions:
   (a) Express $K_{ion} = 2.5 \times 10^{-6}$ as pK_{ion}.
   (b) Express $C_{Ag^{+1}} = 3 \times 10^{-12}$ as $pC_{Ag^{+1}}$.
   (c) Express $K_{eq.}' = 8 \times 10^{-16}$ as $pK_{eq.}$.
   (d) Express $pK_{S.P.} = 9.70$ as $K_{S.P.}$.
   (e) Express $pOH = 6.30$ as $C_{OH^{-1}}$.
   (f) Express $pK_{ion} = 8.64$ as K_{ion}.

5. What is the pH of a 2×10^{-8} M solution of H_2SO_4?

6. For each of the following salts, write balanced equations representing the hydrolysis of those ions that do hydrolyze:

   (a) NaAc.   (e) KCN.
   (b) $(NH_4)_2SO_4$.   (f) $Fe(Ac)_3$.
   (c) $ZnCl_2$.   (g) $Al_2(SO_4)_3$.
   (d) $FeCl_3$.   (h) $MgCO_3$.

7. A 0.04 M solution of NaClO is 0.22% hydrolyzed. What molecules and ions are present in the solution? What are their concentrations?

8. A 0.07 M solution of KCN is 2.0% hydrolyzed. What molecules and ions are present in the solution? What are their concentrations?

9. A 0.25 M solution of $NaHCO_3$ is 0.03% hydrolyzed. What molecules and ions are present in the solution? What are their concentrations? (Ignore dissociation of HCO_3^{-1}.)

10. Calculate hydrolysis constants for each of the following salt solutions. Compute also the pH of the solution and the percentage of hydrolysis.

(a) 0.05 M NaAc; K_{ion}(HAc) $= 1.8 \times 10^{-5}$.
(b) 0.008 M NH$_4$Cl; K_{ion}(NH$_3$) $= 1.8 \times 10^{-5}$.
(c) 0.32 M Na$_2$HPO$_4$; K_{ion}(H$_2$PO$_4^{-1}$) $= 6.2 \times 10^{-8}$ (ignore second step).
(d) 0.5 M Na$_2$S; K_{ion}(HS^{-1}) $= 1.0 \times 10^{-15}$ (ignore second step).
(e) 0.64 M KCN; K_{ion}(HCN) $= 4.0 \times 10^{-10}$.
(f) 0.06 M MgCl$_2$; K_{ion}[Mg(OH)$^{+1}$] $= 2 \times 10^{-4}$ (ignore second step).
(g) 0.40 M NH$_4$Ac (see values above).
(h) 0.003 M NH$_4$CN (see values above).

11. Calculate the pH to be expected at the endpoint in the following titrations (see previous problem for K_{ion} values):

(a) NH$_3$ with HCl.   (c) KOH with H$_2$PO$_4^{-1}$.
(b) NaOH with HCN.   (d) KOH with HS^{-1}.

CHAPTER XIV

Additional Equilibria in Ionic Solutions

1. Ionization of Polyvalent Electrolytes

In Chapter XII we emphasized problems dealing with the first step in the ionization of a weak electrolyte. Many electrolytes, however, are polyvalent and ionize in a sequence of steps:

First step: $\qquad$ $H_2O + H_2S \rightleftarrows HS^{-1} + H_3O^{+1}$ $\qquad$ $K_{ion}(I)$

Second step: $\qquad$ $H_2O + HS^{-1} \rightleftarrows S^{-2} + H_3O^{+1}$ $\qquad$ $K_{ion}(II)$

or by addition of these two steps we have the overall equation:

$$2H_2O + H_2S \rightleftarrows S^{-2} + 2H_3O^{+1} \qquad K_{ion}(\text{overall})$$

If we are given C_{H_2S} and want to find $C_{HS^{-1}}$, we would use the first equation together with its $K_{ion}(I)$.

If we are given $C_{HS^{-1}}$ and want to find $C_{S^{-2}}$, we would use the second equation together with its $K_{ion}(II)$.

If we are given C_{H_2S} and want to find $C_{S^{-2}}$, we would use the overall equation which is equal to $K_{ion}(I)$ times $K_{ion}(II)$.

If we are given C_{H_2S} and want to find both $C_{HS^{-1}}$ and $C_{S^{-2}}$, then we proceed stepwise.

Example: What are the $C_{HS^{-1}}$, $C_{H_3O^{+1}}$ and $C_{S^{-2}}$ in a 0.03 M solution of H$_2$S. $K_{ion}(H_2S) = 1 \times 10^{-7}$; $K_{ion}(HS^{-1}) = 1 \times 10^{-15}$.

Answer: Proceeding as usual, let X = moles/l. of H$_2$S that ionize. Then we have in solution:

$$C_{H_2S} = 0.03 - X$$

$$C_{H_3O^{+1}} = X$$

$$C_{HS^{-1}} = X$$

But it will be objected that some of the HS^{-1} ionizes to produce more H$_3$O^{+1}, and so $C_{H_3O^{+1}}$ is more than X moles/l. and $C_{HS^{-1}}$ is less than X moles/l.

The answer to these objections is this: H$_2$S ionizes only weakly in the first step $[K_{ion}(I) = 1 \times 10^{-7}]$. This permits us to ignore X with respect to 0.03. Similarly, HS^{-1} ionizes even less in the second step, and so we can ignore the changes. that this second ionization produces on $C_{H_3O^{+1}}$ and on $C_{HS^{-1}}$. Then

$$K_{ion}(H_2S) = \frac{C_{H_3O^{+1}} \times C_{HS^{-1}}}{C_{H_2S}}$$

On substitution:

$$1 \times 10^{-7} = \frac{(X)(X)}{0.3 - X} \quad \text{(approximating } 0.3 - X \cong 0.3\text{)}$$

Then

$$1 \times 10^{-7} = \frac{X^2}{0.3} \quad \text{or} \quad X^2 = 0.3 \times 10^{-7} = 3.0 \times 10^{-8}$$

Thus

$$X = 1.7 \times 10^{-4} \text{ moles/l.} = C_{H_3O^{+1}} = C_{HS^{-1}}$$

To find $C_{S^{-2}}$ we now use $K_{ion}(II)$:

$$K_{ion}(II) = \frac{\cancel{C_{H_3O^{+1}}} \times C_{S^{-2}}}{\cancel{C_{HS^{-1}}}}$$

But we have just agreed that $C_{H_3O^{+1}} = C_{HS^{-1}}$, so we can cancel them. Therefore

$$C_{S^{-2}} = K_{ion}(II) = 1 \times 10^{-15} \text{ mole/l.}$$

If there is a common ion added, then all calculations are simplified, as indicated in Chapter XIII.

2. Reactions of Amphoteric Ions

Some substances may react both as weak acids or as weak bases. Thus HCO_3^{-1} may do either:

As acid: $HCO_3^{-1} + H_2O \rightleftarrows H_3O^{+1} + CO_3^{-2}$

As base: $HCO_3^{-1} + H_2O \rightleftarrows OH^{-1} + H_2CO_3$

If we have a solution of $NaHCO_3$ we can decide qualitatively which tendency predominates from a knowledge of the ionization constants. It can be shown that if the product of the K_{ion} for the two steps involved is greater than 1×10^{-14} (i.e., $K_I \times K_{II} > 10^{-14}$) then the acid behavior predominates and the solution is acidic. If, however, the product is less than 10^{-14} (i.e., $K_I \times K_{II} < 10^{-14}$) then the basic behavior predominates and the solution is basic.

For the example chosen, $K_{ion}(H_2CO_3) = 4.3 \times 10^{-7}$ and

$$K_{ion}(HCO_3^{-1}) = 4.7 \times 10^{-11},$$

the product $= 2.0 \times 10^{-17}$, which is less than 10^{-14}. Thus a solution of $NaHCO_3$ is basic. The following list shows similar results for other salts.

Salt	$K_{ion}(I)$	$K_{ion}(II)$	Product $[K_{ion}(I) \times K_{ion}(II)]$
NaHS	$1 \times 10^{-7}(H_2S)$	$1 \times 10^{-15}(HS^{-1})$	1×10^{-22}(basic)
NaHSO$_3$	$1.2 \times 10^{-2}(H_2SO_3)$	$1 \times 10^{-7}(HSO_3^{-1})$	1.2×10^{-9}(acidic)
Na$_2$HPO$_4$	$6.2 \times 10^{-8}(H_2PO_4^{-1})$	$1 \times 10^{-12}(HPO_4^{-2})$	6.2×10^{-20}(basic)
NaH$_2$PO$_4$	$7.5 \times 10^{-3}(H_3PO_4)$	$6.2 \times 10^{-8}(H_2PO_4^{-1})$	4.7×10^{-10}(acidic)
NaHB$_4$O$_7$	$1 \times 10^{-4}(H_2B_4O_7)$	$1 \times 10^{-9}(HB_4O_7^{-1})$	1×10^{-13}(acidic)

The quantitative calculation can be treated just as we treated the hydrolysis of the salt of a weak acid and a weak base. We combine the two equations and make the assumption that both reactions are roughly equal. Thus, for 0.4 M solution NaHCO$_3$:

$$2HCO_3^{-1} \rightleftarrows H_2CO_3 + CO_3^{-2}$$

Let X = concentration of HCO_3^{-1} used up. Then

$$C_{HCO_3^{-1}} = 0.4 - X; \quad C_{H_2CO_3} = C_{CO_3^{-2}} = \frac{X}{2}$$

$$K_{eq.} = \frac{C_{H_2CO_3} \times C_{CO_3^{-2}}}{(C_{HCO_3^{-1}})^2} = \frac{K_{ion}(HCO_3^{-1})}{K_{ion}(H_2CO_3)}$$

Substituting numbers:

$$\frac{\left(\frac{X}{2}\right)\left(\frac{X}{2}\right)}{(0.4 - X)^2} = \frac{4.7 \times 10^{-11}}{4.3 \times 10^{-7}} = 1.1 \times 10^{-4} = \frac{X^2}{4(0.4 - X)^2}$$

Taking square roots of both sides:

$$\frac{X}{2(0.4 - X)} = 1.05 \times 10^{-2}$$

and solving for X we have

$$X = (0.8)(1.05 \times 10^{-2}) - (2.1 \times 10^{-2})X$$

or

$$1.02X = 8.4 \times 10^{-3}$$

Thus

$$X = 8.2 \times 10^{-3} \text{ mole/l.}$$

and

$$C_{HCO_3^{-1}} = 0.4 - X = 0.392 \text{ mole/l.}$$

and

$$C_{H_2CO_3} = C_{CO_3^{-2}} = \frac{X}{2} = 4.1 \times 10^{-3} \text{ mole/l.}$$

$$\% \text{ hydrolysis} = \frac{X}{0.4} \times 100 = \frac{8.2 \times 10^{-3}}{0.4} \times 100 = 2.1\%$$

We may calculate $C_{H_3O^{+1}}$ from either $K_{ion}(I)$ or $K_{ion}(II)$ since both will give the same answer.

$$\frac{C_{H_3O^{+1}} \times C_{HCO_3^{-1}}}{C_{H_2CO_3}} = K_{ion}(H_2CO_3)$$

Solving for $C_{H_3O^{+1}}$:

$$C_{H_3O^{+1}} = \frac{K_{ion}(H_2CO_3) \times C_{H_2CO_3}}{C_{HCO_3^{-1}}}$$

but

$$\frac{C_{H_2CO_3}}{C_{HCO_3^{-1}}} = \frac{C_{CO_3^{-1}}}{C_{HCO_3^{-1}}} = \sqrt{\frac{K_{ion}(II)}{K_{ion}(I)}}$$

Thus on substitution:

$$C_{H_3O^{+1}} = \sqrt{K_{ion}(I) \times K_{ion}(II)}$$

$$= \sqrt{4.3 \times 10^{-7} \times 4.7 \times 10^{-11}} = 4.5 \times 10^{-9} \text{ mole/l.}$$

Finally

$$C_{OH^{-1}} = \frac{K_{ion}(H_2O)}{C_{H_3O^{+1}}} = \frac{1 \times 10^{14}}{4.5 \times 10^{-9}} = 2.2 \times 10^{-6} \text{ mole/l.}$$

The exact solution to this problem gives an almost identical result.

3. Summary on Polyvalent Ions

We can summarize our findings on multivalent acids as follows: The second stage of ionization of a weak electrolyte is always small compared to the first. The concentration of the anion produced in the second step is numerically equal to the value of $K_{ion}(II)$.

For the hydrolysis of an amphoteric substance, we can say the following:

1. From the product of the K_{ion} for the two steps involved, we can tell if the acid or basic behavior will predominate. The concentrations of H_3O^{+1} and OH^{-1} are given by

$$C_{H_3O^{+1}} = \sqrt{K_I \times K_{II}}; \quad C_{OH^{-1}} = \frac{K_{ion}(H_2O)}{\sqrt{K_I \times K_{II}}} \quad \text{(approximate)}$$

2. *If we assume equal amounts of both types of hydrolysis, then the concentration of ion hydrolyzed is*

$$X = \frac{2\,M\,\sqrt{K_I/K_{II}}}{1 + 2\,\sqrt{K_I/K_{II}}} \qquad \text{(approximate)}$$

$$\% \text{ hydrolysis} = \frac{X}{M} \times 100 = \frac{200\,\sqrt{K_I/K_{II}}}{1 + 2\,\sqrt{K_I/K_{II}}}$$

4. Dissociation of Complex Ions

We have thus far emphasized the dissociation of weak electrolytes that contain H^{+1} ions. There are a large group of complex radicals made from metal ions and other groups. Thus the Zn^{+2} ion can form the following complexes: $Zn(OH)_4^{-2}$, $Zn(NH_3)_4^{+2}$, and $Zn(CN)_4^{-2}$. Similarly, the Hg^{+2} ion forms: $HgCl_4^{-2}$, HgI_4^{-2}, and $Hg(CN)_4^{-2}$; and the Ag^{+1} ion forms $Ag(NH_3)_2^{+1}$, $AgCl_3^{-2}$, $Ag(S_2O_3)_2^{-3}$, and $Ag(CN)_2^{-1}$. The types of complex ion which a metal ion can form can be determined only by experiment. However, for every complex ion we can write an equilibrium equation showing its tendency to dissociate into its original components:

$$Zn(OH)_4^{-2} \rightleftarrows Zn^{+2} + 4OH^{-1}$$

$$Zn(NH_3)_4^{+2} \rightleftarrows Zn^{+2} + 4NH_3$$

$$Zn(CN)_4^{-2} \rightleftarrows Zn^{+2} + 4CN^{-1}$$

The law of mass action may be applied to these *homogeneous* equilibria, and we can write an equilibrium constant for each. Thus

$$K_{eq.}[Zn(OH)_4^{-2}] = \frac{C_{Zn^{+2}} \times C^4_{OH^-}}{C_{Zn(OH)_4^{-2}}}$$

This $K_{eq.}$ or dissociation constant, as it is frequently called, may be measured experimentally. Once known it is useful (just like other equilibrium constants) to calculate the concentrations of ions and complex ions in equilibrium with each other.

Example:
$$K_{eq.}[Zn(NH_3)_4^{+2}] = 2.6 \times 10^{-10}$$

What are the ions present in a 0.2 M solution of $Zn(NH_3)_4Cl_2$? What are their concentrations?

Answer: $Zn(NH_3)_4Cl_2$ is a salt. In a 0.2 M solution we will have $C_{Cl^{-1}} = 0.4\,M$ and $C_{Zn(NH_3)_4^{+2}} = 0.2\,M$. However, some of the $Zn(NH_3)_4^{+2}$ complex ions dissociate as follows:

$$Zn(NH_3)_4^{+2} \rightleftarrows Zn^{+2} + 4NH_3$$

Let X = moles per liter of $Zn(NH_3)_4^{+2}$ that dissociate. Then we will have in solution

$$C_{Zn(NH_3)_4^{+2}} = 0.2 - X; \quad C_{Zn^{+2}} = X; \quad C_{NH_3} = 4X$$

By definition:

$$K_{eq.} = \frac{C_{Zn^{+2}} \times C^4_{NH_3}}{C_{Zn(NH_3)_4^{+2}}}$$

Substituting we have

$$2.6 \times 10^{-10} = \frac{(X)(4X)^4}{(0.2 - X)} = \frac{256X^5}{0.2 - X}$$

Let us neglect X compared to 0.2. Our equation simplifies to

$$\frac{256X^5}{0.2} = 2.6 \times 10^{-10}$$

or

$$X^5 = \frac{0.2 \times 2.6 \times 10^{-10}}{256}$$

or

$$X^5 = 2.0 \times 10^{-13}$$

or

$$X^5 = 200 \times 10^{-15}$$

Taking the $\frac{1}{5}$ root of both sides:

$$X = 2.9 \times 10^{-3} \ M.$$

Thus

$$C_{Zn^{+2}} = 2.9 \times 10^{-3} \ M$$

$$C_{NH_3} = 4X = 1.16 \times 10^{-2} \ M$$

$$C_{Zn(NH_3)_4^{+2}} = 0.2 - 0.0029 = 0.197 \ M$$

The percentage of dissociation $= \dfrac{X}{0.2} \times 100 = \dfrac{0.0029}{0.2} \times 100 = 1.45\%$

---

5. Common Ion Effect for Complex Ions

In laboratory practice we generally deal not with pure salts of complex ions but with solutions containing the complex ion in the presence of an excess of the agent used to form the complex.

Thus the $Ag(CN)_2^{-1}$ complex ion is always formed in the presence of an excess of CN^{-1} ions. In such cases the calculations are much simplified if we know the excess concentration of the complexing agent.

Example: A solution contains 0.3 M $Ag(CN)_2^{-1}$ ions and 0.04 M CN^{-1}. What is the concentration of Ag^{+1} ions if $K_{eq}[Ag(CN)_2^{-1}] = 1 \times 10^{-21}$? *Note:* There are, of course, positive ions present also, but they are not of importance for the problem.

Answer: By definition:

$$K_{eq}[Ag(CN)_2{}^{-1}] = \frac{C_{Ag^{+1}} \times C^2{}_{CN^{-1}}}{C_{Ag(CN)_2{}^{-1}}}$$

Solving for $C_{Ag^{+1}}$ and substituting numbers:

$$C_{Ag^{+1}} = K_{eq} \times \frac{C_{Ag(CN)_2{}^{-1}}}{C^2{}_{CN^{-1}}} = 1 \times 10^{-21} \times \frac{0.3}{(0.04)^2}$$

$$= \frac{1 \times 10^{-21} \times 0.3}{0.0016} = 1.9 \times 10^{-19} \text{ mole}/\text{l}.$$

Example: What concentration of NH_3 is needed in a solution containing 0.03 M Ag^{+1} to suppress the $C_{Ag^{+1}}$ to 2×10^{-10} M?

$$K_{eq}[Ag(NH_3)_2{}^{+1}] = 6.8 \times 10^{-8}.$$

Answer: By adding enough NH_3 all 0.03 M Ag^{+1} ions will be converted to 0.03 M $Ag(NH_3)_2{}^{+1}$ ions except for a negligible 2×10^{-10} M.

$$K_{eq} = \frac{C_{Ag^{+1}} \times C^2{}_{NH_3{}^{+1}}}{C_{Ag(NH_3)_2{}^{+1}}}$$

Solving for C_{NH_3} and substituting numbers:

$$C^2{}_{NH_3} = \frac{K_{eq} \times C_{Ag(NH_3)_2{}^{+1}}}{C_{Ag^{+1}}} = \frac{6.8 \times 10^{-8} \times 3 \times 10^{-2}}{2 \times 10^{-10}} = 10.2$$

Taking the square roots of both sides:

$$C_{NH_3} = 3.2 \text{ moles}/\text{l}.$$

Then the total amount of NH_3 needed is $3.2 + 2 \times 0.03 = 3.28 \simeq 3.3$ M, since some of the NH_3 is added to the Ag^{+1}.

---

6. Simultaneous Equilibria

In the usual situation that occurs in laboratory and commercial practice, we find not one equilibrium but often two or even three simultaneous equilibria going on at once. A set of typical situations is outlined in the following examples:

A. Separation of Two Ions by Selective Precipitation with the Ions of a Weak Electrolyte. In a typical scheme in qualitative analysis, a solution may contain two ions such as Zn^{+2} and Cd^{+2} which form insoluble sulfide salts. However, the solubility of the sulfide salts are different, the ZnS being 300 times more soluble than CdS. This difference in solubility is sufficient to permit us to ppt. the less soluble CdS without pptg. the more soluble ZnS if we can control the S^{-2} ion concentration carefully. The S^{-2} ion is the ion of the weak acid H_2S, and its concentration may be controlled by controlling the concentration of the hydrogen ion (H_3O^{+1}) in the solution.

Example: A solution contains 0.04 M Cd^{+2} ions and 0.3 M Zn^{+2} ions. It is proposed to ppt. CdS by making the solution 0.1 M with H_2S. What concentration of H_3O^{+1} is needed to prevent the ZnS from pptg?

$$K_{S.P.}(ZnS) = 4.5 \times 10^{-24}$$

$$K_{S.P.}(CdS) = 1.4 \times 10^{-28}$$

$$K_{ion}(H_2S) = 1.1 \times 10^{-22} \text{ (overall)}$$

Answer: Since we don't want ZnS to ppt., let us consider its equilibrium first:

$$K_{S.P.}(ZnS) = C_{Zn^{+2}} \times C_{S^{-2}}$$

Since the solution is 0.4 M in $C_{Zn^{+2}}$, we want to keep $C_{S^{-2}}$ sufficiently low so that the product $C_{Zn^{+2}} \times C_{S^{-2}}$ is less than $K_{S.P.}(ZnS)$. The maximum permissible $C_{S^{-2}}$ is obtained from the equation:

$$C_{S^{-2}} = \frac{K_{S.P.}(ZnS)}{C_{Zn^{+2}}} = \frac{4.5 \times 10^{-24}}{0.3} = 1.5 \times 10^{-23} M$$

Thus we must not have a $C_{S^{-2}}$ greater than $1.5 \times 10^{-23} M$. Now we turn to the relation between the S^{-2} ion and H^{+1} ion. Since we are given C_{H_2S} we use the equation for the overall ionization:

$$H_2S + 2H_2O \rightleftarrows 2H_3O^{+1} + S^{-2}$$

$$K_{ion}(H_2S) = \frac{C^2_{H_3O^{+1}} \times C_{S^{-2}}}{C_{H_2S}}$$

Solving for $C_{H_3O^{+1}}$:

$$C^2_{H_3O^{+1}} = \frac{C_{H_2S}}{C_{S^{-2}}} \times K_{ion}(H_2S)$$

Substituting:

$$C^2_{H_3O^{+1}} = \frac{0.1}{1.5 \times 10^{-23}} \times 1.1 \times 10^{-22} = 0.73$$

Taking square roots:

$$C_{H_3O^{+1}} = 0.85 \text{ mole}/l.$$

Thus, to keep $C_{S^{-2}}$ below $1.5 \times 10^{-23} M$, $C_{H_3O^{+1}}$ must be at least 0.85 M. Will this $C_{S^{-2}}$ be sufficient to ppt. CdS? We now turn to the $K_{S.P.}(CdS)$.

$$K_{S.P.}(CdS) = C_{Cd^{+2}} \times C_{S^{-2}}$$

Solving for $C_{Cd^{+2}}$:

$$C_{Cd^{+2}} = \frac{K_{S.P.}(CdS)}{C_{S^{-2}}}$$

Substituting:

$$C_{Cd^{+2}} = \frac{1.4 \times 10^{-28}}{1.5 \times 10^{-23}} = 9.3 \times 10^{-6} M$$

We conclude that $C_{S^{-2}} = 1.5 \times 10^{-23} M$ (which can be obtained by adjusting the acidity of the solution until $C_{H_3O^{+1}} = 0.85\ M$) will ppt. CdS effectively (compare $9.3 \times 10^{-6}\ M$ to the original concentration of $0.04\ M$) and still not ppt. ZnS.

Example: A solution contains $0.2\ M$ Mg^{+2} ions and $0.2\ M$ Ca^{+2} ions. Is it possible to separate Ca^{+2} by forming a ppt. of $CaCO_3$ without pptg. $MgCO_3$?

$$K_{S.P.}(CaCO_3) = 4.8 \times 10^{-9}$$

$$K_{S.P.}(MgCO_3) = 1 \times 10^{-5}$$

Answer: The maximum $C_{CO_3^{-2}}$ that we can have in the solution that will not ppt. $MgCO_3$ is given by

$$K_{S.P.}(MgCO_3) = C_{Mg^{+2}} \times C_{CO_3^{-2}}$$

Solving for $C_{CO_3^{-2}}$:

$$C_{CO_3^{-2}} = \frac{K_{S.P.}(MgCO_3)}{C_{Mg^{+2}}}$$

Substituting numbers:

$$C_{CO_3^{-2}} = \frac{1 \times 10^{-5}}{0.2} = 5 \times 10^{-5}\ \text{mole/l.}$$

Will this now be enough to ppt. the Ca^{+2} ion?

$$K_{S.P.}(CaCO_3) = C_{Ca^{+2}} \times C_{CO_3^{-2}}$$

Solving for $C_{Ca^{+2}}$:

$$C_{Ca^{+2}} = \frac{K_{S.P.}(CaCO_3)}{C_{CO_3^{-2}}}$$

Substituting numbers:

$$C_{Ca^{+2}} = \frac{4.8 \times 10^{-9}}{5 \times 10^{-5}} = 9.6 \times 10^{-5}\ \text{mole/l.}$$

Thus this concentration of CO_3^{-2} will ppt. practically all the original Ca^{+2} ions and the separation is possible. How can we obtain this $C_{CO_3^{-2}}$ in the solution? If we just add Na_2CO_3 reagent, we might easily add too much. The answer is that if the pH of the solution is controlled (i.e., control the H_3O^{+1}) we can control the CO_3^{-2} ion concentration even if excess Na_2CO_3 is added. This is generally done by using a buffer solution for the H_3O^{+1} ion, and it can be shown that an alkaline solution containing NH_3 and NH_4^{+1} ions can keep the $C_{CO_3^{-2}}$ within desired limits.

B. Selective Precipitation Using Complex Ions. The control of the concentration of the reagent used to do the precipitating may be done by means of a complex ion rather than by the hydrogen ion. This is frequently the case when anions are separated.

Example: A solution contains $0.4\ M$ Cl^{-1} and $0.4\ M$ I^{-1}. Is it possible to separate the I^{-1} by forming a ppt. of AgI without pptg. AgCl?

$$K_{S.P.}(AgCl) = 1.7 \times 10^{-10}$$

$$K_{S.P.}(AgI) = 8.5 \times 10^{-17}$$

Answer: The maximum $C_{Ag^{+1}}$ that will not ppt. AgCl is given by

$$K_{S.P.}(AgCl) = C_{Ag^{+1}} \times C_{Cl^{-1}}$$

Solving for $C_{Ag^{+1}}$ and substituting:

$$C_{Ag^{+1}} = \frac{K_{S.P.}(AgCl)}{C_{Cl^{-1}}} = \frac{1.7 \times 10^{-10}}{0.4} = 4.3 \times 10^{-10} \ M$$

Is this sufficient to ppt. the I^{-1} ion?

$$K_{S.P.}(AgI) = C_{Ag^{+1}} \times C_{I^{-1}}$$

Solving for $C_{I^{-1}}$ and substituting numbers:

$$C_{I^{-1}} = \frac{K_{S.P.}(AgI)}{C_{Ag^{+1}}} = \frac{8.5 \times 10^{-17}}{4.3 \times 10^{-10}} = 2.0 \times 10^{-7} \ M.$$

Thus a $C_{Ag^{+1}} = 4.3 \times 10^{-10} \ M$ is sufficient to ppt. all the I^{-1} ions (compare 2.0×10^{-7} with 0.4) without pptg. the Cl^{-1} ion.

How can we adjust the $C_{Ag^{+1}}$ to this value? The normal stock solutions are about 0.01 M! The answer is that we must use a buffered solution of Ag^{+1}. A 0.01 M solution of $Ag(NH_3)_2^{+1}$ containing excess NH_3 may be used as a reagent. What excess of NH_3 must it have?

$$K_{eq.}[Ag(NH_3)_2^{+1}] = \frac{C_{Ag^{+1}} \times C^2_{NH_3}}{C_{Ag(NH_3)_2^{+1}}}$$

Solving for C_{NH_3}:

$$C^2_{NH_3} = C_{Ag(NH_3)_2^{+1}} \times \frac{K_{eq.}}{C_{Ag^{+1}}}$$

and substituting numbers:

$$C^2_{NH_3} = 0.01 \times \frac{6.8 \times 10^{-7}}{4.3 \times 10^{-10}} = 15.8$$

or

$$C_{NH_3} = 4 \ M$$

Thus a solution of Ag^{+1} in 4 M NH_3 may be used to ppt. the I^{-1} ion without pptg. the Cl^{-1} ion. With this reagent there is no danger that adding an excess will cause the Cl^{-1} ion to ppt.

Example: A solution contains 0.04 M $Cd(CN)_4^{-2}$ and 0.06 M $Cu(CN)_3^{-2}$ complex ions together with an excess of CN^{-1} ions = 0.2 M. If the solution is now treated with Na_2S until $C_{S^{-2}} = 1 \times 10^{-3}$, will either ion ppt. as the sulfide?

$$K_{S.P.}(CdS) = 1.4 \times 10^{-28} \qquad K_{S.P.}(Cu_2S) = 2.5 \times 10^{-50}$$

$$K_{eq.}[Cd(CN)_4^{-2}] = 1.4 \times 10^{-17} \qquad K_{eq.}[Cu(CN)_3^{-2}] = 5 \times 10^{-28}$$

Answer: Let us first determine the concentrations of Cu^{+1} and Cd^{+2} ions in the buffered solution.

$$K_{eq.} \; [\text{Cu(CN)}_3{}^{-2}] = \frac{C_{\text{Cu}^{+1}} \times C^3{}_{\text{CN}^{-1}}}{C_{\text{Cu(CN)}_3{}^{-2}}}$$

Solving for $C_{\text{Cu}^{+1}}$:

$$C_{\text{Cu}^{+1}} = \frac{C_{\text{Cu(CN)}_3{}^{-2}}}{(C_{\text{CN}^{-1}})^3} \times K_{eq.}$$

Substituting numbers:

$$C_{\text{Cu}^{+1}} = \frac{0.06}{(0.2)^3} \times 5 \times 10^{-28}$$

$$= \frac{6 \times 10^{-2}}{8 \times 10^{-3}} \times 5 \times 10^{-28}$$

$$C_{\text{Cu}^{+1}} = 3.8 \times 10^{-27} \; M$$

$$K_{eq.} \; [\text{Cd(CN)}_4{}^{-2}] = \frac{C_{\text{Cd}^{+2}} \times C^4{}_{\text{CN}^{-1}}}{C_{\text{Cd(CN)}_4{}^{-2}}}$$

Solving for $C_{\text{Cd}^{+2}}$:

$$C_{\text{Cd}^{+2}} = \frac{C_{\text{Cd(CN)}_4{}^{-2}}}{(C_{\text{CN}^{-1}})^4} \times K_{eq.}$$

Substituting numbers:

$$C_{\text{Cd}^{+2}} = \frac{0.04}{(0.2)^4} \times 1.4 \times 10^{-17}$$

$$= \frac{4 \times 10^{-2} \times 1.4 \times 10^{-17}}{1.6 \times 10^{-3}}$$

$$C_{\text{Cd}^{+2}} = 3.5 \times 10^{-16} \; M$$

Let us now see if the $C_{\text{S}^{-2}} = 1 \times 10^{-3} \; M$ is sufficient to ppt. either ion.

$$C^2{}_{\text{Cu}^{+1}} \times C_{\text{S}^{-2}}$$
$$= (3.8 \times 10^{-27})^2 \times 1 \times 10^{-3}$$
$$= 14.5 \times 10^{-57}$$

But this is much less than $K_{\text{S.P.}}(\text{Cu}_2\text{S}) = 2.5 \times 10^{-50}$. Thus Cu_2S will not ppt.

$$C_{\text{Cd}^{+2}} \times C_{\text{S}^{-2}}$$
$$= 3.5 \times 10^{-16} \times 1 \times 10^{-3}$$
$$= 3.5 \times 10^{-19}$$

But this is much greater than $K_{\text{S.P.}}(\text{CdS}) = 1.4 \times 10^{-28}$. Thus the CdS will ppt.

We conclude that under these conditions CdS will ppt. whereas Cu_2S will not, and so the separation of Cu^{+1} and Cd^{+2} is possible.

Example: A solution containing excess $\text{NH}_4{}^{+1}$ ions and NH_3 will be buffered with respect to the OH^{-1} ion. What should the composition of such a reagent be if it is to be used to separate the 0.05 M Mg^{+2} from the 0.08 M Ni^{+2} ion?

$$K_{\text{S.P.}}[\text{Mg(OH)}_2] = 5.5 \times 10^{-12}$$

$$K_{\text{S.P.}}[\text{Ni(OH)}_2] = 1.6 \times 10^{-14}$$

$$K_{\text{ion}}(\text{NH}_3) = 1.8 \times 10^{-5}$$

Answer: Since Mg(OH)_2 is more soluble than Ni(OH)_2, we want to have the maximum $C_{\text{OH}^{-1}}$ present that will not ppt. Mg(OH)_2.

$$K_{\text{S.P.}}[\text{Mg(OH)}_2] = C_{\text{Mg}^{+1}} \times C^2{}_{\text{OH}^{-1}}$$

Solving for $C_{\text{OH}^{-1}}$ and substituting:

$$C^2{}_{\text{OH}^{-1}} = \frac{K_{\text{S.P.}}}{C_{\text{Mg}^{+2}}} = \frac{5.5 \times 10^{-12}}{0.05} = 1.1 \times 10^{-10}$$

Taking square roots:

$$C_{\text{OH}^{-1}} = 1.05 \times 10^{-5} \; M$$

Thus we want our solution to contain C_{OH^-} of 1.05×10^{-5} M or less.   Is this enough to ppt. Ni(OH)$_2$?

$$K_{\text{S.P.}}[\text{Ni(OH)}_2] = C_{Ni^{+2}} \times C^2_{OH^-}$$

Solving for $C_{Ni^{+2}}$ and substituting:

$$C_{Ni^{+2}} = \frac{K_{\text{S.P.}}}{C^2_{OH^-}} = \frac{1.6 \times 10^{-14}}{(1.05 \times 10^{-5})^2} = \frac{1.6 \times 10^{-14}}{1.1 \times 10^{-10}} = 1.45 \times 10^{-4}\ M$$

$$\% \text{ Ni}^{+2} \text{ left in solution} = \frac{1.45 \times 10^{-4}}{0.08} \times 100 = 0.18\%$$

That is the $C_{OH^-} = 1.05 \times 10^{-5}$ M will ppt. all but 0.18% of the Ni^{+2} and will not ppt. any of the Mg^{+2} ions.   This is certainly close to the limits which we would permit but is satisfactory for qualitative analysis.

Finally, what composition of NH$_4^{+1}$, NH$_3$ buffer should we use to give $C_{OH^-} = 1.05 \times 10^{-5}$ M?

$$K_{\text{ion}}(\text{NH}_3) = \frac{C_{NH_4^{+1}} \times C_{OH^-}}{C_{NH_3}}$$

Solving for the ratio $C_{NH_4^{+1}}/C_{NH_3}$ and substituting numbers:

$$\frac{C_{NH_4^{+1}}}{C_{NH_3}} = \frac{K_{\text{ion}}}{C_{OH^-}} = \frac{1.8 \times 10^{-5}}{1.05 \times 10^{-5}} = 1.7$$

Thus any solution in which $C_{NH_4^{+1}}/C_{NH_3} = 1.7$ will do.   A solution containing $C_{NH_4^{+1}} = 1.7$ M and $C_{NH_3} = 1.0$ M will work.

---

7. Summary—Principles of Selective Precipitation

In the last section we have illustrated methods for separating ions based on differences in solubilities of their salts.   The conditions under which these separations are possible are:

1. *If the solubilities of the salts differ sufficiently, then one of the salts can be made to precipitate, leaving the other in solution if the precipitating ion is not present in too high concentrations.   Too high concentrations of the precipitating ion may be avoided if this ion can be buffered.   It may be buffered if it will form a weak acid or complex ion.*

2. *If the solubilities of the salts of the ions do not differ sufficiently, then it may be possible to reduce the concentration of one of the ions to the point where it is not present in high enough quantities to precipitate.   This is possible if one of the ions forms a stronger complex than the other.*

8. Problems

1. Write equations for the stepwise and overall ionizations of each of the following.   Also write a K_{ion} for each equation:

  (a) H$_3$PO$_4$.   (c) H$_2$SiO$_4^{-2}$(ion).
  (b) H$_2$SO$_3$.   (d) Al(OH)$_2^{+1}$(ion).

2. What are the concentrations of the ions present in a 0.05 M solution of H$_2$B$_4$O$_7$, given K_{ion}(H$_2$B$_4$O$_7$) $= 1 \times 10^{-4}$, K_{ion}(HB$_4$O$_7^{-1}$) $= 1 \times 10^{-9}$?

3. What are the concentrations of the ions present in a 0.8 M solution of H_2Se, given $K_{ion}(H_2Se) = 1.7 \times 10^{-4}$, $K_{ion}(HSe^{-1}) = 1 \times 10^{-10}$?

4. What is the pH and the percentage of hydrolysis of a 0.05 M solution of $NaHCO_3$? $K_{ion}(H_2CO_3) = 4.3 \times 10^{-7}$; $K_{ion}(HCO_3^{-1}) = 4.7 \times 10^{-11}$?

5. What is the pH and the percentage of hydrolysis of a 0.02 M solution of $NaHS$? $K_{ion}(H_2S) = 1.1 \times 10^{-7}$; $K_{ion}(HS^{-1}) = 1 \times 10^{-15}$?

6. What is the concentration of PO_4^{-3} ions in a 0.06 M solution of Na_2HPO_4? $K_{ion}(H_2PO_4^{-1}) = 6.2 \times 10^{-8}$; $K_{ion}(HPO_4^{-2}) = 1 \times 10^{-12}$. What is the pH of the solution?

7. What is the concentration of Hg^{+2} ions in a 0.3 M solution of $K_2Hg(CN)_4$? $K_{eq}.[Hg(CN)_4^{-2}] = 4 \times 10^{-42}$.

8. What is the concentration of Ag^{+1} ions in a 0.6 M solution of $NaAg(CN)_2$? $K_{eq}.[Ag(CN)_2^{-1}] = 1 \times 10^{-21}$. What is the $C_{CN^{-1}}$?

9. What concentration of NH_3 will reduce the $C_{Cd^{+2}}$ to 1×10^{-6} M in a solution of 0.3 M $Cd(NH_3)_4^{+2}$ ions? $K_{eq}.[Cd(NH_3)_4^{+2}] = 1 \times 10^{-7}$.

10. A solution of 0.4 M $HgCl_3^{-1}$ ions is made 0.3 M in Cl^{-1} ions. What is $C_{Hg^{+2}}$ in this solution? $K_{eq}.[Hg(Cl_3)^{-1}] = 6 \times 10^{-17}$.

11. What $C_{S^{-2}}$ ion will effect the maximum separation of 0.3 M Mn^{+2} ions and 0.05 M Cd^{+2} ions? $K_{S.P.}(CdS) = 1.4 \times 10^{-28}$; $K_{S.P.}(MnS) = 5.6 \times 10^{-16}$. What $C_{H_3O^{+1}}$ in a 0.1 M H_2S solution will produce this $C_{S^{-2}}$ ion? What percentage of Cd^{+2} will be left in solution?

12. For each of the following pairs of ions, find a single ion that will ppt. one in the presence of the other when both are present in 0.1 M concentration. (Use texts for data on properties.)

    (a) Br^{-1} and Cl^{-1}.   (d) SO_4^{-2} and CO_3^{-2}.
    (b) Ag^{+1} and Cu^{+2}.   (e) CrO_4^{-2} and SO_4^{-2}.
    (c) Sn^{+2} and Hg^{+2}.   (f) Zn^{+2} and Ni^{+2}.

13. A solution contains 0.03 M Zn^{+2} ions and 0.02 M Mn^{+2} ions. Can these be separated by pptg. ZnS? $K_{S.P.}(ZnS) = 4.5 \times 10^{-24}$; $K_{S.P.}(MnS) = 5.6 \times 10^{-16}$. What $C_{S^{-2}}$ is needed for best separation? If a 0.1 M solution of H_2S is used, what $C_{H_3O^{+1}}$ is needed to give this $C_{S^{-2}}$? $K_{ion}(H_2S) = 1.1 \times 10^{-22}$.

14. What $C_{CO_3^{-2}}$ is needed to ppt. the 0.003 M Cd^{+2} ion in the presence of the 0.04 M Ca^{+2} ion. $K_{S.P.}(CdCO_3) = 2.5 \times 10^{-14}$; $K_{S.P.}(CaCO_3) = 4.8 \times 10^{-9}$. What percentage of Cd^{+2} is left in solution? What $C_{H_3O^{+1}}$ must be present in a 0.1 M solution of $NaHCO_3$ to give this $C_{CO_3^{-2}}$? $K_{ion}(HCO_3^{-1}) = 4.7 \times 10^{-11}$.

15. A solution contains 0.08 M Ba^{+2} ions and 0.08 M Sr^{+2} ions. What $C_{CrO_4^{-2}}$ ion will ppt. the maximum amount of $BaCrO_4$ without pptg. $SrCrO_4$? $K_{S.P.}(BaCrO_4) = 2 \times 10^{-10}$; $K_{S.P.}(SrCrO_4) = 3.6 \times 10^{-5}$. What must the pH of a 0.2 M K_2CrO_4 solution be to give the $C_{CrO_4^{-2}}$ ion? $K_{ion}(HCrO_4^{-1}) = 3.2 \times 10^{-7}$.

16. Can 0.1 M Br^{-1} ions and 0.1 M I^{-1} ions be separated using Ag^{+1} as a reagent? What must be $C_{Ag^{+1}}$ be to effect maximum separation? What excess concentration of $S_2O_3^{-2}$ ions must be present in a solution containing 0.1 M $Ag(S_2O_3)_2^{-3}$ ions to buffer the Ag^{+1} to give the desired concentration? $K_{S.P.}(AgBr) = 3.3 \times 10^{-13}$; $K_{S.P.}(AgI) = 8.5 \times 10^{-17}$; $K_{eq}.[Ag(S_2O_3)_2^{-3}] = 1 \times 10^{-13}$.

17. What concentrations of Ac^{-1} ions and HAc would you use to give a buffer solution of OH^{-1} ions that would ppt. the 0.1 M Fe^{+3} ion as $Fe(OH)_3$ without pptg. the 0.1 M Cr^{+3} ion. $K_{S.P.}[Cr(OH)_3] = 6.7 \times 10^{-31}$; $K_{S.P.}[Fe(OH)_3] = 4 \times 10^{-38}$; $K_{ion}(NH_3) = 1.8 \times 10^{-5}$.

CHAPTER XV

Oxidation and Reduction

1. Multivalence

In Chapter VII we discussed the valences of elements and groups present in binary compounds, that is, compounds behaving as though they contained only two distinct groups.

It was pointed out at the end of that chapter (p. 79) that many elements display the property of multivalence. That is, they have different valences (combining power) in different binary compounds. Thus nitrogen (N) may form NO (valence = 2), N_2O (valence = 1); N_2O_3 (valence = 3); NO_2 (valence = 4); N_2O_5 (valence = 5).

There are many reactions in which the apparent binary valence undergoes a change. To these reactions, our principle of equivalence will not be directly applicable. In order to develop methods for handling such reactions conveniently we shall enlarge our simple theory of binary valence so that it may deal with reactions in which there are changes in valence. These reactions are called oxidation-reduction reactions and may be related to processes in which electrons are transferred.

2. A New System of Valences—Oxidation Numbers

In the new system of valences we shall now develop, we shall start by creating a standard and a set of rules for assigning valence. To distinguish these new valences from the old binary valences, we shall call them oxidation numbers.

Rules: 1. *All free elements shall be assigned the oxidation number of zero (to indicate that they are not in combination).*

  2. *When H is present in a compound, it will be assigned an oxidation number of $+1$ (except in hydrides, when it is -1).*

  3. *The sum of all oxidation numbers of the elements present in a compound must be zero (to indicate that all valences are used up).*

  4. *The sum of all oxidation numbers in a complex ion or radical must equal the charge on the ion or radical (to indicate the residual combining power of the ion or radical).*

From these rules we can now proceed to find the oxidation numbers of all the other elements. We see that hydrogen is our standard.

Thus, in H_2O the oxidation number of O is -2 since 2H make $+2$ and H_2O is a compound in which all oxidation numbers must be zero. In H_2O_2 the oxidation number of O is -1.

Corollary: In compounds, O will always have the oxidation number -2 except in peroxide, where it is -1.

Proceeding in this manner we see that Al is $+3$ in Al_2O_3; Mn is $+2$ in MnO, but $+4$ in MnO_2; Fe is $+2$ in FeO, but $+3$ in Fe_2O_3; S is $+4$ in SO_2, but -2 in H_2S.

To take a few radicals: Cl is $+1$ in ClO^{-1}, $+3$ in the ClO_2^{-1} ion, $+5$ in the ClO_3^{-1} ion, $+7$ in ClO_4^{-1}, but -1 in the Cl^{-1} ion. Cr is $+3$ in the Cr^{+3} ion, but $+6$ in the CrO_4^{-2} ion. Mn is $+2$ in the Mn^{+2} ion, but $+7$ in the MnO_4^{-1} ion.

These rules permit us to assign oxidation numbers to all elements in any type of compound, ion or radical. These numbers have a $+$ or $-$ sign, thus differing from our binary valence numbers.

The oxidation number indicates the combining power (based on $H = +1$) of the elements in any state of combination. The units of oxidation valence, so defined, are equivalents per mole. Thus the oxidation number of Zn in Zn^{+2} ion is $+2$ equivalents Zn^{+2} per mole Zn^{+2}.

Do problem 1 at the end of the chapter.

3. Oxidation and Reduction

Definition: When the oxidation number of an element increases in a reaction, the element is said to be oxidized. When the oxidation number of an element is lowered in a reaction, the element is said to be reduced.

Thus, when O_2 gas reacts with Zn (metal) to form ZnO:

$$2Zn + O_2 \rightarrow 2ZnO$$

zinc has increased in oxidation number (from zero in free Zn to $+2$ in ZnO) and oxygen has decreased (from zero in free O_2 to -2 in ZnO). We say that Zn has been oxidized and oxygen has been reduced. Because of the rule that all oxidation numbers in a compound must add to zero, we will find that oxidation and reduction always occur together and in equivalent amounts. If one element is oxidized, another element must always be reduced to maintain the balance of oxidation numbers. Thus in the above case for every Zn atom that increased from 0 to $+2$, an equal number of O atoms had to decrease from 0 to -2 to preserve the balance of zero in ZnO.

Oxidation-reduction reactions (redox for short) may always be recognized by computing the valences of all the elements in each substance. If one of these has undergone a change, then the reaction is a redox reaction. If there is no such change, then the reaction is not a redox reaction.

In the following illustrations the oxidation numbers of the elements are written in parentheses. The equations are skeleton equations and not balanced.

$$\overset{(+2)\ (-2)}{\text{Ca O}} + \overset{(+1)(-2)}{\text{H}_2\text{ O}} \to \overset{(+2)\ (-2)(+1)}{\text{Ca (O H)}_2} \qquad \text{(not redox)}$$

$$\overset{(+1)(+5)(-2)}{\text{Ag N O}_3} + \overset{(+1)(-1)}{\text{Na Cl}} \to \overset{(+1)(-1)}{\text{Ag Cl}}\downarrow + \overset{(+1)(+5)(-2)}{\text{Na N O}_3} \qquad \text{(not redox)}$$

$$\overset{(0)}{\text{Al}} + \overset{(0)}{\text{O}_2} \to \overset{(+3)(-2)}{\text{Al}_2\text{ O}_3} \qquad \text{(redox)}$$

$$\overset{(+2)(-2)}{\text{N O}} + \overset{(0)}{\text{O}_2} \to \overset{(+4)(-2)}{\text{N O}_2} \qquad \text{(redox)}$$

$$\overset{(0)}{\text{Cu}} + \overset{(+1)(+5)(-2)}{\text{H N O}_3} \to \overset{(+2)(+5)\ (-2)}{\text{Cu (N O}_3)_2} + \overset{(+2)(-2)}{\text{N O}} + \overset{(+1)(-2)}{\text{H}_2\text{ O}} \qquad \text{(redox)}$$

$$\overset{(+6)\ (-2)}{\text{Cr O}_4^{-2}} + \overset{(+1)\ (-2)}{\text{H}_3\text{ O}^{+1}} \rightleftarrows \overset{(+6)\ (-2)}{\text{Cr}_2\text{ O}_7^{-2}} + \overset{(+1)(-2)}{\text{H}_2\text{ O}} \qquad \text{(not redox)}$$

$$\overset{(0)}{\text{Cl}_2} + \overset{(+1)(-2)}{\text{H}_2\text{ O}} \rightleftarrows \overset{(+1)(-1)}{\text{H Cl}} + \overset{(+1)(+1)(-2)}{\text{H Cl O}} \qquad \text{(redox)}$$

$$\overset{(0)}{\text{Zn}^0} + \overset{(+1)}{\text{Ag}^{+1}} \to \overset{(+2)}{\text{Zn}^{+2}} + \overset{(0)}{\text{Ag}^0}\downarrow \qquad \text{(redox)}$$

4. Redox Reactions as Electron Transfers

The changes in oxidation numbers can be related to transfers of electrons and consequent change in charge. Thus when metallic Zn reacts with Ag^{+1} ions to liberate free Ag metal and produce Zn^{+2} ions, we can look at this process from the point of view of electron transfer.

The Zn metal (zero oxidation number) went to the Zn^{+2} ion ($+2$ oxidation number). This occurred by each Zn atom's losing 2 negatively charged electrons:

$$Zn^0 \to Zn^{+2} + 2e^{-1}$$

Similarly:

$$Ag^{+1} \to Ag^0 + 1e^{-1}$$

We will soon see that all such changes in oxidation number can be associated with transfers of electrons. We thus expand our definition.

Definitions: Oxidation (the increase in oxidation number) is a loss of electrons. *Reduction* (the decrease in oxidation number) is a gain of electrons.

This association of oxidation and reduction with transfer of electrons leads to a completely consistent scheme for discussing these reactions. It has the added advantage of permitting us to write individual equations to represent the oxidation and reduction and thus directly indicating the electron transfers. Finally, it enables us to include in a single scheme not only redox reactions but also the individual electrode reactions which occur in electrolysis.

For these reasons, the concept of electron transfer has become a most valuable one for discussing redox reactions, and we shall now proceed to a discussion of the conventions employed in writing these individual electron-transfer equations or ion-electron equations as they are called.

5. Ion-Electron Reactions

We shall now develop a method of separating a skeleton redox equation into a pair of ion-electron equations representing the oxidation and the reduction. The procedure is as follows:

1. The skeleton equation must be given! This is generally obtained from direct experiment.
2. Write oxidation numbers above each element.
3. Pick out the ion, molecule, or radical containing the element undergoing oxidation and the ion, molecule, or radical containing the element in its oxidized form. This pair will form the basis for the oxidation equation.
4. Select the similar pair of substances containing the element undergoing reduction and its reduced form. These will form the basis for the reduction equation.
5. The individual oxidation and reduction equations are now balanced; first chemically and finally electrically by means of electrons.

Example:

$$\overset{(0)}{Al} + \overset{(+2)(-1)}{Cu\ Cl_2} \rightarrow \overset{(+3)(-1)}{Al\ Cl_3} + \overset{(0)}{\underline{Cu}} \qquad \text{(skeleton equation)}$$

Al undergoes oxidation, going from zero to $+3$. Cu undergoes reduction, going from $+2$ to zero. We write:

Oxidation: $\qquad\qquad\qquad\qquad Al \rightarrow Al^{+3} \qquad\qquad\qquad$ (skeleton equation)

Note: We write the Al^{+3} ion rather than the $AlCl_3$ molecule, since it is the Al^{+3} ion that exists in water solution.

This equation is balanced chemically. It may be balanced electrically by adding 3 electrons (e^{-1}):

Oxidation: $Al \rightarrow Al^{+3} + 3e^{-1}$ (balanced ion-electron equation)

The equation means: 1 mole of Al (or 1 atom Al) yields 1 mole of Al^{+3} ion (or 1 ion of Al^{+3}) plus 3 moles of electrons (or 3 electrons). It is balanced electrically since the total charge is the same on both sides. In a similar fashion we can write:

Reduction: $2e^{-1} + Cu^{+2} \rightarrow Cu$ (balanced)

Example:

$$\overset{(+1)(-2)}{H_2 \ S} + \overset{(0)}{Cl_2} \rightarrow \overset{(+1)(-1)}{H \ Cl} + \overset{(0)}{S}$$ (skeleton equation)
$$\text{(reaction in water solution)}$$

Proceeding as before, S is oxidized from -2 to zero.   Cl is reduced from 0 to -1.

Reduction: $Cl_2 \rightarrow Cl^{-1}$ (skeleton equation)

Note: We write Cl_2 since it is Cl_2 gas which contains the Cl. Also, we write Cl^{-1} rather than HCl, since in water solution, HCl is ionized into Cl^{-1} ions.

The balanced equation is:

Reduction: $2e^{-1} + Cl_2 \rightarrow 2Cl^{-1}$

The oxidation equation is:

Oxidation: $H_2S \rightarrow S$ (skeleton equation)

Note: We write H_2S rather than S^{-2} ion, since H_2S is a weak electrolyte.

To balance this equation chemically we must add $2H^{+1}$ ions to the right side. (We will write H^{+1} instead of H_3O^{+1} for the sake of simplicity.) A look at the skeleton equation tells us that hydrogen ion is indeed a product since the acid HCl is produced.   Thus

Oxidation: $H_2S \rightarrow S + 2H^{+1}$

To balance electrically we add 2 electrons.

Oxidation: $H_2S \rightarrow S + 2H^{+1} + 2e^{-1}$ (balanced)

---

6. Single Ion-Electron Reactions

From the preceding we see that it is always possible to write a single ion-electron equation if we know the state of the substance before and after the transfer of electrons.

Example: Write a balanced ion-electron equation for the oxidation of $FeCl_2$ to $FeCl_3$.

Answer:

$$Fe^{+2} \rightarrow Fe^{+3} + 1e^{-1}$$ (oxidation)

Example: Write a balanced equation for the reduction of $Hg(NO_3)_2$ to $Hg_2(NO_3)_2$.

Answer:

$$2e^{-1} + 2Hg^{+2} \rightarrow Hg_2^{+2} \qquad \text{(reduction)}$$

Example: Write a balanced equation for the oxidation of H_2SO_4 to $H_2S_2O_8$.

Answer:

$$2SO_4^{-2} \rightarrow S_2O_8^{-2} + 2e^{-1} \qquad \text{(oxidation)}$$

Example: Write a balanced equation for the oxidation of Cr^{+3} ions to CrO_4^{-2} ions.

Answer:

Oxidation: $\qquad\qquad Cr^{+3} \rightarrow CrO_4^{-2} \qquad\qquad$ (skeleton)

Now clearly this cannot be balanced chemically unless we add something to supply the O atoms for the CrO_4^{-2} ion. In such cases we use the ever-present H_2O to supply this oxygen. But we will have H left over. We leave this as H^{+1} ions. The equation thus becomes:

Oxidation: $\qquad Cr^{+3} + 4H_2O \rightarrow CrO_4^{-2} + 8H^{+1}$ (balanced chemically)

To balance electrically we need 3 electrons:

Oxidation: $\qquad Cr^{+3} + 4H_2O \rightarrow CrO_4^{-2} + 8H^{+1} + 3e^{-1} \qquad$ (balanced)

In the above examples, we can see illustrated a few conventions which are used in writing ion-electron equations. These are applicable to water solutions with which we shall be dealing exclusively.

1. Always write the element in the form of the species which actually exists in water solution (ion or molecule).
2. Since H^{+1}, OH^{-1}, and H_2O always exist in water solution, we can use them to aid in balancing equations chemically.

Example: Write the equation for the oxidation of H_2O to O_2 gas.

Answer:

Oxidation: $\qquad\qquad H_2O \rightarrow O_2\uparrow \qquad\qquad$ (skeleton equation)

$$2H_2O \rightarrow O_2\uparrow \qquad\qquad \text{(step 1)}$$

$$2H_2O \rightarrow O_2\uparrow + 4H^{+1} \qquad\qquad \text{(step 2)}$$

Oxidation: $\qquad 2H_2O \rightarrow O_2 + 4H^{+1} + 4e^{-1} \qquad\qquad$ (balanced)

Example: Write the equation for the reduction of $KMnO_4$ to $MnCl_2$.

Answer:

Oxidized species: $\overset{(+7)}{MnO_4^{-1}}$ ions $\qquad\qquad\qquad$ *Reduced species:* $\overset{(+2)}{Mn^{+2}}$ ions

Reduction: $MnO_4^{-1} \rightarrow Mn^{+2}$ (skeleton equation)

$$MnO_4^{-1} \rightarrow Mn^{+2} + 4H_2O$$ (step 1)

$$8H^{+1} + MnO_4^{-1} \rightarrow Mn^{+2} + 4H_2O$$ (step 2)

$$5e^{-1} + 8H^{+1} + MnO_4^{-1} \rightarrow Mn^{+2} + 4H_2O$$ (balanced)

Do problem 2 at the end of the chapter.

7. Balancing Redox Equations

The principle of equivalence may now be stated for redox equations:

The number of electrons produced by an oxidation must be equal to the number of electrons used by the reduction.

This principle now enables us to balance redox equations.   The procedure is as follows:

1. Label the oxidation states of all elements in the skeleton equation.
2. From these, pick out the oxidized and reduced forms of each element undergoing changes and write individual, balanced ion-electron equations for the oxidation and reduction.
3. Add the oxidation and reduction steps in such fashion that the electrons cancel on both sides.
4. Cancel quantities that appear on both sides.

Example: Balance the following skeleton equation:

$$HCl + KMnO_4 \rightarrow Cl_2\uparrow + KCl + MnCl_2 + H_2O$$

Answer: Oxidation: Cl^{-1} (-1) goes to Cl_2 (gas) (0).
Reduction: Mn ($+7$) in the MnO_4^{-1} ion goes to the Mn^{+2} ion ($+2$).

Oxidation		*Reduction*	
(step 1)	$Cl^{-1} \rightarrow Cl_2$	$MnO_4^{-1} \rightarrow Mn^{+2}$	(step 1)
(step 2)	$2Cl^{-1} \rightarrow Cl_2$	$MnO_4^{-1} \rightarrow Mn^{+2} + 4H_2O$	(step 2)
(balanced)	$2Cl^{-1} \rightarrow Cl_2 + 2e^{-1}$	$8H^{+1} + MnO_4^{-1} \rightarrow Mn^{+2} + 4H_2O$	(step 3)
		$5e^{-1} + 8H^{+1} + MnO_4^{-1} \rightarrow Mn^{+2} + 4H_2O$	(balanced)

We note now that each oxidation releases $2e^{-1}$ and each reduction requires $5e^{-1}$.   Thus 5 oxidation steps will provide just enough electrons (10) for 2 reduction steps.   We thus combine them in the ratio of 5 to 2:

Oxidation: $2Cl^{-1} \rightarrow Cl_2 + 2e^{-1}$ (multiplying by 5)

Reduction: $5e^{-1} + 8H^{+1} + MnO_4^{-1} \rightarrow Mn^{+2} + 4H_2O$ (multiplying by 2) and add:

$$10e^{-1} + 10Cl^{-1} + 16H^{+1} + 2MnO_4^{-1} \rightarrow 5Cl_2 + 2Mn^{+2} + 8H_2O + 10e^{-1}$$

and, canceling electrons, we obtain the balanced ionic equation:

$$10Cl^{-1} + 16H^{+1} + 2MnO_4^{-1} \rightarrow 5Cl_2 + 2Mn^{+2} + 8H_2O$$

Generally the balanced ionic equation is all we want or will use since the ionic equation tells us the ions and molecules that actually take part in the reaction. Thus the above equation says that $2MnO_4^{-1}$ ions are needed for 16 H^{+1} ions and 10 Cl^{-1} ions. The K^{+1} ions provided by $KMnO_4$ do not actually take part in the reaction, and we could equally well have used $NaMnO_4$ or $LiMnO_4$ to provide the MnO_4^{-1} ions. Similarly, although in the original equation HCl is the source of H^{+1} ions and Cl^{-1} ions, the ionic equation tells us that, of 16 molecules of HCl, only 10 Cl^{-1} ions and 16 H^{+1} ions will be used. The extra 6 Cl^{-1} do not take part in the reaction, and, indeed, we see from the skeleton equation that some of the original Cl^{-1} ions end up in KCl and $MnCl_2$. These latter Cl^{-1} ions have not been oxidized!

Example: Balance the following skeleton equation:

$$SO_2 + Na_2Cr_2O_7 + H_2SO_4 \rightarrow Na_2SO_4 + Cr_2(SO_4)_3 + H_2O$$

Answer: Oxidation: S($+4$) in SO_2 goes to S($+6$) in the SO_4^{-2} ion.
Reduction: Cr($+6$) in the $Cr_2O_7^{-2}$ ion goes to Cr($+3$) in the Cr^{+3} ion.

	Oxidation	Reduction	
(step 1)	$SO_2 \rightarrow SO_4^{-2}$	$Cr_2O_7^{-2} \rightarrow Cr^{+3}$	(step 1)
(step 2)	$2H_2O + SO_2 \rightarrow SO_4^{-2}$	$Cr_2O_7^{-2} \rightarrow 2Cr^{+3} + 7H_2O$	(step 2)
(step 3)	$2H_2O + SO_2 \rightarrow SO_4^{-2} + 4H^{+1}$	$14H^{+1} + Cr_2O_7^{-2} \rightarrow 2Cr^{+3} + 7H_2O$	(step 3)
(balanced)	$2H_2O + SO_2 \rightarrow SO_4^{-2} + 4H^{+1} + 2e^{-1}$	$6e^{-1} + 14H^{+1} + Cr_2O_7^{-2} \rightarrow 2Cr^{+3} + 7H_2O$	(balanced)

Oxidation: $2H_2O + SO_2 \rightarrow SO_4^{-2} + 4H^{+1} + 2e^{-1}$ ($\times 3$)

Reduction: $6e^{-1} + 14H^{+1} + Cr_2O_7^{-2} \rightarrow 2Cr^{+3} + 7H_2O$ ($\times 1$)

and add

$$6e^{-1} + 6H_2O + 3SO_2 + 14H^{+1} + Cr_2O_7^{-2} \rightarrow$$
$$3SO_4^{-2} + 12H^{+1} + 2Cr^{+3} + 7H_2O + 6e^{-1}$$

Canceling $6e^{-1}$ and subtracting $6H_2O$ and $12H^{+1}$ from both sides:

$$3SO_2 + 2H^{+1} + Cr_2O_7^{-2} \rightarrow 3SO_4^{-2} + 2Cr^{+3} + H_2O$$

Note: If we add $2Na^{+1}$ and $1SO_4^{-2}$ to both sides we can obtain the balanced molecular equation:

$$3SO_2 + H_2SO_4 + Na_2Cr_2O_7 \rightarrow Na_2SO_4 + Cr_2(SO_4)_3 + H_2O$$

Do problem 3 at the end of the chapter.

8. Principle of Equivalence for Redox Reactions

If we have the balanced ionic equation we can do problems with them just as we have done before.   However, the principle of equivalence permits us to do such calculations without the balanced equation if only we know the oxidized and reduced states of each substance. The principle is:

Equal numbers of equivalents of oxidizing and reducing substance will always react with each other to produce equal numbers of equivalents of oxidized and reduced products.

To use this law we must reexamine what we mean by an equivalent of oxidizing or reducing agent.

Definition: The *equivalent weight* of a substance taking part in a redox reaction is that weight of the substance which will accept (oxidized form) or lose (reduced form) 1 mole of electrons in the reaction.

Algebraically:

$$\text{Equivalent weight} = \frac{\text{Molecular weight}}{\text{Moles of electrons transferred per mole of substance}}$$

Definition:

Redox valence = Number of moles of electrons transferred per mole of substance

Combing these definitions, we can write a relation connecting the units of equivalents with units of moles for a redox material:

$$\text{Redox equivalents} = \text{Moles} \times \text{Redox valence}$$

Thus when 1 mole of Zn metal goes to 1 mole of the Zn^{+2} ion, it loses 2 moles of electrons.   Thus 1 equivalent of Zn metal will be half a mole.   Similarly in the reverse reaction (the reduction) $\frac{1}{2}$ mole of the Zn^{+2} ion = 1 equivalent Zn^{+2} ion.   The following table gives a number of such relations:

Oxidized Form	Reduced Form	Number of Equivalents in 1 Mole	
		Oxidized Form	Reduced Form
Cu^{+2} ion	Cu (metal)	2	2
Fe^{+3} ion	Fe^{+2} ion	1	1
Fe^{+3} ion	Fe (metal)	3	3
Cl_2 (gas)	Cl^{-1} ion	2	1
CrO_4^{-2} ion	Cr^{+3} ion	3	3
O_2 (gas)	H_2O	4	2
$Cr_2O_7^{-2}$ ion	Cr^{+3} ion	6	3
NO_3^{-1} ion	NO (gas)	3	3

We observe that the redox valence (the number of equivalents per mole) depends on the particular reaction. Thus, when the Fe^{+3} ion is reduced to the Fe^{+2} ion, it has a valence of 1, but when the Fe^{+3} ion is reduced to the Fe metal, it has a valence of 3. This is a great cause of ambiguity, so much so that many chemists no longer use the units of equivalents in speaking of redox reactions. If, however, the nature of the reaction is understood, the ambiguity disappears. We must always state the reaction when we speak of redox equivalents.

The above definition of equivalent provides us with a conversion factor for going from units of equivalents to units of moles, the conversion factor being the redox valence—that is, the number of moles of electrons transferred per mole of material.

Do problem 4 at the end of the chapter.

9. Redox Calculations

We are now ready to use our principle of equivalence to do chemical calculations. To refresh his memory, the reader should review Chapter VIII on solutions.

Example: How many grams of HCl will be oxidized to free Cl_2 by 60 g. of K_2CrO_4, the latter producing Cr^{+3} ions.

Answer: The valence change of the Cl is 1 (from -1 to 0). The valence change of the Cr is 3 (from $+6$ to $+3$). Applying our general method for such problems:

$$60 \text{ g. } K_2CrO_4 = 60 \text{ g. } K_2CrO_4 \left(\frac{1 \text{ mole } K_2CrO_4}{194 \text{ g. } K_2CrO_4}\right) \times \left(\frac{3 \text{ eq. } K_2CrO_4}{1 \text{ mole } K_2CrO_4}\right)$$

$$\times \left(\frac{1 \text{ eq. } HCl}{1 \text{ eq. } K_2CrO_4}\right) \times \left(\frac{1 \text{ mole } HCl}{1 \text{ eq. } HCl}\right) \times \left(\frac{36.5 \text{ g. } HCl}{1 \text{ mole } HCl}\right)$$

$$= \frac{60 \times 3 \times 36.5}{194} \text{ g. } HCl = 33.9 \text{ g. } HCl$$

Example: How many liters STP of O_2 will be reduced to H_2O by 30 g. of SO_2 in acid solution? (SO_2 goes to the SO_4^{-2} ion.)

Answer: Valence change of O is 2 (from 0 to -2). Valence change of S is 2 (from $+4$ to $+6$)

$$30 \text{ g. } SO_2 = 30 \text{ g. } SO_2 \left(\frac{1 \text{ mole } SO_2}{64 \text{ g. } SO_2}\right)\left(\frac{2 \text{ eq. } SO_2}{1 \text{ mole } SO_2}\right)\left(\frac{1 \text{ eq. } O_2}{1 \text{ eq. } SO_2}\right)$$

$$\left(\frac{1 \text{ mole } O_2}{4 \text{ eq. } O_2}\right)\left(\frac{22.4 \text{ l. STP } O_2}{1 \text{ mole } O_2}\right)$$

$$= \frac{30 \times 2 \times 22.4}{64 \times 4} \text{ l. STP } O_2 = 5.25 \text{ l. STP } O_2$$

Note: There are 4 equivalents of O in 1 mole of O_2 since there are 2 moles of O in 1 mole of O_2 and each O has a valence of 2.

Doing problems dealing with water solutions, we employ the same methods as we used previously.

Example: How many milliliters of 1.36 M $CuSO_4$ solution will react with 1.7 g. Zn metal, the products being Cu metal and Zn^{+2} ions?

Answer:

$$1.70 \text{ g. } Zn = 1.70 \text{ g. } Zn \left(\frac{1 \text{ mole } Zn}{65.4 \text{ g. } Zn}\right)\left(\frac{2 \text{ eq. } Zn}{1 \text{ mole } Zn}\right)\left(\frac{1 \text{ eq. } Cu^{+2}}{1 \text{ eq. } Zn}\right)$$

$$\left(\frac{1 \text{ mole } Cu^{+2}}{2 \text{ eq. } Cu^{+2}}\right) \times \left(\frac{1 \text{ l. soln.}}{1.36 \text{ moles } Cu^{+2}}\right)\left(\frac{1000 \text{ ml.}}{1 \text{ l.}}\right)$$

$$= \frac{1.70 \times 2 \times 1000}{2 \times 65.4 \times 1.36} \text{ ml. soln.} = 18.1 \text{ ml. soln.}$$

Example: How many milliliters of 0.68 M $KMnO_4$ will react with 42 ml. of 0.16 M $NaHSO_3$, the products being Mn^{+2} ions and SO_4^{-2} ions.

Answer: Let us call the $KMnO_4$ solution A, and $NaHSO_3$ solution B.

$$42 \text{ ml. soln. } B = 42 \text{ ml. soln. } B \left(\frac{0.16 \text{ mmole } SO_3^{-2}}{1 \text{ ml. soln. } B}\right)\left(\frac{2 \text{ meq. } SO_3^{-2}}{1 \text{ mmole } SO_3^{-2}}\right)$$

$$\left(\frac{1 \text{ meq. } MnO_4^{-1}}{1 \text{ meq. } SO_3^{-2}}\right) \times \left(\frac{1 \text{ mmole } MnO_4^{-1}}{5 \text{ meq. } MnO_4^{-1}}\right)\left(\frac{1 \text{ ml. soln. } A}{0.68 \text{ mmole } MnO_4^{-1}}\right)$$

$$= \frac{42 \times 0.16 \times 2}{5 \times 0.68} \text{ ml. soln. } A = 3.95 \text{ ml. } KMnO_4$$

Note the use of millimoles and milliequivalents here for convenience.

Example: 15.8 ml. of 0.42 M $FeCl_3$ will oxidize 38.0 ml. of a solution of CaI_2 to I_2 (element).   If the $FeCl_3$ is reduced to Fe^{+2}, what is the concentration of the KI solution?

Answer: Call the $FeCl_3$ solution A, and the KI solution B.

$$15.8 \text{ ml. soln. } A = 15.8 \text{ ml. soln. } A \left(\frac{0.42 \text{ mmoles } Fe^{+3}}{1 \text{ ml. soln. } A} \right) \left(\frac{1 \text{ meq. } Fe^{+3}}{1 \text{ mmole } Fe^{+3}} \right)$$

$$\times \left(\frac{1 \text{ meq. } I^{-1}}{1 \text{ meq. } Fe^{+3}} \right) \left(\frac{1 \text{ mmole } I^{-1}}{1 \text{ meq. } I^{-1}} \right)$$

$$= 15.8 \times 0.42 \text{ mmoles } I^{-1} = 6.64 \text{ mmoles } I^{-1}$$

$$\text{Molarity} = \frac{\text{mmoles } CaI_2}{\text{ml. soln.}} = \frac{6.64 \text{ mmoles } I^{-1} \left(\dfrac{1 \text{ mmole } CaI_2}{2 \text{ mmoles } I^{-1}} \right)}{38.0 \text{ ml. soln.}}$$

$$= \frac{6.64}{2 \times 38.0} \frac{\text{mmoles } CaI_2}{\text{ml. soln.}} = 0.087 \ M \ CaI_2$$

10. Problems

1. Calculate the oxidation numbers of each element in the following:

(a) Cr_2O_3.	(e) K_2O_2 (peroxide).	(i) $HClO_3$.
(b) HNO_2.	(f) MnO_2.	(j) K_2MnO_4.
(c) SbH_3.	(g) H_3PO_4.	(k) $Na_2B_4O_7$.
(d) Na_2SO_4.	(h) H_3PO_3.	(l) $H_2S_2O_7$.

2. Write balanced ion-electron equations for each of the following:
  (a) Oxidation of H_2S to K_2SO_3.
  (b) Oxidation of Bi metal to Na_3BiO_3.
  (c) Reduction of MnO_2 to Mn^{+2}.
  (d) Reduction of HPO_4^{-2} to HPO_3^{-2}.
  (e) Oxidation of NH_3 to NO.
  (f) Oxidation of Cl^{-1} to ClO_2 gas.
  (g) Reduction of $Cr_2O_7^{-2}$ to Cr metal.
  (h) Oxidation of NO gas to HNO_3.

3. Write balanced ionic equations for each of the following reactions (add H_2O if needed):
  (a) $NO_2 + HClO \rightarrow HNO_3 + HCl$
  (b) $Na_2O_2 (s) + CrCl_3 \rightarrow Na_2CrO_4 + NaCl$
  (c) $Cu + HNO_3 \rightarrow Cu(NO_3)_2 + NO + H_2O$
  (d) $Mg + HNO_3 \rightarrow Mg(NO_3)_2 + N_2 + H_2O$
  (e) $Cu + H_2SO_4 \rightarrow CuSO_4 + SO_2 + H_2O$
  (f) $Zn + HNO_3 \rightarrow Zn(NO_3)_2 + NH_4NO_3 + H_2O$
  (g) $NaIO_3 + H_2S \rightarrow I_2 + Na_2SO_3$
  (h) $CuS + HNO_3 \rightarrow Cu(NO_3)_2 + NO_2 + H_2O + S$
  (i) $HCl + HNO_3 \rightarrow NOCl + Cl_2 + H_2O$
  (j) $CuCl_2 + KCN \rightarrow K_2Cu(CN)_3 + (CN)_2\uparrow + KCl$

4. Make the following conversions:

(a) 8 equivalents of $KMnO_4$ to moles of $KMnO_4$ (product is Mn^{+2}).

(b) 0.3 mole of HCl to equivalent of HCl (product is Cl_2).

(c) 0.46 equivalent of Zn metal to grams of Zn (product is Zn^{+2}).

(d) 14.2 g. of $KMnO_4$ to equivalents of $KMnO_4$ (product is MnO_2).

(e) 12 mg. of $KMnO_4$ to milliequivalents of $KMnO_4$ (product is Mn^{+2}).

(f) 68 mmoles $K_2Cr_2O_7$ to equivalents of $K_2Cr_2O_7$ (product is Cr^{+3}).

(g) 8.4 meq. HNO_3 to milligrams of HNO_3 (product is NO).

5. How many grams of I_2 can be oxidized to KIO_3 by 16 g. of $HClO$? (Product is HCl.)

6. How many cubic centimeters STP of O_2 gas are needed to oxidize 1.8 g. of KI in solution to I_2? (O_2 is reduced to H_2O.)

7. How many liters STP of Cl_2 gas can be made from NaCl by oxidation with 24 g. of $K_2Cr_2O_7$? (Product is Cr^{+3}.)

8. How many milligrams of CuS will be oxidized to free S by 210 mg. of HNO_3? (Product is NO gas.)

9. 90 ml. of a 0.43 M solution of H_2O_2 will oxidize 64 ml. of a solution of NaI to I_2. If the H_2O_2 is reduced to H_2O, what is the concentration of the NaI?

10. 16.4 ml. of a 0.33 M solution of $K_2Cr_2O_7$ will oxidize 24.0 ml. of a solution of $FeCl_2$ to $FeCl_3$. If Cr^{+3} is the product what is the molarity of the $FeCl_2$ solution?

11. How many milliliters of a 0.24 M solution of Na_2SO_3 will be oxidized to Na_2SO_4 by 180 ml. of 0.32 M $KMnO_4$ solution? (The product is Mn^{+2}.)

12. How many milliliters of a 0.085 M solution of $Na_2S_2O_3$ will be oxidized to $Na_2S_4O_6$ by a 180 ml. of a 0.16 M solution of $KClO_3$? (The product is the Cl^{-1} ion.)

CHAPTER XVI

Predicting Redox Reactions

1. Reversibility of Redox Reactions

Any single ion-electron equation is reversible. That is, under the proper circumstances it can be made to proceed in either direction. Thus the equation for the oxidation of Zn metal to Zn^{+2} ion:

(oxidation) $$Zn^0 \rightleftarrows Zn^{+2} + 2e^{-1}$$ (reduction)

The reverse reaction, Zn^{+2} ion going to Zn metal, is a reduction.

If we put Zn metal in $CuSO_4$ solution the Zn will be oxidized to the Zn^{+2} ion by the Cu^{+2} ion which in turn goes to Cu metal.

$$Zn^0 + Cu^{+2} \rightarrow Zn^{+2} + Cu^0$$

If, however, we put a piece of Mg metal in a solution of $ZnSO_4$, then the Zn^{+2} will be reduced to Zn metal while the Mg metal is itself oxidized to Mg^{+2} ion.

$$Mg^0 + Zn^{+2} \rightarrow Zn^0 + Mg^{+2}$$

The familiar electromotive series of metals is nothing more or less than an expression of the relative tendency of the metals to displace each other from ionic solution. The active metals at the top of the list (Li, Na, K, Mg, etc.) will displace the less active metals below them. That is, the tendency of Li metal to lose an electron ($Li^0 \rightarrow Li^{+1} + 1e^{-1}$) and become Li^{+1} ion is greater than the tendency of any other metal to lose an electron. Or, putting it in reverse, Li^{+1} ion has the least attraction for electrons of any of the metal ions.

This tendency of metals to lose electrons (become oxidized) can be measured quantitatively as well as qualitatively.

2. Measurement of Oxidation Potentials—A Chemical Battery

If a piece of Zn rod is placed in a solution containing Zn^{+2} ions (e.g., $ZnCl_2$) and a piece of Cu rod is placed in a solution containing

174

Cu^{+2} ions (e.g., $CuCl_2$) and the two solutions are connected by a tube containing any electrolyte (e.g., KCl), then there will be a voltage between the Zn and Cu rods.   If a wire is connected to the two rods, a current will flow through it.   The current will continue to flow until all the Zn metal or all the Cu^{+2} ions are exhausted.   This is an example of a chemical battery.   Electrons flow through the wire from the cathode to anode.

In the solution Cl^{-1} ions (or other anions) move from the $CuCl_2$ beaker where Cu^{+2} ions are disappearing, through the salt bridge, to the $ZnCl_2$ beaker to neutralize the Zn^{+2} ions which are being formed.

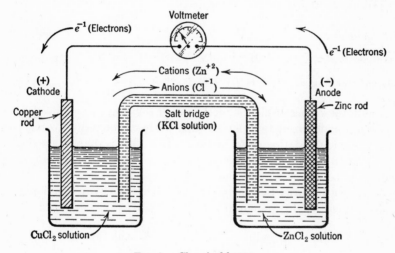

FIG. 3.   Chemical battery.

At the cathode:	$Cu^{+2} + 2e^{-1} \rightarrow Cu$ (metal)	(reduction)
At the anode:	Zn (metal) $\rightarrow Zn^{+2} + 2e^{-1}$	(oxidation)

The only function of the salt bridge is to allow the anions to move and thus complete the circuit.   (*Note:* Cations (+) move in the reverse direction.)

The voltage which is measured in this set-up is a direct measure of the tendency of the Zn metal to displace Cu^{+2} from solution.   If a more active metal than Zn is used, then the voltage is higher.   If a less active metal than Cu is used, the voltage will also be higher.

The greater the difference in activity between two metals, the greater will be their voltage in a chemical battery.

The information gained by measuring such voltages can be expressed in terms of a chart if we can choose a standard against which to measure such voltages.

3. Standard Oxidation Potentials—The Hydrogen Electrode

The standard which has been chosen is the hydrogen electrode. A beaker of a strong acid containing $C_{H_3O^{+1}} = 1.00\ M$ is taken. A piece of rough platinum foil is placed in this solution, and hydrogen at 1 atm. pressure is bubbled through the solution. This constitutes the hydrogen electrode. If we replaced the beaker of $CuCl_2$ and Cu metal in Figure 3 by this hydrogen electrode and measured the voltage, we would find that it would be precisely 0.762 v. (if the Zn^{+2} ion concentration were 1 M). The zinc is more active than hydrogen and tends to displace it from solution. In this case we can write the electrode reaction:

At the anode: $\qquad\qquad Zn^0 \rightarrow Zn^{+2} + 2e^{-1}$ $\qquad\qquad$ (oxidation)

At the cathode: $\qquad\quad 2H^{+1} + 2e^{-1} \rightarrow H_2{}^0\uparrow$ $\qquad\qquad$ (reduction)

Overall reaction: $\quad Zn^0 + 2H^{+1} \rightarrow H_2{}^0\uparrow + Zn^{+2}$

The total voltage which is measured (0.762 v.) can be looked upon as being made up of two parts. One is the voltage due to reaction at the anode (oxidation of Zn metal). The other is the voltage due to the reaction at the cathode (reduction of the H^{+1} ion). We can never measure the absolute potential of either reaction separately. However, if we arbitrarily take as our standard that the hydrogen potential is zero, then the zinc potential must be +0.762 v.

$$E(\text{total}) = E(\text{reduction of } H^{+1}) + E(\text{oxidation of Zn})$$

Thus: $\quad \underset{\text{(observed)}}{0.762\ \text{v.}} = \underset{\text{(choice)}}{0} \qquad + E(\text{oxidation of Zn})$

Potentials measured in this manner against the hydrogen electrode, at 25°C. and with all concentrations = 1 M, are called standard oxidation potentials ($E°_{ox.}$). They are positive if the reaction displaces H^{+1} from solution as H_2 gas. They are negative if the H_2 gas is more active and displaces the other substance.

Table XV shows some potentials measured in this manner.

This table will now give the potential for any combination of electrode couples. Thus, if we measure the $Zn|Zn^{+2}$ electrode against the $Sn|Sn^{+2}$ electrode, the total voltage is the algebraic difference between their standard oxidation potentials:

$$E(\text{total}) = E°_{ox.}(\text{higher}) - E°_{ox.}(\text{lower})$$

$$E(Zn|Zn^{+2}||Sn^{+2}|Sn) = (+0.762) - (+0.136) = 0.626\ \text{v.}$$

TABLE XV*
SOME STANDARD OXIDATION POTENTIALS

Oxidation Reaction	$E^\circ_{ox.}$ (Standard Oxidation Potential)
Na $\to$ Na^{+1} + $1e^{-1}$	+2.712 v.
Mg $\to$ Mg^{+2} + $2e^{-1}$	+2.34 v.
Al $\to$ Al^{+3} + $3e^{-1}$	+1.67 v.
Zn $\to$ Zn^{+2} + $2e^{-1}$	+0.762 v.
Fe $\to$ Fe^{+2} + $2e^{-1}$	+0.440 v.
Sn $\to$ Sn^{+2} + $2e^{-1}$	+0.136 v.
H$_2$ $\to$ 2H^{+1} + $2e^{-1}$	0.000 v. (standard)
Cu $\to$ Cu^{+2} + $2e^{-1}$	−0.345 v.
2I^{-1} $\to$ I$_2$ + $2e^{-1}$	−0.535 v.
Fe^{+2} $\to$ Fe^{+3} + $1e^{-1}$	−0.771 v.
Ag $\to$ Ag^{+1} + $1e^{-1}$	−0.800 v.
2Cl^{-1} $\to$ Cl$_2$ + $2e^{-1}$	−1.358 v.

* For the purpose of such a table it doesn't matter which electrode we choose as standard or what value we give it. The differences between two electrodes, which is all we care about, will still be the same.

and since Zn is higher it will displace Sn, the reaction being

$$\text{Zn} + \text{Sn}^{+2} \to \text{Sn} + \text{Zn}^{+2} \quad (E = 0.626 \text{ v.})$$

Example: What voltage will be generated by the battery consisting of a Zn|Zn^{+2} electrode and a Cu|Cu^{+2} electrode?

Answer:

$$E(\text{Zn}|\text{Zn}^{+2}||\text{Cu}^{+2}|\text{Cu}) = (+0.762) - (-0.345)$$

$$= 1.107 \text{ v.}$$

Since Zn is higher, it will displace Cu, the reaction being

$$\text{Zn} + \text{Cu}^{+2} \to \text{Cu} + \text{Zn}^{+2}$$

Do problem 1 at the end of the chapter.

4. Summary

1. *Almost every ion-electron reaction is reversible.*

2. *We can measure the tendency of any ion-electron reaction to proceed as an oxidation or reduction by placing the substances (at a 1 M concentration) in a vessel and measuring the voltage of this electrode compared to the hydrogen electrode.*

3. *If the reaction displaces* H^{+1} *from solution as* H$_2$ *gas then the ion-electron equation goes as an oxidation and its standard potential is positive.* ($E^\circ_{ox.} > 0$)

4. *If the reaction permits* H$_2$ *gas to go into solution as* H^{+1} *ions then the reaction proceeds as a reduction and its standard oxidation potential is negative.* ($E^\circ_{ox.} < 0$)

5. *If any two, individual ion-electron reactions are compared, the one with the higher standard oxidation potential will proceed as an oxidation. The one with the lower standard oxidation potential will be forced to proceed as a reduction.*

6. *The total potential generated by any two ion-electron reactions will be given by the algebraic difference of their standard oxidation potentials.*

From the above we see that if we have a complete list of standard oxidation potentials we can predict the direction that the redox reaction corresponding to these reactions will take.

Example: If a piece of Ag metal is put into a solution of $SnCl_2$, will it displace the Sn?

Answer: The $E^o_{ox.}$ for $Ag|Ag^{+1}$ is -0.800 v. The $E^o_{ox.}$ for $Sn|Sn^{+2}$ is $+0.136$ v. Thus Sn has a greater tendency to go to Sn^{+2} than Ag has to go to Ag^{+1}. No reaction occurs.

---

5. Effect of Concentration—The Nernst Equation

In most laboratory experiments we seldom have solutions at concentrations of 1 M. They are almost always higher or lower. How does this affect our ability to predict reactions?

Let us take a typical ion-electron reaction:

$$Zn \rightleftarrows Zn^{+2} + 2e^{-1} \qquad E^o_{ox.} = +0.762 \text{ v.}$$

What happens if we put a piece of Zn into a solution whose concentration of Zn^{+2} ion is less than 1 M? By applying Le Châtelier's principle we see that the equilibrium is shifted to the right, that is, by removing Zn^{+2} we increase the tendency of the forward reaction. The oxidation tendency is increased. If we were to measure the potential of this electrode with $C_{Zn^{+2}}$ less than 1 M, we would find it higher than $+0.762$ v.

Conversely, if we used a $C_{Zn^{+2}}$ greater than 1 M, we would shift the equilibrium in the opposite direction and *decrease* the oxidation tendency. The observed potential of such an electrode would be smaller.

There is an equation which tells us precisely to what extent the EMF is changed by changing the concentration. It is known as the Nernst equation:

$$E_{ox.}(\text{observed}) = E^o_{ox.} - \frac{2.3RT}{nF} \log \frac{C_{ox.}}{C_{red.}}$$

in which R is the universal gas constant, T is the absolute temperature, F is the number of coulombs in 1 faraday (96,500) and n is the number of electrons transferred in the oxidation. $C_{\text{ox.}}$ is the concentration of the oxidized forms, and $C_{\text{red.}}$ is the concentration of the reduced forms. At room temperature, substituting numbers for the constants, this equation becomes

$$E_{\text{ox.}}(\text{obs.}) = E^{\circ}_{\text{ox.}} - \frac{0.06}{n} \log \frac{C_{\text{ox.}}}{C_{\text{red.}}} \qquad \text{(at 25°C.)}$$

Thus an electrode consisting of a rod of Zn in a solution in which $C_{\text{Zn}^{+2}} = 0.01\ M$ would be ($n = 2$ for this electrode):

$$E_{\text{ox.}}(\text{obs.}) = 0.762 - \frac{0.06}{2} \log 0.01 \qquad (\log 0.01 = -2)$$

$$= 0.762 - 0.03 \times (-2) = 0.762 + 0.06$$

$$= +0.822\ \text{v.}$$

Note: We omit $C_{\text{red.}}$ when the reduced form is a solid, as zinc is.

Example: What is the $E_{\text{ox.}}$ of an electrode consisting of Cu metal in a solution of $1 \times 10^{-6}\ M$ Cu^{+2} ions?

Answer:

$$E_{\text{ox.}}\ (\text{obs.}) = E^{\circ}_{\text{ox.}} - \frac{0.06}{2} \log C_{\text{Cu}^{+2}}$$

$$= -0.345 - 0.03 \log (1 \times 10^{-6})$$

$$= -0.345 - 0.03(-6) = -0.345 + 0.18$$

$$= -0.165\ \text{v.}$$

That is, as we should expect, the oxidation tendency of the reaction $Cu \rightarrow Cu^{+2} + 2e^{-1}$ is increased (the voltage is less negative).

In general we can say that, if n is the number of electrons transferred, then: (1) For every power of 10 by which the concentration of an oxidized species decreases, the $E^{\circ}_{\text{ox.}}$ is increased by $0.06/n$ volts. (2) For every power of 10 by which the concentration of a reduced species decreases, the $E^{\circ}_{\text{ox.}}$ is decreased by $0.06/n$ volts.

6. More Complex Ion-Electron Equations

The treatment we have just described is applicable not only to simple metal|metal ion reactions, but also to any reversible ion-electron equations.

We find for the oxidation of Mn^{+2} to MnO_4^{-1} in acid solution:

$$Mn^{+2} + 4H_2O \rightleftarrows MnO_4^{-1} + 8H^{+1} + 5e^{-1} \qquad (E^{\circ}_{\text{ox.}} = -1.52\ \text{volts})$$

The Nernst equation for such a reaction becomes

$$E_{ox.}(\text{obs.}) = (-1.52) - \frac{0.06}{5} \log \frac{C_{MnO_4^{-1}} \times C^8_{H^{+1}}}{C_{Mn^{+2}}} \quad \text{(as usual, water is left out)}$$

Example: What is the potential of the $Mn^{+2}|MnO_4^{-1}$ oxidation in a solution in which $C_{Mn^{+2}} = 1 \times 10^{-8}\ M$, $C_{H^{+1}} = 1 \times 10^{-5}\ M$, and $C_{MnO_4^{-1}} = 1 \times 10^{-2}\ M$?
Answer:

$$E_{ox.}(\text{obs.}) = -1.52 - \frac{0.06}{5} \log \frac{(1 \times 10^{-2}) \times (1 \times 10^{-5})^8}{1 \times 10^{-8}}$$

$$= -1.52 - \frac{0.06}{5} \log (1 \times 10^{-34})$$

$$= -1.52 - \frac{0.06}{5} \times (-34) = -1.52 + 0.41$$

$$= -1.11 \text{ v.}$$

The tendency of the forward reaction is increased (oxidation). The tendency of the back reaction is decreased (reduction).

Do problem 3 at the end of the chapter.

7. Strength of Oxidizing and Reducing Agents

When an ion-electron reaction has a high positive $E^o_{ox.}$ we interpret this as meaning that it has a great tendency to go forward. Thus

$$Na \rightleftarrows Na^{+1} + 1e^{-1} \quad E^o_{ox.}(Na|Na^{+1}) = +2.71 \text{ v.}$$

We can interpret this as meaning that Na metal is easily oxidized (has small affinity for electrons). When we couple this reaction with any other ion-electron equation having a lower $E^o_{ox.}$.

$$Zn \rightleftarrows Zn^{+2} + 2e^{-1} \quad E^o_{ox.}(Zn|Zn^{+2}) = +0.76 \text{ v.};$$

the higher $E^o_{ox.}$ of the $(Na|Na^{+1})$ reaction causes the $(Zn|Zn^{+2})$ to reverse and proceed as a reduction. This may also be interpreted as saying that Na metal is a *powerful reducing agent* since it causes other ion-electron reactions to proceed backwards, that is, as reductions.

In a similar fashion, the couple $(Cl^{-1}|Cl_2)$ has a low $E^o_{ox.} = -1.36$ v. This means that the reaction $2Cl^{-1} \rightleftarrows Cl_2 + 2e^{-1}$ has a small tendency to proceed in the forward direction and, conversely, a great tendency to proceed in the reverse direction, that is, as a reduction. In terms of electron affinity, we say that the Cl^{-1} ion has a great affinity for its electrons. If we combine this with any ion-electron reaction having a higher $E^o_{ox.}$ (e.g., $2Br^{-1} \rightleftarrows Br_2 + 2e^{-1}$, $E^o_{ox.} = -1.07$ v.), the latter will proceed forward as an oxidation. Thus we would say that the $(Cl^{-1}|Cl_2)$ couple is a *good oxidizing agent* since it causes other couples to proceed as oxidations.

We can summarize these statements:

Standard Oxidation Potential	Tendency of Forward Reaction	Tendency of Reverse Reaction	Affinity for Electrons	Strength as Oxidizing Agent	Strength as Reducing Agent
High (positive)	High	Low	Small	Weak	Strong
Low (negative)	Low	High	Great	Strong	Weak

Do problem 8 at the end of the chapter.

8. Equilibrium Constants for Redox Reactions

When two redox reactions have the same value of $E^o_{ox.}$ they have precisely the same tendency to proceed as oxidations; consequently, if the electrodes are connected as in a chemical battery, no voltage will be observed. If the substances are mixed, no reaction occurs. The system is in a state of equilibrium. If we know the concentrations of all materials, we can calculate the equilibrium constant. Thus it is possible from voltage measurements to calculate the equilibrium constants in a redox reaction.

If we consider the pair of equations:

$$Zn \rightleftarrows Zn^{+2} + 2e^{-1} \qquad E^o_{ox.}(Zn|Zn^{+2}) = +0.76 \text{ v.}$$

$$Fe \rightleftarrows Fe^{+2} + 2e^{-1} \qquad E^o_{ox.}(Fe|Fe^{+2}) = +0.44 \text{ v.}$$

$$E^o(\text{cell}) \qquad = \quad 0.32 \text{ v.}$$

we see that the Zn metal is a more powerful reducing agent and will drive the Fe^{+2} ion out of solution. If we put a piece of Zn metal in a solution containing Fe^{+2} ions, the reaction will be:

$$Zn + Fe^{+2} \rightarrow Zn^{+2} + Fe$$

Suppose now we lower the concentration of Fe^{+2} ions and increase the $C_{Zn^{+2}}$. By Le Châtelier's principle, the above reaction, which is really an equilibrium, shifts to the left. If these concentrations are just right, we can reach equilibrium. The Nernst equation tells us what the concentrations are at this point:

$$E_{obs.}(Zn|Zn^{+2}) = E^o_{ox.}(Zn|Zn^{+2}) - \frac{0.06}{2} \log C_{Zn^{+2}}$$

$$E_{obs.}(Fe|Fe^{+2}) = E^o_{ox.}(Fe|Fe^{+2}) - \frac{0.06}{2} \log C_{Fe^{+2}}$$

When equilibrium is reached,

$$E_{obs.}(Zn|Zn^{+2}) = E_{obs.}(Fe|Fe^{+2})$$

At this point then

$$E^\circ_{ox.}(Zn|Zn^{+2}) - 0.03 \log C_{Zn^{+2}} = E^\circ_{ox.}(Fe|Fe^{+2}) - 0.03 \log C_{Fe^{+2}}$$

or, rearranging,

$$E^\circ_{cell} = E^\circ_{ox.}(Zn|Zn^{+2}) - E^\circ_{ox.}(Fe|Fe^{+2}) = 0.03 \log C_{Zn^{+2}}$$
$$- 0.03 \log C_{Fe^{+2}}$$

or

$$E^\circ_{cell} = 0.03 \log \frac{C_{Zn^{+2}}}{C_{Fe^{+2}}}$$

But $E^\circ_{cell} = 0.32$ v., and substituting:

$$\log \frac{C_{Zn^{+2}}}{C_{Fe^{+2}}} = \frac{0.32}{0.03} = 10.7$$

Taking antilogs:

$$\frac{C_{Zn^{+2}}}{C_{Fe^{+2}}} = 5 \times 10^{+10}$$

But, by definition $C_{Zn^{+2}}/C_{Fe^{+2}} = K_{eq.}$ for the overall reaction. Thus

$$K_{eq.} = 5 \times 10^{10}$$

Since $K_{eq.}$ is so large we can calculate that the reaction proceeds practically to completion.

The preceding illustration shows us how $E^\circ_{ox.}$ can be used to calculate equilibrium constants for redox reactions. Quite generally

$$E^\circ_{cell} = E^\circ_{ox.}(higher) - E^\circ_{ox.}(lower) = \frac{0.06}{n} \log K_{eq.}$$

If we know the individual $E^\circ_{ox.}$, we can always calculate $K_{eq.}$.

Example: Calculate the $K_{eq.}$ for $Sn + Pb^{+2} \rightleftarrows Sn^{+2} + Pb$.

$$E^\circ_{ox.}(Sn|Sn^{+2}) = +0.136 \text{ v.} \quad E^\circ_{ox.}(Pb|Pb^{+2}) = +0.126 \text{ v.}$$

Answer:

$$E^\circ_{cell} = E^\circ_{ox.}(Sn|Sn^{+2}) - E^\circ_{ox.}(Pb|Pb^{+2}) = 0.010 \text{ v.}$$

Thus

$$E^\circ_{cell} = \frac{0.06}{n} \log K_{eq.}$$

Solving for $\log K_{eq.}$ and substituting:

$$\log K_{eq.} = \frac{2}{0.06} \times (0.010) = 0.33$$

Therefore:

$$K_{eq.} = 2.1 \quad \left(\text{By definition, } K_{eq.} = \frac{C_{Sn^{+2}}}{C_{Pb^{+2}}} \right)$$

Example: Calculate the $K_{eq.}$ for $2Cr + 3Fe^{+2} \rightleftarrows 2Cr^{+3} + 3Fe$.

$E^{\circ}_{ox.}(Cr|Cr^{+3}) = +0.71 \text{ v.}; \quad E^{\circ}_{ox.}(Fe|Fe^{+2}) = +0.49 \text{ v.}$

Answer: We must be careful here since the n's are different for the two couples.

$$E^{\circ}_{cell} = E^{\circ}_{ox.}(Cr|Cr^{+3}) - E^{\circ}_{ox.}(Fe|Fe^{+2}) = \frac{0.06}{3} \log C_{Cr^{+3}} - \frac{0.06}{2} \log C_{Fe^{+2}}$$

Then

$$E^{\circ}_{cell} = 0.71 - 0.49 = \frac{0.06}{3 \times 2} \log C^2_{Cr^{+3}} - \frac{0.06}{2 \times 3} \log C^3_{Fe^{+2}}$$

Note: We want the same coefficients before the logs. We can multiply the bottoms by 2 and 3, respectively, and compensate for this by raising the concentrations to the 2 and 3 powers. Thus: $\log x = \frac{1}{2} \log x^2 = \frac{1}{3} \log x^3$.
Then

$$0.22 = 0.01(\log C^2_{Cr^{+3}} - \log C^3_{Fe^{+2}}) = 0.01 \log \frac{C^2_{Cr^{+3}}}{C^3_{Fe^{+2}}}$$

or

$$\log \frac{C^2_{Cr^{+3}}}{C^3_{Fe^{+2}}} = 22 \quad \text{and} \quad \frac{C^2_{Cr^{+3}}}{C^3_{Fe^{+2}}} = 10^{22}$$

Thus:

$$K_{eq.} = \frac{C^2_{Cr^{+3}}}{C^3_{Fe^{+2}}} = 10^{22}$$

The redox $K_{eq.}$ calculated in this fashion can now be used to tell how far towards completion a reaction will go.

Example: A small piece of Cr metal is put into a solution containing $C_{Fe^{+2}} = 1 \times 10^{-3} \, M$ and an excess of Cr^{+3} ions; $C_{Cr^{+3}} = 0.2 \, M$. What will the $C_{Fe^{+2}}$ be when equilibrium is reached? ($E^{\circ}_{ox.}$ are given.)

Answer: The reaction is

$$2Cr + 3Fe^{+2} \rightarrow 2Cr^{+3} + 3Fe$$

From the previous example we see that

$$K_{eq.} = \frac{C^2_{Cr^{+3}}}{C^3_{Fe^{+2}}} = 1 \times 10^{22}$$

As the reaction proceeds towards equilibrium, $C_{Cr^{+3}}$ increases. However, since it is 0.2 M to start with, the additional Cr^{+3} ions from the displacement of Fe^{+2} will not increase this very much (i.e., $\frac{2}{3} \times 1 \times 10^{-3} \, M$ is negligible compared to 0.2). Thus set $C_{Cr^{+3}} = 0.2$. Then

$$C^3_{Fe^{+2}} = \frac{C^2_{Cr^{+2}}}{K_{eq.}} = \frac{(0.2)^2}{1 \times 10^{22}} = 4 \times 10^{-24}$$

Taking cube roots:

$$C_{Fe^{+2}} = 1.6 \times 10^{-8} \text{ mole}/\text{l}.$$

9. Problems

1. From tables of E°_{ox}. calculate the voltages of the following when used as chemical batteries.

  (a) $Zn + 2Ag^{+1} \rightarrow Zn^{+2} + 2Ag$.
  (b) $Mg + Cl_2 \rightarrow Mg^{+2} + 2Cl^{-1}$.
  (c) $Cl_2 + 2Br^{-1} \rightarrow Br_2 + 2Cl^{-1}$.
  (d) $Fe + 2H^{+1} \rightarrow Fe^{+2} + H_2$.
  (e) $3Pb + 8H^{+1} + 2NO_3^{-1} \rightarrow 3Pb^{+2} + 2NO + 4H_2O$.
  (f) $2MnO_4^{-1} + 10Cl^{-1} + 8H^{+1} \rightarrow 2Mn^{+2} + 5Cl_2 + 4H_2O$.
  (g) $Cu + SO_4^{-2} + 2H^{+1} \rightarrow Cu^{+2} + SO_3^{-2} + H_2O$.
  (h) $Cl_2 + H_2O \rightarrow H^{+1} + Cl^{-1} + HClO$.

2. Write K_{eq}. for each of the reactions in problem 1, and compute K_{eq}. from the standard E°_{ox}, using the Nernst equation.

3. Compute the observed potential for the following electrodes:

  (a) $(Zn|Zn^{+2})$ when $C_{Zn^{+2}} = 1 \times 10^{-6} M$. $E^{\circ}_{ox.} = +0.76$ v.
  (b) $(Fe^{+2}|Fe^{+3})$ when $C_{Fe^{+2}} = 2M$; $C_{Fe^{+3}} = 4 \times 10^{-3} M$. $E^{\circ}_{ox.} = -0.77$ v.
  (c) $(Cu|Cu^{+2})$ when $C_{Cu^{+2}} = 1 \times 10^{-14} M$. $E^{\circ}_{ox.} = -0.345$ v.
  (d) $(Cl^{-1}|Cl_2)$ when $C_{Cl^{-1}} = 6 \times 10^{-8} M$. $E^{\circ}_{ox.} = -1.358$ v.

4. What is the oxidation potential of the electrode consisting of a piece of Zn metal placed into a saturated solution of ZnS? $E^{\circ}_{ox.} = +0.76$ v.; $K_{S.P.}(ZnS) = 4.5 \times 10^{-24}$.

5. What is the oxidation potential of the electrode consisting of a piece of Ag metal placed in a saturated solution of AgI? $E^{\circ}_{ox.} = -0.800$ v.; $K_{S.P.}(AgI) = 8.5 \times 10^{-17}$.

6. What is the oxidation potential of the electrode consisting of a piece of Ag metal in a saturated solution of AgI, containing an excess I^{-1} concentration of $1 \times 10^{-2} M$. (Use data from problem 5.) (Hint: Calculate $C_{Ag^{+1}}$ in solution.)

7. A solution containing Cu^{+2} ions is saturated with H_2S at a $C_{H_3O^{+1}}$ of $1 \times 10^{-2} M$. The C_{H_2S} is 0.10 M. What oxidation potential will this solution have when a piece of Cu metal is placed in it? $E^{\circ}_{ox.}(Cu|Cu^{+2}) = -0.35$ v.; $K_{ion}(H_2S)$ overall $= 1.1 \times 10^{-22}$; $K_{S.P.}(CuS) = 4 \times 10^{-36}$.

8. From the Table XV in section 3, which substance is the strongest oxidizing agent? Which substance is the strongest reducing agent? Which set of reactions will give the largest voltage in a chemical battery? Which set of reactions will give the smallest voltage in a chemical battery?

9. (a) What will happen when Fe metal is placed in HCl solution?
  (b) What will happen when Cu metal is placed in HCl solution?
  (c) Will free I_2 oxidize Fe^{+2} ions when placed in a solution?
  (d) What will happen when Cu metal and free iodine are brought together in a solution?

CHAPTER XVII

Rates of Chemical Reactions

1. Specific Reaction Rate

By "rate" of chemical reaction we mean the quantity of matter which is being used up or produced per unit of time. The units are generally moles of substances per second.

If the total volume of the reacting system is doubled, then, all other conditions being constant, the amount of matter produced per second is doubled also (i.e., the rate is doubled). To get around this dependence on volume we define an intensive property, the specific reaction rate.

Definition: The specific reaction rate is the quantity of matter being transformed per second, per unit volume of the reaction system.

The usual unit of specific reaction rate is moles per liter-second.

Example:
$$H_2 + I_2 \rightarrow 2HI.$$

In a 25-l. vessel at 280°C., it is found that the rate of production of HI is 3.0×10^{-2} mole HI/sec. What is the specific reaction rate for this reaction?
Answer: By definition:

$$\text{S.R.R.} = \frac{\text{Rate of reaction}}{\text{Volume}}$$

$$= \frac{3.0 \times 10^{-2} \text{ mole HI/sec.}}{25 \text{ l.}}$$

Thus
$$\text{S.R.R.} = 1.2 \times 10^{-3} \text{ mole HI/l.-sec.}$$

---

2. Dependence of Rate on Concentration—Law of Mass Action

It is found experimentally that for many reactions the rate of reaction is proportional to the concentrations of the reacting species raised to powers given by the coefficients in the balanced equation. Although many reactions do not obey this law (especially in gas phase), it is of considerable value for the others. This rule is known as the *law of mass action*.

We can express this law as follows for the reaction of H_2 and I_2:

$$H_2 + I_2 \rightleftarrows 2HI$$

Specific rate (production of HI) $= k_f \times C_{H_2} \times C_{I_2}$

and for the reverse reaction:

Specific rate (decomposition of HI) $= k_r \times C^2_{HI}$

The constants, k_f and k_r, are called the *specific reaction rate constants*. When all concentrations are 1 mole/l., then the specific reaction rate is equal to the specific reaction rate constant.

These specific reaction rate constants may be measured experimentally. Once known they can be used to compute the reaction rate at any concentration, if the particular reaction follows the law of mass action. However, their values change with temperature, and so they can be used only for the temperature at which they have been measured.

Their units will depend on the particular equation. If the concentrations are all in moles per liter, then k_f above has the units of $\dfrac{\text{moles HI} \times \text{liters}}{\text{moles } H_2 \times \text{moles } I_2 \times \text{seconds}}$ and k_r has the units of $\dfrac{\text{liters}}{\text{moles HI-seconds}}$. Since we shall always use concentrations of moles per liter, we shall not bother to insert units for the k's.

Example: The specific reaction rate constant for the formation of HI at 400°C. is 0.43. What is the specific rate of formation of HI in a vessel at 400°C. if $C_{H_2} = 0.04$ mole/l. and $C_{I_2} = 0.006$ mole/l.?

Answer:

$$\text{Specific rate} = k \times C_{H_2} \times C_{I_2} \qquad \text{(by law of mass action)}$$

$$= 0.43 \times (0.04) \times (0.006)$$

$$= 1.03 \times 10^{-4} \text{ mole HI/l.-sec.}$$

Example:

$$2NO + O_2 \rightarrow 2NO_2$$

The specific reaction rate constant for the formation of NO_2 at 0°C. is 3.9×10^{-4}. What is the specific rate of formation of NO_2 in a vessel in which $C_{NO} = 0.07$ mole/l. and $C_{O_2} = 0.32$ mole/l.?

Answer:

$$\text{Specific rate} = k \times C^2_{NO} \times C_{O_2} \quad\quad \text{(by law of mass action)}$$
$$= 3.9 \times 10^{-4} \times (0.07)^2(0.32)$$
$$= 3.9 \times 10^{-4} \times (4.9 \times 10^{-3}) \times (0.32)$$
$$= 6.1 \times 10^{-7} \text{ mole NO}_2/\text{l.-sec.}$$

Note: Actually, for every reaction, chemists must first determine experimentally whether or not the rate law follows the law of mass action!

3. Dependence of Rate on Temperature—Arrhenius Equation

It is found experimentally that a small increase in temperature will increase the rates of simple reactions by a large amount. (For a few complex reactions such as the reaction of $2NO + O_2 \rightarrow 2NO_2$, the effect of increasing temperature is to decrease the reaction rate.)

The magnitude of this effect of increasing temperature will depend on what we call the "activation energy of the reaction." The activation energy of a reaction may be interpreted as the minimum energy which the molecules must have in order to break their bonds and react. Activation energies are measured experimentally for each reaction. Those reactions that have a large activation energy will be more sensitive to temperature changes than reactions having a low activation energy.

Roughly it is found that many reactions will double their specific rates when the temperature is increased by 10°C. However, this will depend somewhat on the temperature and on the activation energy of the reaction. Table XVI shows how reactions having different activation energies will be affected when the temperature is raised 10°C.

From the chart we see that a reaction having an activation energy of 54 kcal./mole will have its speed increased 4-fold at 300°K. by a 10°C. rise in temperature but only 1.55-fold at 700°K. by the same temperature change.

The relation between the specific reaction rate constants at different temperatures was discovered by Arrhenius and may be expressed algebraically:

Arrhenius' Equation:

$$\log \frac{k_1}{k_2} = \frac{(T_1 - T_2) \times E_{act.}}{2.3 \times R \times T_1 T_2}$$

In this equation, k_1 is the rate constant at the absolute temperature, T_1, and k_2 is the rate constant at the absolute temperature, T_2. $E_{act.}$ is

TABLE XVI

FACTORS BY WHICH REACTION RATES ARE CHANGED BY A 10°C. CHANGE
IN TEMPERATURE

(For reactions with different activation energies at different temperatures)

Temperature		Activation Energy				
(t, °C.)	T, °K.	18 kcal./mole	36 kcal./mole	54 kcal./mole	72 kcal./mole	90 kcal./mole
(27)	300	2	3	4	5	6
(127)	400	1.6	2.1	2.7	3.3	3.9
(227)	500	1.36	1.7	2.1	2.4	2.8
(327)	600	1.25	1.5	1.75	2.0	2.25
(427)	700	1.2	1.36	1.55	1.7	1.92

the activation energy in calories per mole and R is the universal gas constant = 2 cal./mole-°K.

The Arrhenius equation may be used to obtain rate constants at one temperature, if the rate constant at any other temperature is known.

Example: The specific rate constant for the reaction of H_2 with I_2 to form HI is 0.43 at 400°C. If the activation energy is 40 kcal./mole, what is the specific rate constant at 500°C.?

Answer: From the Arrhenius equation:

$$\log \frac{k_1}{k_2} = \frac{(T_1 - T_2)E_{act.}}{2.3 \times R \times T_1 \times T_2}$$

Substituting: $T_1 = 773°K.$, (500°C.); $T_2 = 673°K.$ (400°C.); $R = 2$ cal./mole-°K.; $E_{act.} = 4.0 \times 10^4$ cal./mole; and $k_2 = 0.43$.

$$\log \left(\frac{k_1}{0.43}\right) = \frac{(773°K - 673°K) \times 4.0 \times 10^4 \text{ cal./mole}}{2.3 \times 2 \text{ cal./mole-°K.} \times 673°K. \times 773°K.}$$

$$= \frac{100 \times 4.0 \times 10^4}{2.3 \times 2 \times 673 \times 733} = 1.76$$

Taking antilogs:

$$\frac{k_1}{0.43} = 58$$

Thus

$$k_1 = 58 \times 0.43 = 25$$

Note: If we used our crude rule of doubling the rate for every 10°C. rise in temperature, we would have an increase of $2^{10} \cong 1000$ since there are 10 increases of 10°C. going from 400°C. to 500°C. This method would give $k_1 = 430$.

If we used the nearest factor from Table XVI, namely 1.36, we would have $(1.36)^{10}$ for the increase, which = 21.6, which is an excellent check.

The experimentally observed increase is 54-fold, i.e., $k_1 = 23.2$. Thus the Arrhenius equation was in error by only 8%.

---

4. Dependence of Equilibrium Constants on Temperature

It is found that the Arrhenius equation applies to many other constants besides reaction rate constants. Thus all equilibrium constants obey the Arrhenius equation. In these cases the heat of reaction is used to replace the activation energy.

Arrhenius' Equation for Equilibrium Constants

$$\log \frac{K_{eq.1}}{K_{eq.2}} = \frac{(T_1 - T_2) \times H_r}{2.3 \times R \times T_1 \times T_2}$$

As an example we may apply it to the $K_{ion}(H_2O)$. At 25°C., $K_{ion}(H_2O) = 1.0 \times 10^{-14}$. The heat of the reaction:

$$2H_2O \rightleftarrows OH^{-1} + H_3O^{+1}$$

is exactly equal to minus the heat of neutralization of a strong acid and a strong base, namely 13 kcal./mole. Let us calculate $K_{ion}(H_2O)$ at 50°C.

$$\log \frac{K_{eq.1}}{K_{eq.2}} = \frac{(323°K. - 298°K.) \times 13,000 \text{ cal./mole}}{2.3 \times 2 \text{ cal./mole-°K.} \times 293°K. \times 323°K.}$$

$$= \frac{25 \times 1.3 \times 10^4}{2.3 \times 2 \times 298 \times 323} = 0.735$$

Taking antilogs:

$$\frac{K_{eq.1}}{K_{eq.2}} = 5.44$$

Therefore

$$K_{eq.1} = 5.44 \times 1 \times 10^{-14} = 5.44 \times 10^{-14}$$

The observed value for K at 50°C. is 5.47×10^{-14}, an excellent check.

5. Problems

1. H_2 and Br_2 will react to form HBr at a rate of 1.5×10^{-4} mole HBr/sec. in a 300-cc. flask. What is the specific rate of this reaction?

2. Under given conditions the specific rate of reaction of Sn^{+2} ions with Hg^{+2} ions to produce Sn^{+4} and Hg_2^{+2} ions is 1.7×10^{-3} mole Sn^{+4} ions/l.-sec. What is the rate under the same conditions, if the reactants fill a 12-l. vessel?

3. Write expressions showing the dependence of the following reactions on concentration (assume law of mass action).

(a) $2NO + Cl_2 \rightarrow 2NOCl$.

(b) $2N_2O_5 \rightarrow 4NO_2 + O_2$.

(c) $Cl_2 + 2HBr \rightarrow 2HCl + Br_2$.

(d) $Cl_2 + Br_2 \rightarrow 2ClBr$.

4. If the specific reaction rate constant of reaction 3(a) is 2.1×10^{-3}, calculate the specific rate when $C_{NO} = 1.8$ moles/l. and $C_{Cl_2} = 0.6$ mole/l.

5. It is found that the specific rate of reaction 3(c) is found to be 3.5×10^{-4} when $C_{Cl_2} = 0.04$ M and $C_{HBr} = 2.6$ M. Calculate the specific reaction rate constant for this reaction.

6. Compute the change in specific reaction rate constant for the following, using the Arrhenius equation:

(a) $k = 3.5 \times 10^{-4}$ at 200°C. What is it at 150°C. if $E_{act.} = 24$ kcal./mole?

(b) $k = 2.7 \times 10^{-2}$ at −80°C. What is it at 30°C. if $E_{act.} = 12$ kcal./mole?

(c) $k = 7.5 \times 10^{-8}$ at 400°C. What is it at 600°C. if $E_{act.} = 63$ kcal./mole?

Compare these calculated values with the value predicted by the rough rule of doubling the rate for every 10°C. rise.

7. For the reaction, $CO_2 (g) + H_2 (g) \rightleftarrows CO (g) + H_2O (g)$, it is found that $K_{eq.} = 0.534$ at 686°C. and 1.571 at 986°C. Using the Arrhenius equation, compute the heat of this reaction. Is the reaction exothermic or endothermic?

APPENDIX I

Some Mathematical Definitions and Operations

1. Algebraic Operations

Algebra is an abstract science which deals with defined entities, numbers, and defined operations which may be performed on them. The great power of algebra lies in its system of abbreviation, that is, its compact language. This compactness permits us to express very complex relations very briefly.

Most of the operations of algebra have associated with them inverse operations. Thus addition $(+)$ has the inverse operation, subtraction $(-)$. Performing an operation and its inverse in succession leaves the quantity operated on unchanged. Thus, if we add a number to a quantity and then subtract the same number, the original quantity is unchanged. This may be expressed compactly by means of an equation. If we let $X =$ the original quantity and $N =$ the number added, then

$$X + N - N = X$$

Multiplication $(\times)$ is a compact method for expressing a continued addition. Thus 2×5 means $5 + 5$; 3×4 means $4 + 4 + 4$. Division $(\div)$ is the inverse of multiplication. If we multiply a quantity (X) by a number (N) and then divide by N, the original quantity is unchanged:

$$X \times N \div N = X$$

Some operations commute with other operations. That is, if the order of operations is reversed, the result is the same.

Operations commute with their inverse operations and with themselves. Thus

$$5 \times 4 \times 3 = 5 \times 3 \times 4 = 3 \times 5 \times 4, \text{ etc.}$$

Also

$$(5 \times 4) \div 2 = (5 \div 2) \times 4$$

Addition and subtraction do not commute with multiplication or division. Thus $(12 + 2) \times 3$ is not equal to $(12 \times 3) + 2$.

2. Exponents

The operation of continued multiplication by a certain quantity is abbreviated by an exponent. Thus 4^3 means $4 \times 4 \times 4$; X^5 means $X \cdot X \cdot X \cdot X \cdot X$. From this we can deduce some simple rules of operations on such quantities:

Combining Exponents.

$$5^3 \times 5^2 \text{ means } (5 \times 5 \times 5) \times (5 \times 5) = 5^5$$

or, in general,

$$X^a \cdot X^b = X^{a+b}$$

When multiplying quantities having different exponents we add the exponents. Note, however, we may not simplify $5^3 \times 4^2$ further. The base quantities having different exponents must be the same.

$$(5^3)^4 \text{ means } (5^3) \times (5^3) \times (5^3) \times (5^3) = 5^{12}$$

Thus when we raise a quantity (expressed as an exponent) to a power, the two exponents are multiplied. In general $(X^a)^b = X^{a \cdot b}$. Manipulation involving exponents can always be checked if the definitions are kept in mind.

Rule: Any quantity raised to exponent zero is 1. Thus $X^0 = 1$.

Negative Exponents. The operation of continued division by a given quantity is abbreviated by a negative exponent. Thus if we want to divide a quantity by 10 three times, this operation may be represented by multiplication by

$$10^{-3} = \frac{1}{10} \times \frac{1}{10} \times \frac{1}{10} = \frac{1}{10^3}$$

The reciprocal of a number is that number with a negative exponent. Thus

$$\frac{1}{2} = 2^{-1}; \quad \frac{1}{X} = X^{-1}; \quad \frac{1}{10} = 10^{-1}; \quad \frac{1}{X^4} = X^{-4}$$

Note that the inverse of the operation of multiplication by X^a is division by X^a or multiplication by X^{-a}; the application of both these operations cancel each other: $(X^a) \cdot (X^{-a}) = 1$.

Fractional Exponents. The inverse operation to raising a quantity to a given power is called taking the root of the quantity. This may be expressed by a fractional exponent.

Thus $9^{\frac{1}{2}}$ (the $\frac{1}{2}$ root or square root of 9) means the number which when multiplied by itself twice will give 9. The answer is, of course 3.

The operations of squaring and taking square roots are inverse and commute. Thus:

$$(3^2)^{\frac{1}{2}} = (3^{\frac{1}{2}})^2 = 3^1$$

$$(5^3)^{\frac{1}{3}} = (5^{\frac{1}{3}})^3 = 5^1.$$

The same rules for combination apply to integral and fractional exponents. Thus

$$(3^{\frac{1}{2}}) \times 3^2 = 3^{2+\frac{1}{2}} = 3^{\frac{5}{2}}.$$

3. Numbers Expressed as Powers of 10

It is a great convenience to express both large and small numbers as powers of 10. Thus

$$1{,}000{,}000{,}000 = 1 \times 10^9$$

$$176{,}000 = 176 \times 10^3 = 17.6 \times 10^4 = 1.76 \times 10^5$$

$$0.001 = 1 \times 10^{-3}$$

$$0.000047 = 47 \times 10^{-6} = 4.7 \times 10^{-5}$$

To convert such a number expressed as an exponent back to a number, we have a simple rule:

For Positive Exponents: Shift the decimal point forward by the number of places indicated by the exponent.
For Negative Exponents: Move the decimal place back as many places as the exponent.

The use of exponents allows us to make operations much less cumbersome.

Whenever we have a group of numbers to multiply and divide, if the numbers are very large or small, express all numbers as numbers between 1 and 10 multiplied by some power of 10. Group all the numbers and powers of 10 separately and then perform the operations.

Examples:

$$\frac{720{,}000}{48{,}000} = \frac{7.2 \times 10^5}{4.8 \times 10^4} = \frac{7.2}{4.8} \times 10^1 = 15$$

$$\frac{12{,}000 \times 0.006}{0.036 \times 250} = \frac{1.2 \times 10^4 \times 6 \times 10^{-3}}{3.6 \times 10^{-2} \times 2.5 \times 10^2} = \frac{1.2 \times 6 \times 10^1}{3.6 \times 2.5}$$

$$= \frac{7.2}{9.0} \times 10^1 = 0.8 \times 10 = 8.$$

4. Logarithms to the Base 10

We define the logarithm (log) of a number to the base 10 as that exponent to which 10 must be raised to give the number. Thus: $10^x = N$, may be taken to mean that the log of N is X: $\log N = X$ (in the base 10).

For very simple numbers:

$$\log 10 = \log 10^1 = 1$$

$$\log 100 = \log 10^2 = 2$$

$$\log 0.01 = \log 10^{-2} = -2$$

$$\log 1 = \log 10^0 = 0 \qquad \text{(since } 10^0 = 1)$$

Theorem: The logarithm of a product of two or more numbers is equal to the sum of the logarithms of the numbers. Thus

$$\log (N \times M) = \log N + \log M$$

Example:

$$\log (10 \times 100) = \log 10 + \log 100 = 1 + 2 = 3$$

Theorem: The logarithm of a number raised to some exponent is equal to the exponent times the log of the number. Thus

$$\log (X^a) = a \cdot (\log X)$$

Examples:

$$\log (10^4) = 4 \cdot \log 10 = 4 \times 1 = 4$$

$$\log \frac{1}{1000} = \log (1000^{-1}) = -1 \cdot \log 1000 = -3$$

$$\log \left(\frac{N}{M}\right) = \log (N \times M^{-1}) = \log N + \log M^{-1}$$

$$= (\log N) - 1 \cdot (\log M) = \log N - \log M$$

$$\log \left(\frac{100}{1000}\right) = \log 100 + \log (1000^{-1}) = \log 100 - \log 1000$$

$$= 2 - 3 = -1$$

Tables have been prepared for finding the logarithms of numbers that are not simple powers of 10. If we wish to find the logarithm of such a number it is simplest first to express the number as a power of 10.

To find the logarithm of 230 we observe that 230 lies between 100 (log = 2) and 1000 (log = 3). Then log 230 will be between 2 and 3. The number before the decimal point of a logarithm is called the *characteristic*. The remainder of the logarithm after the decimal point is called the *mantissa*.

The *characteristic* of log 230 will be 2. To find the mantissa we look in our logarithm tables under 23 or 230 (we will find the same mantissa for each). We obtain 0.3617 (four-place log tables) or 0.36173 (five-place log tables). We add the characteristic to the mantissa and obtain log 230 = 2.3617.

Examples:

$$\log 36{,}400 = \log (3.64 \times 10^4) \qquad \text{(characteristic} = 4)$$

$$= 4.5611$$

$$\log 0.0075 = \log (7.5 \times 10^{-3}) \qquad \text{(characteristic} = 3)$$

$$= -3 + 0.8751$$

$$= -2.1249$$

---

5. Antilogarithms

The inverse operation to finding the logarithm, given the number, is to find the number (antilogarithm), given the logarithm. Thus we may be told that the logarithm of a number is 2 and asked to find the number. This is, of course, simple since the log of 100 is 2. Thus the number whose log is 2 is 100, or conversely, the antilog 2 = 100. Note that the operations log and antilog commute and cancel each other.

To find the antilog of a number we must express the number with a positive mantissa since the log tables give values only for positive mantissas.

Example: Find the antilog of 1.301.
Answer: First note that log 10 = 1 and log 100 = 2. Thus the number lies between 10 and 100. We write

$$1.301 = 1 + 0.301$$

We can now look up 0.301 in the log tables, and we find that 200 has the value 0.301 as its mantissa. The number is thus $2.00 \times 10^2 = 200$.

Example: Find the antilog of -2.730.
Answer: We first write $-2.730 = -3 + 0.270$, that is, we write the number with a positive mantissa. We can now look up this positive mantissa and find that

186 is the nearest number having the mantissa 0.270.   The antilog of -2.730 is then $1.86 \times 10^{-3} = 0.00186$.

We can always check:

$$\log (0.00186) = \log (1.86 \times 10^{-3})$$
$$= \log 1.86 + \log (10^{-3})$$
$$= \log 1.86 - 3 = 0.270 - 3$$
$$= -2.730$$

6. Using Logarithms To Do Problems

We may use logarithms to simplify calculations for us:

Example: Find X, given:

$$X = \frac{27.6 \times 873}{0.076 \times 96{,}200}$$

Answer: We can, of course, work this out by longhand.   However, it is simpler if we use logarithms and exponents.   Let us write it using exponents:

$$X = \frac{2.76 \times 10^1 \times 8.73 \times 10^2}{7.6 \times 10^{-2} \times 9.62 \times 10^4} = \frac{2.76 \times 8.73}{7.6 \times 9.62} \times 10^1$$

We now proceed to evaluate the fraction $\dfrac{2.76 \times 8.73}{7.6 \times 9.62}$ using logarithms:

$$\log \left(\frac{2.76 \times 8.73}{7.6 \times 9.62} \right) = \log 2.76 + \log 8.73 - \log 7.6 - \log 9.62$$

(by rule about products)

$$\begin{bmatrix} \log 2.76 = 0.4409 & \quad \log 7.6 \ = 0.8808 \\ \log 8.73 = 0.9410 & \quad \log 9.62 = 0.9832 \\ \hline \qquad 1.3819 & \qquad 1.8640 \end{bmatrix}$$

$$= 1.3819 - 1.8640 = -0.4821$$
$$= -1 + 0.5179$$

Now by looking up the antilog of 0.5179 we find it to be 330.   Thus

$$\frac{2.76 \times 8.73}{7.6 \times 9.62} = 3.30 \times 10^{-1} = 0.330$$

and

$$X = \frac{2.76 \times 8.73}{7.6 \times 9.62} \times 10^1 = 0.330 \times 10^1 = 3.30$$

Example: What is the sixth root of 18.76?   We write:

$$X = 18.76^{1/6}$$

Taking logarithms of both sides:

$$\log X = \log (18.76)^{\frac{1}{6}} = \frac{1}{6} \times \log 18.76$$

by our rules about logarithms of exponents. Thus

$$\log X = \frac{1}{6} \times \log (1.876 \times 10^1)$$

$$= \frac{1}{6} \times (1.2732) = 0.2122$$

Taking antilogs of both sides:

$$X = 1.630 \quad (\text{i.e., } 1.630^6 = 18.76)$$

Note: If we want only 1% accuracy all of these types of problems may be performed with a slide rule. Log tables are needed for greater accuracy.

---

7. Getting the Decimal Point in a Problem

The method of writing numbers as powers of 10 provides us with a simple method of obtaining the decimal point in a calculation involving many operations.

To do this we write the numbers as powers of 10. We then make an approximate calculation in which we replace each coefficient by the nearest integer and perform the operations. This approximate answer will be close to the correct answer and tell us where the decimal belongs.

Example: Calculate the value of $X = \dfrac{394 \times 7.25 \times 0.0642}{0.0428 \times 9{,}680 \times 22.8}$.

We express this in powers of 10:

$$X = \frac{3.94 \times 10^2 \times 7.25 \times 6.42 \times 10^{-2}}{4.28 \times 10^{-2} \times 9.68 \times 10^3 \times 2.28 \times 10^1}$$

$$= \frac{3.94 \times 7.25 \times 6.42}{4.28 \times 9.68 \times 2.28} \times 10^{-2}$$

The approximation gives:

$$X = \frac{4 \times 7 \times 6}{4 \times 10 \times 2} \times 10^{-2} = \frac{42}{20} \times 10^{-2}$$

$$= 2.1 \times 10^{-2} = 0.021$$

The correct answer must be close to 0.021. If we now perform all operations on a slide rule without worrying about the decimal, we find $X = 1945$. The correct answer is then $X = 0.01945$.

---

8. Significant Figures

An experimental measurement is no better than the instrument used. If we are measuring a length with a ruler marked off in millimeters as the smallest division, then we express our result to the nearest millimeter.* The length 273 mm. measured in this fashion indicates that the actual length may lie anywhere between 272.5 mm. and 273.5 mm. It is closest to 273 mm. which is written.

The answer 273 mm. is said to be expressed to three significant figures. The number 58 contains two significant figures. In order to obtain a uniform system of expressing results so that the number of significant figures is apparent, many scientists will express their findings in powers of 10. The total number of digits given when this is done indicates the number of significant figures in the answer. The following list shows some results expressed this way.

Result	Number of Significant Figures	Expressed as a Power of 10
21,000	2	2.1×10^4
	3	2.10×10^4
	4	2.100×10^4
0.00035	2	3.5×10^{-4}
	3	3.50×10^{-4}
	4	3.500×10^{-4}
	5	3.5000×10^{-4}

When written in this fashion, as powers of 10, it will be immediately clear from the total number of digits how many significant figures are indicated.

9. Adding Significant Figures

The principal reason for reporting significant figures in scientific experiments is that we can then tell how far to go in interpreting and using the result.

If a chemist weighs the amount of Ag to be used in an experiment to the nearest gram and records 18 g., we interpret this as meaning that the true weight might be anywhere between 17.5 and 18.5 g. If now another chemist weighs some more silver in a more sensitive balance and records the weight as 1.25 g. and adds it to the first sample, how shall we record the total weight? If we add we obtain

* Generally we would try to estimate the length to 0.1 mm.

19.25 g.   However, the first result was recorded only to the nearest gram, and it is not meaningful to repeat the total weight to any more significant figures.   It should be recorded simply as 19 g.

In adding significant figures, the result cannot be expressed with any more precision than the crudest measurement in the sum.

Example: Add the following lengths: 102.5 cm., 32.76 cm., 0.008 cm., and 915 cm.

Answer:

$$
\begin{array}{l}
102.5 \\
32.76 \\
0.008 \\
915. \qquad \leftarrow \text{crudest measurement} \\
\hline
1050.268
\end{array}
$$

The answer is 1050 cm. since the crudest figure (915 cm.) is not reported to better than 1 cm.

---

10. Multiplying and Dividing Significant Figures

In multiplying and dividing significant figures, the final result cannot contain any more significant figures than the least number of significant figures in any of the quantities used.   Thus

$$\frac{982 \times 22 \times 14}{362 \times 756} = 0.55259 \quad \text{(by longhand division)}$$

However, the answer should be recorded as 0.55 since there is a number (actually two, 14 and 22) which is recorded to only two significant figures.

APPENDIX II

Table of Common Units

Length:

1 meter (m.) = 100 centimeters (cm.)
1 centimeter (cm.) = 10 millimeters (mm.)
1 centimeter (cm.) = 100,000,000 (1×10^8) angstroms (A)
1 inch (in.) = 2.54 centimeters = 25.4 millimeters
1 yard (yd.) = 3 feet (ft.)
1 mile = 5280 ft.

Area:

1 square centimeter (cm.^{2}) = 1×10^{-4} square meters (m.^{2})
1 square centimeter (cm.^{2}) = 100 square millimeters (mm.^{2})
1 square inch (in.^{2} or sq. in.) = 6.452 square centimeters (cm.^{2})

Volume:

1 liter (l.) = 1000 milliliters (ml.)
1 milliliter (ml.) = 1 cubic centimeter (cc.) (cm.^{3}) (to three significant figures)
1 cubic centimeter (cc.) = 1000 cubic millimeters (mm.^{3})
1 cubic inch (in.^{3}) = 16.387 cubic centimeters
1 quart (qt.) = 2 pints (pt.) = 0.25 gallon (gal.) = 32 ounces (fluid, oz.) = 0.946 l.

Mass:

1 kilogram (kg.) = 1000 grams
1 gram (g.) = 1000 milligrams
1 milligram (mg.) = 1000 micrograms (μg.)
1 pound (lb.) = 454 grams (three significant figures) = 16 ounces
1 ton = 907 kilograms = 9.07×10^{11} micrograms

Density:

Density = $\dfrac{\text{Mass}}{\text{Volume}}$ (usually expressed as g./cm.^{3})
1 g./cm.^{3} = 62.4 lb./ft.^{3}

Pressure:

$$\text{Pressure} = \frac{\text{Force}}{\text{Area}} \text{ (usually expressed as atmospheres; mm. of mercury; lb./sq. in.)}$$

1 atmosphere (atm.) = 14.7 lb./sq. in. = 760 mm. Hg.

Temperature: Temperature may be expressed in any of four scales, centigrade (°C.), Rankine (°R.), Fahrenheit (°F.), or absolute (°K.). The standards for these scales are the freezing point of water at 1 atm. pressure and the boiling point of water at 1 atm. pressure.

	Rankine	Fahrenheit	Centigrade *CELSIUS or*	Absolute
Boiling point	492°R.	212°F.	100°C.	373°K.
Freezing point	672°R.	32°F.	0°C.	273°K.

$$°K. = °C. + 273$$
$$°F. = \tfrac{9}{5}°C. + 32$$
$$°R. = °F. + 459$$

Energy: *Heat energy* is generally expressed in calories:

1000 calories (cal.) = 1 kilocalorie (kcal.)

Mechanical energy is expressed in foot-pounds (ft.-lb.) or ergs.

1 foot-pound = 0.32 calorie

1 erg = 1 dyne-centimeter

1×10^7 ergs = 1 joule = 0.24 calorie

Electrical energy is usually expressed in joules.

1 joule = 1 watt-second = 0.24 calorie

1 kilowatt-hour = 1000 watt-hours

1 kilowatt-hour = 864 kilocalories = 864,000 calories

Force:

1 dyne = force necessary to give 1 gram of mass an acceleration of 1 cm./sec.^{2}

Force of gravity = 980 dynes/gram

Electricity: The most common unit used for expressing the *difference in potential energy* between two bodies or two points in space is the *volt*. A position of low voltage is at a low potential energy compared to a position of high voltage.

It always requires energy to move electrical charges from low-potential energy levels to high-potential energy levels.

Charges will tend naturally to move from a high potential to a low potential, and in doing this they produce kinetic energy. (An analogy can be drawn between electrical potential energy and gravitational potential energy.)

Masses always tend naturally to move closer to the center of the earth, and in doing this they release energy (e.g., waterfalls—as the water descends it moves faster).

The *motion of charges* is an *electric current*. This is most frequently the motion of electrons which possess negative charges, but it may be the motion of any body which possess a charge, e.g., ions in solution.

The common unit for measuring the number of electric charges is the coulomb.

$$1 \text{ equivalent of charge} = 96,500 \text{ coulombs} = 1 \text{ faraday}$$

The faraday represents 1 mole of electrons or 1 equivalent of electric charges.

In 1 faraday there are 6.02×10^{23} units of charge. If we consider the electron which has one unit of electric charge:

$$1 \text{ faraday} = 1 \text{ mole of electrons} = 6.02 \times 10^{23} \text{ electrons}$$

When electric charges are transported in a closed circuit at the rate of 1 coulomb of charge per second a current of 1 ampere is said to be flowing in the circuit.

$$1 \text{ ampere} = 1 \text{ coulomb/second}$$

$$\text{Coulombs} = \text{Amperes} \times \text{Seconds}$$

Concentration:

$$\text{Density} = \text{Mass/Volume} \quad \text{(usually in g./cc.)}$$

$$\text{Per cent by weight} = \frac{\text{Mass of solute}}{\text{Mass of total solution}} \times 100$$

$$\begin{cases} \text{Molarity} = \dfrac{\text{Moles of solute}}{\text{Liters of solution}} \\ \text{Moles of Solute} = \text{Molarity} \times \text{Liters of solution} \end{cases}$$

$L = \dfrac{\text{MOLES SOLUTE}}{\text{MOLARITY}}$

$$\begin{cases} \text{Normality} = \dfrac{\text{Equivalents of solute}}{\text{Liters of solution}} \\ \text{Equivalents of solute} = \text{Normality} \times \text{Liters of solution} \end{cases}$$

Molality = Moles of solute/1000 g. of solvent

APPENDIX III

Answers to Problems

Chapter I

1. (a) 2 milliinches.
   (b) 10 millimiles.
   (c) 12 kilodresses.
   (d) 100 megayears.
   (e) 7000 megawatts.
   (f) 3.5 microtons.
2. (a) 3500 bucks.
   (b) 0.000075 meters.
   (c) 42,000 watts.
   (d) 160,000 pounds.
   (e) 0.000000095 grams.
   (f) 0.0027 gallons.
   (g) 1600 sheep.
3. Intensive: (a), (c), (e); extensive: (b), (d), (f).
4. 0.0553 lb.
5. 16×10^{-6} kg.
6. 1.33×10^{-7} ton.
7. 2.27×10^7 dollars = 22.7 megabucks.
8. 1.67×10^5 cm.^{2}.
9. 40.8 m.^{3}.
10. 2.32×10^{-5} in. = 5.9×10^{-5} cm. = 0.59 micron.
11. 1.35 tons/yd.^{3}.
12. 24.9 miles/hr. = 1.11×10^3 cm./sec.
13. 976 cm./sec.^{2} = 3.51×10^4 m./min.^{2}.
14. 35.2 kg.-m./min.^{2}.
15. 27.5 in.^{3} = 452 cm.^{3}.
16. 7.80 g./cm.^{3}.
17. 22,000 mg.
18. Rate = 0.893 egg/hen-day; time = 56 days.
19. 1.70×10^{26} atoms O.
20. (a) 1×10^{15} molecules; (b) 6×10^{13} molecules.

Chapter II

1. (a) 97.4 g.
   (b) 78.0 g.
   (c) 159.6 g.
   (d) 158 g.
   (e) 249.7 g.
   (f) 78.0 g.
   (g) 562 g.
   (h) 96.0 g.
2. (a) 0.353 mole.
   (b) 0.172 g.
   (c) 837 g.
   (d) 0.138 mmoles.
   (e) 0.59 mole.
   (f) 6190 mmoles.
   (g) 0.096 mole.
3. (a) 4 mmoles HNO_3.   (b) 16 g. NaCl.   (c) 4 moles $Ca(NO_3)_2$.
4. (a) 1.44×10^{23} molecules.
   (b) 1.02×10^{21} molecules.
   (c) 1.15×10^{-7} mole.
   (d) 7.7×10^{24} molecules.
   (e) 3.4×10^{-24} ton.
5. 0.588 mmole S.
6. 1.87×10^{-4} mole NO_2.
7. 1.55×10^{-22} cc.

8. (a) 1.16 mmoles Cl_2.
    (b) 7820 l. STP NO gas.
    (c) 10.6 cc. STP H_2S gas.
    (d) 0.215 kg. SF_6.
9. 79.4 g./mole.
10. 140 g./mole.
11. 502.723 g.
12. 83.5 g./mole.
13. 70.0 g./mole.
14. (a) 1.28×10^{-19} cm.^{3}.   (b) 1.6×10^{-22} cm.^{3}.   (c) 5.4 A.

Chapter III

1. True formulae are (a), (f), and (h).
2. 3.36 moles O.
3. 7.12 moles S.
4. 1.56 moles O.
5. 1.575×10^{-3} mole.
6. 0.012 mole H_2O_2.
7. 189 mmoles B.
8. 0.40 mole B.
9. 277 mmoles S.
10. 4.10 g. O.
11. 104 mg. Na.
12. 3.52×10^5 g. Ca.
13. 7.1×10^{20} atoms O.
14. (a) Na = 22.3%; Br = 77.7%.
    (b) Ca = 43.5%; C = 26.1%; N = 30.4%.
    (c) K = 41.1%; S = 33.7%; O = 25.2%.
    (d) Na = 16.1%; C = 4.2%; O = 72.7%; H = 7.0%.
    (e) C = 40.0%; H = 6.7%; O = 53.3%.
    (f) C = 58.6%; H = 4.1%; N = 11.3%; O = 26.0%.
15. (a) $CaBr_2$.
    (b) C_3O_2.
    (c) $Al_2(CO_3)_3$.
    (d) Sr_2SiO_4.
    (e) Mn_3S_4.
    (f) $CaCl_2 \cdot 6H_2O$.
16. C_6H_{12}; H_2O_2; $C_5H_{10}O_5$; Hg_2Cl_2; H_4F_4.
17. $CuSO_4 \cdot 5H_2O$.
18. Cr_2S_3.
19. $PtCl_4$.
20. $CuCl_2 \cdot 6NH_3$.

Chapter IV

1. Refer to text.
2. 0.70 mole HCl.
3. 1.00 moles Cl_2.
4. 0.0253 mole K_3PO_4.
5. 1770 cc. STP SO_2.
6. (a) 259 g. FeS.
    (b) 66 l. STP H_2S gas.
7. 6.86 l. STP O_2 gas.
8. 2.04 moles NaOH.
9. 32.2 cc. STP O_2 gas.
10. 2970 kg. H_2SO_4.
11. 1600 l.
12. 13900 cc. STP CO_2.
13. 0.564 g. $KMnO_4$.
14. 536 g. Al_4C_3; 803 g. H_2O; 803 cc. H_2O
15. 22.2 kg. C_6H_{14}.
16. 50.9 kg. hydrate.
17. (a) 1.2 moles Zn; 0.8 mole $ZnCl_2$; 0.8 mole H_2.
    (b) 2.37 g. HCl; 29.2 g. $ZnCl_2$; 0.43 g. H_2.
18. (a) 5.3 moles HNO_3; 4 moles $Cu(NO_3)_2$; 2.7 moles NO; 5.3 moles H_2O.
    (b) 19.5 g. Cu; 13.4 g. $Cu(NO_3)_2$; 1.4 g. NO; 1.7 g. H_2O.

Chapter V

2. (a) 9.8×10^5 ergs.
    (b) 443 cm./sec.
3. (a) 2.09×10^{10} ergs.
    (b) 0.0143 kcal.
    (c) 1.92 cal.
    (d) 6 microjoules.

4. (a) 423°K.
   (b) −460°F.
   (c) −273°C.
   (d) 727°C.
   (e) 441°F.
   (f) −40°F.
5. 15°K.; 27°F.
7. 45,400 cal.
9. 1,785 cal.
11. 0.25 cal./g.-°C.
13. 0.102 cal./g.-°C.
15. (a) −57.8 kcal. (exothermic).
    (b) −212.1 kcal. (exothermic).
    (c) +40.4 kcal. (endothermic).
16. (a) −143.9 kcal./mole.
    (b) −300.8 kcal./mole.
17. 92.7 l. STP O_2 (g).
19. 108,000 cal.; 9.72 kcal./mole.

(g) 200°K.
(h) 509.6°R.
(i) −449.6°F.
(j) 1391.6°R.
(k) 50°K.

6. 184 cal.
8. 1.06 × 10^{10} ergs/lb. °F.
10. Low temperature.
12. 40 a.m.u.; Ca.
14. 1.26 × 10^{-15} erg.
(d) −77.7 kcal. (exothermic).
(e) −67.0 kcal. (exothermic).
(f) −184.6 kcal. (exothermic).
(c) −91.7 kcal./mole.
(d) −286.8 kcal./mole.
18. 188 kcal.
20. (a) 1440 cal./mole.
    (b) 40,000 cal.
    (c) 36,000 cal.

Chapter VI

1. 0.526 atm.
3. 81.6 cm. Hg; 1.07 atm.
4. (a) 3.33 × 10^5 dynes/cm.^{2}.
   (b) 0.46 atm.
5. 6.37 × 10^4 dynes/cm.^{2}.
7. 2 l.
9. 32.1 l.
11. 349 cc.
13. (a) Initial volume.
    (b) Initial temperature.
    (c) Final volume.
15. 72.0 g./mole.
17. 35.8 g./mole.
19. 1.15 g./l.
21. 2.07 × 10^{11} molecules/cc.
23. 80 g./mole.

2. 25.4 cm. Hg; 0.334 atm.

(c) 15.5 cm. Hg.
(d) 6.0 × 10^{-5} atm.
6. 1790 lb./sq. in.
8. 225 cm. Hg.
10. 117.5°K. = −155.5°C.
12. 246 cc. STP.
14. (a) 6.24 × 10^4 cc.-mm. Hg/mole-°K.
    (b) 1.21 l.-lb./sq. in./mole-°K.
    (c) 8.31 × 10^7 ergs/mole-°K.
16. 3.62 l
18. 108.5 g./mole.
20. 2.14 mg./cc.
22. 2.86 g./l.; 2.63 g./l.
24. 58.1 g./mole; 2.59 g./l.

Chapter VII

1. 29.5 g.
2. 100 g.
3. 15.5 g.
4. (a) 6 eq. $FeCl_3$.
   (b) 0.783 eq. Zn.
   (c) 26 meq. Pb.
   (d) 0.0956 eq. $CaSO_4$.
   (e) 1.785 eq. CCl_4.
5. (a) 4.9 g. $CuSO_4$.
   (b) 21.0 g. NaOH.
   (c) 12.6 g. $Ca_3(PO_4)_2$.

(f) 0.225 mole H_2S.
(g) 57 g. $AlBr_3$.
(h) 16.0 g. $CuSO_4$.
(i) 0.0607 eq. O_2.
(j) 15.7 cc. Cl_2STP.
(d) 24.5 g. H_2SO_4.
(e) 9.0 g. Zn.

6. 47.3 g./eq.   **7.** 28.0 g./eq.
8. 262 g./eq.   **9.** 156.8 g./eq.
10. (a) 1.   (e) 6.   (i) 3.
    (b) 4.   (f) 2.   (j) 4.
    (c) 3.   (g) 7.   (k) 2⅔.
    (d) 5.   (h) 4.

Chapter VIII

1. Mass; volume.   **2.** Density.
3. (a) 6 N.   (f) 97.5 g./l.
    (b) 0.05 M.   (g) 0.043 N.
    (c) 0.035 M.   (h) 0.90 Molal.
    (d) 0.125 M.   (i) 5.53%.
    (e) 0.5 mmole/ml.
4. 0.060 mole $Al_2(SO_4)_3$.   **5.** 3.55 g. = 48 mmoles = 96 meq.
6. 1.200 g. = 0.0179 eq. = 2.98 mmoles.
7. 40.8 cc.   **8.** 5.67 ml.
9. Add water to 43.0 g. $Ca(NO_3)_2$ until the final volume is 150 ml.
10. Add water to 0.912 g. Na_2CO_3 until final volume is 240 ml.
11. Add 15 ml. water to 10 ml. stock solution.
12. Add 13.59 ml. water to 1.41 ml. stock solution.
13. 1.96 M K_2SO_4; 0.70 M $NaNO_3$.
14. Add 70 cc. water to 10 cc. stock solution.
15. 3.18 g. Cu = 50 mmoles Cu.
16. 9.2 ml. water for every 1 ml. stock solution.
17. 12 mmoles Zn.   **18.** 0.360 g. Al.
19. 4.50 g. $BaCl_2$; 5.04 g. $BaSO_4$.   **20.** 717 cc. STP HCl gas; 32 mmoles KCl.
21. 11.3 ml.; 68 meq. $CaSO_4$.   **22.** 123.5 ml.; 9.41 g. Na_3PO_4.
23. 78.1 g./eq.   **24.** 0.51 M.
25. 13.8 M; 13.8 N; 0.904.   **26.** 12.0 M; 12.0 N; 16.1 molal.
27. HNO_3 is 15.2 N; 4.2 ml.

Chapter IX

1. (a) 0.0467 mole fraction; 2.72 Molal.   (c) 0.0299 mole fraction; 1.71 Molal.
    (b) 0.225 mole fraction; 4.99 Molal.   (d) 0.0258 mole fraction; 1.47 Molal.
2. Vapor pressure = 38.6 mm. Hg (Mole fraction phenol = 0.121).
3. Vapor pressure = 146.9 mm. Hg (Mole fraction glucose = 0.0164).
4. 2.50 Molal solution.   **5.** 135 g./mole.
6. 57.6 g./mole.   **7.** 228 g. diethylene glycol.
8. 113 g./mole.   **9.** 24.1 atm.
10. 2700 g./mole.   **11.** 1.674°C.
12. 0.52°C.

Chapter X

3. $C_{CO} = C_{H_2O} = 0.19$ mole/l. $C_{CO_2} = C_{H_2} = 0.21$ mole/l.
4. $C_{NO_2} = 0.42$ mole/l.   **5.** $K_{eq.} = 28.6$.
6. $C_{H_2} = C_{I_2} = 7.0 \times 10^{-3}$ mole/l. $C_{HI} = 5.6 \times 10^{-2}$ mole/l.
7. $K_{eq.} = C_{H_2O\,(g)}$; no change.   **8.** 27.11 M; no.
9. (a) $K_{eq.} = C_{CCl_4\,(g)}$.   (b) 10.3 M.   (c) Decreases; nothing.

Chapter XI

2. (a) 4.97×10^{-3} faraday.
   (b) 8.0×10^{-9} coulomb.
   (c) 1.35×10^5 coulombs.
   (d) 6.56×10^4 coulombs.

(e) 19,300 coulombs.
(f) 4800 coulombs.
(g) 2.36 amp.-hr.

3. 5.18 g. Cr; 3.34 l. STP Cl_2 gas.   4. 0.41 mmole H_2; 0.21 mmole O_2.
5. 1785 sec. = 29.75 min.; 0.0925 mole O_2.

Chapter XII

2. $1.4 \times 10^{-5} M$.
4. $2.9 \times 10^{-9} M$.
5. (a) 3.4×10^{-13}.
   (b) 4.9×10^{-9}.
6. (a) $5.0 \times 10^{-9} M$.
   (b) $8.0 \times 10^{-10} M$.
8. (a) $5.5 \times 10^{-6} M$.
   (b) 0.0117 M.

3. $2.1 \times 10^{-3} M$.

(c) 3.0×10^{-16}.
(d) 1.5×10^{-72}.
7. (a) $4.3 \times 10^{-4} M$.
   (b) $9.3 \times 10^{-5} M$.
9. Yes, a ppt. of CuCl forms.

10. No ppt.
12. (a) AgI ppt.
    (b) $C_{Ag^{+1}} = 1.7 \times 10^{-8} M$.
    (c) $C_{I^{-1}} = 5 \times 10^{-9} M$.

11. No ppt.
13. (a) $C_{S^{-2}} = 1.5 \times 10^{-23} M$.
    (b) $C_{Cd^{+2}} = 9.3 \times 10^{-6} M$; separation is possible.

14. $C_{SO_4^{-2}} = 1.2 \times 10^{-3} M$ will not ppt. $CaSO_4$ but will ppt. $BaSO_4$. $C_{Ba^{+2}} = 8.3 \times 10^{-8} M$ is left.
15. See text.
16. (a) $C_{H_3O^{+1}} = C_{NO_2^{-1}} = 0.015\ M$; $C_{HNO_2} = 0.485\ M$; $K_{ion} = 4.6 \times 10^{-4}$.
    (b) $C_{H_3O^{+1}} = C_{F^{-1}} = 0.00536\ M$; $C_{HF} = 0.035\ M$; $K_{ion} = 8.2 \times 10^{-4}$.
    (c) $C_{NH_4^{+1}} = C_{OH^{-1}} = 1.2 \times 10^{-3}\ M$; $C_{NH_3} = 0.079\ M$; $K_{ion} = 1.8 \times 10^{-5}$.
    (d) $C_{H_3O^{+1}} = C_{HS^{-1}} = 1.8 \times 10^{-5}\ M$; $C_{H_2S} = 0.003\ M$; $K_{ion} = 1.1 \times 10^{-7}$.
    (e) $C_{H_3O^{+1}} = C_{HCO_3^{-1}} = 1.6 \times 10^{-4}\ M$; $C_{H_2CO_3} = 0.060\ M$; $K_{ion} = 4.3 \times 10^{-7}$.
17. (a) $C_{H_3O^{+1}} = C_{ClO^{-1}} = 1.06 \times 10^{-4}\ M$; $C_{HClO} = 0.20\ M$;
        $C_{OH^{-1}} = 9.4 \times 10^{-11}\ M$; 0.053% ionized.
    (b) $C_{H_3O^{+1}} = C_{HCO_3^{-1}} = 9.3 \times 10^{-5}\ M$; $C_{H_2CO_3} = 0.020\ M$;
        $C_{OH^{-1}} = 1.07 \times 10^{-10}\ M$; 0.47% ionized.
    (c) $C_{H_3O^{+1}} = C_{Ac^{-1}} = 2.7 \times 10^{-4}\ M$; $C_{HAc} = 3.7 \times 10^{-3}\ M$;
        $C_{OH^{-1}} = 3.7 \times 10^{-11}\ M$; 6.75% ionized.
    (d) $C_{NH_4^{+1}} = C_{OH^{-1}} = 2.85 \times 10^{-3}\ M$; $C_{NH_3} = 0.45\ M$;
        $C_{H_3O^{+1}} = 3.5 \times 10^{-12}\ M$; 0.63% ionized.
    (e) $C_{H_3O^{+1}} = C_{HPO_4^{-2}} = 2.0 \times 10^{-4}\ M$; $C_{H_2PO_4^{-1}} = 0.65\ M$;
        $C_{OH^{-1}} = 5 \times 10^{-11}\ M$; 3×10^{-2}% ionized.
18. $C_{Ac^{-1}} = 0.036\ M$.
19. $C_{H_3O^{+1}} = 2.2 \times 10^{-3} M$.
20. $C_{H_3O^{+1}} = 5 \times 10^{-3} M$.
21. There are many answers to each part.   The following are possible answers:
    (a) HAc and NaAc.
    (b) NH_3 and NH_4Cl.
    (c) HF and HCl.
    (d) HNO_2 and HCl.

    (e) $Pb(Ac)_2$ and NaAc.
    (f) H_2S and HCl.
    (g) H_2CO_3 and HCl.
    (h) $NaHCO_3$ and NH_4Cl.   (Why not HCl?)
22. Ratio of Ac^{-1}/HAc = 0.9; thus 1 M HAc plus 0.9 M NaAc.
23. Ratio of HCl/HAc = 0.045; thus 1.0 M HAc and 0.045 M HCl.

24. (a) $\dfrac{(\text{Moles Ag}^{+1})(\text{Moles Cl}^{-1})}{(\text{Liters})^2}$

(b) $\dfrac{(\text{Moles Pb}^{+2})(\text{Moles Cl}^{-1})^2}{(\text{Liters})^3}$

26. $6.5 \times 10^{-7} \dfrac{(\text{g. Ag}^{+1})(\text{g. Cl}^{-1})}{(\text{L.})^2}$

25. (a) $\dfrac{(\text{Moles H}_3\text{O}^{+1})(\text{Moles Ac}^{-1})}{(\text{Moles HAc})(\text{Liters})}$

(b) $\dfrac{(\text{Moles H}_3\text{O}^{+1})(\text{Moles F}^{-1})}{(\text{Moles HF})(\text{Liters})}$

27. $3.4 \times 10^{-4} \dfrac{(\text{g. H}_3\text{O}^{+1})(\text{g. Ac}^{-1})}{(\text{g. HAc})(\text{l.})}$

Chapter XIII

1. (a) $\dfrac{(\text{Moles H}_3\text{O}^{+1})(\text{Moles OH}^{-1})}{(\text{Liters})^2}$.

(b) $3.23 \times 10^{-12} \dfrac{(\text{Grams H}_3\text{O}^{+1})(\text{Grams OH}^{-1})}{(\text{Liter})^2}$.

2. (a) $\text{Cl}^{-1} = \text{H}_3\text{O}^{+1} = 0.005 \ M; \ 2 \times 10^{-12} \ M \ \text{OH}^{-1}$.

(b) $\text{Na}^{+1} = \text{Cl}^{-1} = 0.34 \ M; \ \text{H}_3\text{O}^{+1} = \text{OH}^{-1} = 1 \times 10^{-7} \ M$.

(c) $1.20 \ M \ \text{K}^{+1}; \ 0.60 \ M \ \text{SO}_4^{-2}; \ \text{H}_3\text{O}^{+1} = \text{OH}^{-1} = 1 \times 10^{-7} \ M$.

(d) $\text{Na}^{+1} = \text{OH}^{-1} = 0.75 \ M; \ \text{H}_3\text{O}^{+1} = 1.3 \times 10^{-14} \ M$.

(e) $\text{K}^{+1} = \text{OH}^{-1} = 3 \times 10^{-5} \ M; \ \text{H}_3\text{O}^{+1} = 3.3 \times 10^{-10} \ M$.

(f) $\text{Zn}^{+2} = 2 \times 10^{-4}; \ \text{Cl}^{-1} = 4 \times 10^{-4}; \ \text{H}_3\text{O}^{+1} = \text{OH}^{-1} = 1 \times 10^{-7}$

3. (a) $p\text{H} = 3.0; \ p\text{OH} = 11.0$.   (e) $p\text{H} = 0.92; \ p\text{OH} = 13.08$.

(b) $p\text{H} = 2.70; \ p\text{OH} = 12.30$.   (f) $p\text{H} = 13.72; \ p\text{OH} = 0.28$.

(c) $p\text{H} = 10.0; \ p\text{OH} = 4.0$.   (g) $p\text{H} = 12.83; \ p\text{OH} = 1.17$.

(d) $p\text{H} = 3.47; \ p\text{OH} = 10.53$.   (h) $p\text{H} = 3.14; \ p\text{OH} = 10.86$.

4. (a) 5.60.   (d) 2×10^{-10}.

(b) 11.52.   (e) 5×10^{-7}.

(c) 15.10.   (f) 2.3×10^{-9}.

5. $p\text{H} = 6.92$.   **6.** See text.

7. $\text{Na}^{+1} = 0.04 \ M; \ \text{ClO}^{-1} \cong 0.04 \ M; \ \text{HClO} = \text{OH}^{-1} = 8.8 \times 10^{-5} \ M;$
$\text{H}_3\text{O}^{+1} = 1.14 \times 10^{-10} \ M$.

8. $\text{K}^{+1} = 0.07 \ M; \ \text{CN}^{-1} = 0.0686 \ M; \ \text{HCN} = \text{OH}^{-1} = 0.0014 \ M;$
$\text{H}_3\text{O}^{+1} = 7 \times 10^{-12} \ M$.

9. $\text{Na}^{+1} = 0.25 \ M; \ \text{HCO}^{-3} \cong 0.25 \ M; \ \text{H}_2\text{CO}_3 = \text{OH}^{-1} = 7.5 \times 10^{-5} \ M;$
$\text{H}_3\text{O}^{+1} = 1.3 \times 10^{-10} \ M$.

10.

	$K_{\text{hyd.}}$	$p\text{H}$	% Hydrolysis
(a)	5.0×10^{-10}	8.72	0.01%
(b)	5.6×10^{-10}	5.68	0.026%
(c)	1.6×10^{-7}	10.37	0.072%
(d)	10.0	13.68	96%
(e)	2.5×10^{-5}	11.60	0.62%
(f)	5×10^{-11}	5.77	0.0028%
(g)	3.1×10^{-5}	7.0	0.56%
(h)	1.4	9.34	54%

11. (a) $p\text{H} \cong 4.6$.   (c) $p\text{H} \cong 10.6$.

(b) $p\text{H} \cong 11.7$.   (d) $p\text{H} \cong 14.5$.

Chapter XIV

2. $C_{\text{H}_3\text{O}^{+1}} = C_{\text{HB}_4\text{O}_7^{-1}} = 2.2 \times 10^{-3} \ M; \ C_{\text{H}_2\text{B}_4\text{O}_7} = 0.048 \ M;$
$C_{\text{OH}^{-1}} = 4.5 \times 10^{-12} \ M; \ C_{\text{B}_4\text{O}_7^{-2}} = 1 \times 10^{-9} \ M$.

3. $C_{\text{H}_3\text{O}^{+1}} = C_{\text{HSe}^{-1}} = 0.012 \ M; \ C_{\text{H}_2\text{Se}} = 0.78 \ M;$
$C_{\text{OH}^{-1}} = 8.5 \times 10^{-13} \ M; \ C_{\text{Se}^{-2}} = 1 \times 10^{-10} \ M$.

4. 2.1%; $pH = 8.35$.　　　　　　**5.** 0.019%; $pH = 10.98$.

6. $C_{PO_4^{-3}} = C_{H_2PO_4^{-1}} = 2.4 \times 10^{-4}$; $pH = 9.60$.

7. $C_{Hg^{+2}} = 1.4 \times 10^{-9} M$.

8. $C_{Ag^{+1}} = 5.3 \times 10^{-8} M$; $C_{CN^{-1}} = 1.06 \times 10^{-7} M$.

9. $C_{NH_3} = 0.42 M$.　　　　　　**10.** $C_{Hg^{+2}} = 8.9 \times 10^{-16} M$.

11. $C_{S^{-2}} = 1.9 \times 10^{-15} M$; $C_{H_3O^{+1}} = 7.3 \times 10^{-5} M$; Cd^{+2} left $= 1.5 \times 10^{-10}\%$.

13. Yes; $C_{S^{-2}} = 2.8 \times 10^{-14} M$; $C_{H_3O^{+1}} = 2.0 \times 10^{-5} M$.

14. $C_{CO_3^{-2}} = 1.2 \times 10^{-7} M$; Cd^{+2} left $= 0.007\%$; $C_{H_3O^{+1}} = 3.9 \times 10^{-5} M$.

15. $C_{CrO_4^{-2}} = 4.5 \times 10^{-4} M$; $pH = 3.85$.

16. Yes; $C_{Ag^{+1}} = 3.3 \times 10^{-12} M$; $C_{S_2O_3^{-2}} = 0.055 M$.

17. $C_{OH^{-1}} = 1.9 \times 10^{-10} M$; ratio of $Ac^{-1}/HAc = 0.34$.

Chapter XV

1. (a) Cr $(+3)$; O (-2).
(b) H $(+1)$; N $(+3)$; O (-2).
(c) Sb (-3); H $(+1)$.
(d) Na $(+1)$; S $(+6)$; O (-2).
(e) K $(+1)$; O (-1).
(f) Mn $(+4)$; O (-2).
(g) H $(+1)$; P $(+5)$; O (-2).
(h) H $(+1)$; P $(+3)$; O (-2).
(i) H $(+1)$; Cl $(+5)$; O (-2).
(j) K $(+1)$; Mn $(+6)$; O (-2).
(k) Na$(+1)$; B $(+3)$; O (-2).
(l) H $(+1)$; S $(+6)$; O (-2).

2. See text.　　　　**3.** See text.

4. (a) 1.6 moles $KMnO_4$.
(b) 0.3 eq. HCl.
(c) 15.0 g. Zn.
(d) 0.270 eq. $KMnO_4$.
(e) 0.38 meq. $KMnO_4$.
(f) 0.408 eq. $K_2Cr_2O_7$.
(g) 176 mg. HNO_3.

5. 12.9 g. I_2.　　　　　　**6.** 60.8 cc. STP O_2 gas.

7. 5.49 l. STP of Cl_2 gas.　　**8.** 478 mg. CuS.

9. 0.605 M NaI.　　　　　　**10.** 1.52 M $FeCl_2$.

11. 600 ml.　　　　　　**12.** 2030 ml. $Na_2S_2O_3$ solution.

Chapter XVI

1. (a) 1.56 v.
(b) 3.70 v.
(c) 0.288 v.
(d) 0.44 v.
(e) 1.09 v.
(f) 0.16 v.
(g) -0.15 v. (does not go).
(h) -0.27 v. (goes in reverse).

2. (a) $K_{eq.} = 10^{52}$.

(b) $K_{eq.} = 10^{123}$.

(c) $K_{eq.} = 4 \times 10^9 = \dfrac{C^2_{Cl^{-1}} \times C_{Br_2}}{C^2_{Br^{-1}} \times C_{Cl_2}}$.

(d) $K_{eq.} = 2 \times 10^{14}$.

(e) $K_{eq.} = 10^{109} = \dfrac{C^3_{Pb^{+2}} \times C^2_{NO}}{C^8_{H^{+1}} \times C^2_{NO_3^{-1}}}$.

(f) $K_{eq.} = 5 \times 10^{26}$.

(g) $K_{eq.} = 1 \times 10^{-5}$.

(h) $K_{eq.} = 3.2 \times 10^{-5}$.

3. (a) $E = +0.94$ v.
(b) $E = -0.61$ v.
(c) $E = +0.075$ v.
(d) $E = -1.791$ v.

4. $E = +1.11$ v.　　　　**5.** $E = -0.317$ v.

6. $C_{Ag^{+1}} = 8.5 \times 10^{-15} M$. $E = +0.044$ v.

7. $C_{S^{-2}} = 1.1 \times 10^{-19} M$; $C_{Cu^{+2}} = 3.6 \times 10^{-19} M$; $E = +0.20$ v.

8. Strongest oxidizing agent is Cl_2 gas　Strongest reducing agent is Na metal.
Largest voltage is $Na^{+1}|Na||Cl^{-1}|Cl_2 = 4.07$ v.
Smallest voltage is $Fe^{+2}|Fe^{+3}||Ag^{+1}|Ag = 0.029$ v.

9. See text.

Chapter XVII

1. 5×10^{-4} mole HBr/l.-sec.   2. 2.04×10^{-2} mole Sn^{+4}/sec.
3. See text.   4. 4.08×10^{-3} mole NOCl/l.-sec.
5. 1.29×10^{-3}.
6. (a) $k_{150} = 1.72 \times 10^{-5}$.   (b) $k_{30} = 2.19 \times 10^3$.   (c) $k_{600} = 3.43 \times 10^{-3}$.
7. $H_R = +8.64$ kcal.; endothermic.

INDEX

LOGARITHMS

Natural Numbers.	0	1	2	3	4	5	6	7	8	9	1	2	3	4	5	6	7	8	9
											PROPORTIONAL PARTS.								
10	0000	0043	0086	0128	0170	0212	0253	0294	0334	0374	4	8	12	17	21	25	29	33	37
11	0414	0453	0492	0531	0569	0607	0645	0682	0719	0755	4	8	11	15	19	23	26	30	34
12	0792	0828	0864	0899	0934	0969	1004	1038	1072	1106	3	7	10	14	17	21	24	28	31
13	1139	1173	1206	1239	1271	1303	1335	1367	1399	1430	3	6	10	13	16	19	23	26	29
14	1461	1492	1523	1553	1584	1614	1644	1673	1703	1732	3	6	9	12	15	18	21	24	27
15	1761	1790	1818	1847	1875	1903	1931	1959	1987	2014	3	6	8	11	14	17	20	22	25
16	2041	2068	2095	2122	2148	2175	2201	2227	2253	2279	3	5	8	11	13	16	18	21	24
17	2304	2330	2355	2380	2405	2430	2455	2480	2504	2529	2	5	7	10	12	15	17	20	22
18	2553	2577	2601	2625	2648	2672	2695	2718	2742	2765	2	5	7	9	12	14	16	19	21
19	2788	2810	2833	2856	2878	2900	2923	2945	2967	2989	2	4	7	9	11	13	16	18	20
20	3010	3032	3054	3075	3096	3118	3139	3160	3181	3201	2	4	6	8	11	13	15	17	19
21	3222	3243	3263	3284	3304	3324	3345	3365	3385	3404	2	4	6	8	10	12	14	16	18
22	3424	3444	3464	3483	3502	3522	3541	3560	3579	3598	2	4	6	8	10	12	14	15	17
23	3617	3636	3655	3674	3692	3711	3729	3747	3766	3784	2	4	6	7	9	11	13	15	17
24	3802	3820	3838	3856	3874	3892	3909	3927	3945	3962	2	4	5	7	9	11	12	14	16
25	3979	3997	4014	4031	4048	4065	4082	4099	4116	4133	2	3	5	7	9	10	12	14	15
26	4150	4166	4183	4200	4216	4232	4249	4265	4281	4298	2	3	5	7	8	10	11	13	15
27	4314	4330	4346	4362	4378	4393	4409	4425	4440	4456	2	3	5	6	8	9	11	13	14
28	4472	4487	4502	4518	4533	4548	4564	4579	4594	4609	2	3	5	6	8	9	11	12	14
29	4624	4639	4654	4669	4683	4698	4713	4728	4742	4757	1	3	4	6	7	9	10	12	13
30	4771	4786	4800	4814	4829	4843	4857	4871	4886	4900	1	3	4	6	7	9	10	11	13
31	4914	4928	4942	4955	4969	4983	4997	5011	5024	5038	1	3	4	6	7	8	10	11	12
32	5051	5065	5079	5092	5105	5119	5132	5145	5159	5172	1	3	4	5	7	8	9	11	12
33	5185	5198	5211	5224	5237	5250	5263	5276	5289	5302	1	3	4	5	6	8	9	10	12
34	5315	5328	5340	5353	5366	5378	5391	5403	5416	5428	1	3	4	5	6	8	9	10	11
35	5441	5453	5465	5478	5490	5502	5514	5527	5539	5551	1	2	4	5	6	7	9	10	11
36	5563	5575	5587	5599	5611	5623	5635	5647	5658	5670	1	2	4	5	6	7	8	10	11
37	5682	5694	5705	5717	5729	5740	5752	5763	5775	5786	1	2	3	5	6	7	8	9	10
38	5798	5809	5821	5832	5843	5855	5866	5877	5888	5899	1	2	3	5	6	7	8	9	10
39	5911	5922	5933	5944	5955	5966	5977	5988	5999	6010	1	2	3	4	5	7	8	9	10
40	6021	6031	6042	6053	6064	6075	6085	6096	6107	6117	1	2	3	4	5	6	8	9	10
41	6128	6138	6149	6160	6170	6180	6191	6201	6212	6222	1	2	3	4	5	6	7	8	9
42	6232	6243	6253	6263	6274	6284	6294	6304	6314	6325	1	2	3	4	5	6	7	8	9
43	6335	6345	6355	6365	6375	6385	6395	6405	6415	6425	1	2	3	4	5	6	7	8	9
44	6435	6444	6454	6464	6474	6484	6493	6503	6513	6522	1	2	3	4	5	6	7	8	9
45	6532	6542	6551	6561	6571	6580	6590	6599	6609	6618	1	2	3	4	5	6	7	8	9
46	6628	6637	6646	6656	6665	6675	6684	6693	6702	6712	1	2	3	4	5	6	7	7	8
47	6721	6730	6739	6749	6758	6767	6776	6785	6794	6803	1	2	3	4	5	5	6	7	8
48	6812	6821	6830	6839	6848	6857	6866	6875	6884	6893	1	2	3	4	4	5	6	7	8
49	6902	6911	6920	6928	6937	6946	6955	6964	6972	6981	1	2	3	4	4	5	6	7	8
50	6990	6998	7007	7016	7024	7033	7042	7050	7059	7067	1	2	3	3	4	5	6	7	8
51	7076	7084	7093	7101	7110	7118	7126	7135	7143	7152	1	2	3	3	4	5	6	7	8
52	7160	7168	7177	7185	7193	7202	7210	7218	7226	7235	1	2	2	3	4	5	6	7	7
53	7243	7251	7259	7267	7275	7284	7292	7300	7308	7316	1	2	2	3	4	5	6	6	7
54	7324	7332	7340	7348	7356	7364	7372	7380	7388	7396	1	2	2	3	4	5	6	6	7